# CARNEGIE LEARNING MATH SERIES COURSE 2

## STUDENT SKILLS PRACTICE

### 4TH EDITION

SANDY BARTLE FINOCCHI

WILLIAM S. HADLEY

MARY LOU METZ

MARY LYNN RAITH

JANET SINOPOLI

JACLYN SNYDER

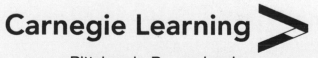

Carnegie Learning >

Pittsburgh, Pennsylvania

# Carnegie Learning >

437 Grant St., Suite 1906
Pittsburgh, PA 15219
Phone 888.851.7094
Customer Service Phone 888.851.7094, option 3

*www.carnegielearning.com*

**Printing History**
First Edition 2011
Second Edition 2014
Third Edition 2015
Fourth Edition 2016

**ISBN: 978-1-60972-136-7**

Printed in the United States of America by Cenveo Corporation
1 2 3 4 5 6 7 8 9 CC 18 17 16

# Lesson 1.1 Skills Practice

NAME _____ DATE _____

## Show Someone You Care- Send Flowers!
### Introduction to Ratios and Rates

## Vocabulary

Write the term or phrase from the box that best completes each statement.

| ratio   rate   unit rate   proportion   scaling up   scaling down   equivalent ratios |

1. _____ means to multiply the numerator and the denominator of a ratio by the same factor.

2. A _____ is a ratio that compares two quantities that are measured in different units.

3. _____ means to divide the numerator and the denominator of a ratio by the same factor.

4. A _____ is a comparison using division.

5. A _____ is an equation that states that two ratios are equal.

6. A _____ is a comparison of two measurements in which the denominator has a value of one unit.

7. _____ are ratios that represent the same part-to-part relationship or the same part-to-whole relationship.

## Problem Set

Write each statement as a ratio using colons and in fractional form.

1. There are 5 boys for every 3 girls.

   5 boys : 3 girls, $\frac{5 \text{ boys}}{3 \text{ girls}}$

2. There are 2 basketballs for every soccer ball.

3. There are 4 bananas in each fruit basket.

© Carnegie Learning

1

4. There are 50 gallons of water used after 4 showers.

5. There are 3 blueberry muffins in each variety pack of 6 muffins.

6. You purchase a dozen roses for $42.

7. There are 4 grape juice boxes in each variety pack of 10 juice boxes.

8. Each bagel costs $0.45.

Complete the model to answer each question.

9. For every 3 boys at soccer camp, there are 2 girls. If there are 20 children at soccer camp, how many are girls?

There are 8 girls at soccer camp.

NAME_____ DATE _____

**10.** In a Friendship Bouquet, 2 out of every 5 roses are pink. If there are 6 pink roses, how many total roses are in the bouquet?

**11.** In an apartment building, there are 4 tenants who own cats for every 1 tenant who owns fish. If there are 5 tenants who own fish, how many tenants own cats?

1

**12.** Each three pack of tennis balls costs $5.75. How many tennis balls can you buy for $23?

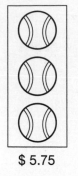

$ 5.75

**13.** Four light bulbs cost $3.20. How much does it cost to buy 14 light bulbs?

$ 3.20

**14.** Three pens cost $1.80. How many pens can you buy for $6?

$ 1.80

© Carnegie Learning

**NAME**_____ **DATE** _____

Scale up the ratio to complete each proportion.

**15.** $\dfrac{24 \text{ hours}}{1 \text{ day}} = \dfrac{?}{3 \text{ days}}$

$\dfrac{24}{1} \xrightarrow[\times 3]{\times 3} \dfrac{72}{3}$

72 hours

**16.** $\dfrac{12 \text{ bagels}}{1 \text{ dozen}} = \dfrac{36 \text{ bagels}}{?}$

**17.** $\dfrac{4 \text{ oranges}}{3 \text{ apples}} = \dfrac{?}{15 \text{ apples}}$

**18.** $\dfrac{5 \text{ fiction books}}{2 \text{ non-fiction books}} = \dfrac{?}{6 \text{ non-fiction books}}$

**19.** $\dfrac{12 \text{ eggs}}{\$3.25} = \dfrac{48 \text{ eggs}}{?}$

**20.** $\dfrac{6 \text{ scones}}{\$6.30} = \dfrac{18 \text{ scones}}{?}$

**21.** $\dfrac{8 \text{ artichokes}}{\$4.50} = \dfrac{?}{\$9.00}$

**22.** $\dfrac{1 \text{ pack of gum}}{\$0.75} = \dfrac{?}{\$2.25}$

1

Scale down the ratio to complete each proportion.

**23.** $\dfrac{72 \text{ oz red paint}}{48 \text{ oz blue paint}} = \dfrac{3 \text{ oz red paint}}{?}$

$\dfrac{72}{48} \overset{\div 24}{\underset{\div 24}{=\!\!\!\Rightarrow}} \dfrac{3}{2}$

2 oz blue paint

**24.** $\dfrac{15 \text{ red tulips}}{9 \text{ yellow tulips}} = \dfrac{5 \text{ red tulips}}{?}$

**25.** $\dfrac{138 \text{ students}}{6 \text{ teachers}} = \dfrac{?}{1 \text{ teacher}}$

**26.** $\dfrac{112 \text{ energy bars}}{14 \text{ value packs}} = \dfrac{?}{1 \text{ value pack}}$

**27.** $\dfrac{12 \text{ eggs}}{\$3.60} = \dfrac{1 \text{ egg}}{?}$

**28.** $\dfrac{8 \text{ pack of yogurt cups}}{\$2.56} = \dfrac{1 \text{ yogurt cup}}{?}$

**29.** $\dfrac{12 \text{ pencils}}{\$1.32} = \dfrac{?}{\$0.22}$

**30.** $\dfrac{4 \text{ lb bananas}}{\$2.36} = \dfrac{?}{\$1.18}$

NAME_____ DATE_____

Scale down the rate to determine each unit rate.

**31.** $\dfrac{75 \text{ miles}}{3 \text{ hours}}$

$$\dfrac{75}{3} \xrightarrow[\div 3]{\div 3} \dfrac{25}{1}$$

25 miles per hour

**32.** $\dfrac{130 \text{ miles}}{2 \text{ hours}}$

**33.** $\dfrac{\$48}{4 \text{ pounds}}$

**34.** $\dfrac{\$4}{8 \text{ pounds}}$

**35.** $\dfrac{45 \text{ students}}{3 \text{ teachers}}$

**36.** $\dfrac{153 \text{ miles}}{9 \text{ gallons}}$

**37.** $\dfrac{24 \text{ bracelets}}{6 \text{ hours}}$

**38.** $\dfrac{\$28}{8 \text{ gallons}}$

NAME_____ DATE _____

## Making Punch
## Ratios, Rates, and Mixture Problems

## Problem Set
Use ratios to answer each question.

1. Gerain and Deon are each making trail mix. Gerain's recipe calls for 3 parts raisins to 2 parts almonds. Deon's recipe calls for 4 parts raisins to 3 parts almonds. Which recipe has a higher concentration of almonds?

   Gerain's recipe: $\dfrac{2 \text{ parts almonds}}{5 \text{ total parts}} = \dfrac{14}{35}$

   Deon's recipe: $\dfrac{3 \text{ parts almonds}}{7 \text{ total parts}} = \dfrac{15}{35}$

   Because $\dfrac{15}{35} > \dfrac{14}{35}$, Deon's recipe has a higher concentration of almonds.

2. Taisha and Shakina are each making punch. Taisha's recipe calls for 5 parts pineapple juice to 3 parts orange sherbet. Shakina's recipe calls for 8 parts pineapple juice to 6 parts orange sherbet. Which recipe will have a stronger orange flavor?

1

3. Jin and Nami are each making Hawaiian snack mix. Jin's recipe calls for 5 parts dried pineapple to 2 parts macadamia nuts. Nami's recipe calls for 3 parts dried pineapple to 1 part macadamia nuts. Which recipe has a higher concentration of macadamia nuts?

4. Juanita and Lydia are each making lemonade. Juanita's recipe calls for 4 parts lemon juice to 2 parts sugar syrup. Lydia's recipe calls for 5 parts lemon juice to 3 parts sugar syrup. Which recipe has a stronger lemon flavor?

5. Leon and Cisco are each making snack mix. Leon's recipe calls for 8 parts pretzels to 3 parts peanuts. Cisco's recipe calls for 6 parts pretzels to 2 parts peanuts. Which recipe has a higher concentration of peanuts?

NAME_____ DATE _____

6. Belinda and Cristina are each making a wildflower seed mix to plant in their gardens. Belinda's mix calls for 8 parts poppy seeds to 5 parts daisy seeds. Cristina's mix calls for 10 parts poppy seeds to 8 parts daisy seeds. Which mix will produce a higher concentration of poppy flowers?

1

Use ratios to answer each question.

**7.** Carmen is making a strawberry drink. The recipe calls for 5 parts strawberry juice to 3 parts water. Carmen would like to make 64 fluid ounces of the strawberry drink. How many fluid ounces of strawberry juice and water does Carmen need?

Number of fluid ounces in one part of the recipe:

$$\frac{64 \text{ fluid ounces}}{8 \text{ parts}} = \frac{8 \text{ fluid ounces}}{1 \text{ part}}$$

Number of fluid ounces of strawberry juice:

$$\frac{8 \text{ fluid ounces}}{1 \text{ part}} = \frac{x}{5 \text{ parts}}$$

$$(1)(x) = (8)(5)$$

$$x = 40$$

Number of fluid ounces of water:

$$\frac{8 \text{ fluid ounces}}{1 \text{ part}} = \frac{x}{3 \text{ parts}}$$

$$(1)(x) = (8)(3)$$

$$x = 24$$

Carmen will need 40 fluid ounces of strawberry juice and 24 fluid ounces of water to make 64 fluid ounces of strawberry drink.

**NAME** _____ **DATE** _____

8. Elena is making a grape drink. The recipe calls for 2 parts grape juice concentrate to 6 parts water. Elena would like to make 80 fluid ounces of the grape drink. How many fluid ounces of grape juice concentrate and water does Elena need?

1

9. Jose is making a trail mix. The recipe calls for 3 parts golden raisins to 2 parts cashews. Jose would like to make 30 cups of trail mix. How many cups of golden raisins and cashews does Jose need?

NAME_____ DATE _____

**10.** Miguel is making a snack mix. The recipe calls for 6 parts of spicy tortilla chips to 3 parts of corn chips. Miguel would like to make 45 cups of snack mix. How many cups of spicy tortilla chips and corn chips does Miguel need?

1

**11.** Carla is making a bean salad. The recipe calls for 4 parts green beans to 3 parts yellow wax beans. Carla would like to make 56 ounces of bean salad. How many ounces of green beans and yellow wax beans does Carla need?

NAME_____ DATE _____

**12.** Shawna is making smoothies. The recipe calls for 2 parts yogurt to 3 parts blueberries. Shawna wants to make 10 cups of smoothie mix. How many cups of yogurt and blueberries does Shawna need?

1

**NAME**_____ **DATE** _____

## For the Birds
### Rates and Proportions

## Vocabulary

Define the term in your own words.

**1.** convert

## Problem Set

Write the ratio described by each problem situation. Write the ratio as a decimal. Round to the nearest thousandth, if necessary.

**1.** An adult female elephant weighs about 8000 pounds. A newborn baby elephants weighs about 200 pounds. Write the ratio of the baby elephant's weight to the adult female elephant's weight.

$$\frac{200 \text{ lb}}{8000 \text{ lb}} = 0.025$$

**2.** An adult pygmy shrew weighs about 3.5 grams. A newborn pygmy shrew weighs just about 0.25 gram. Write the ratio of the newborn pygmy shrew's weight to the adult pygmy shrew's weight.

**3.** An adult tiger weighs about 650 pounds. A baby tiger weighs about 2 pounds at birth. Write the ratio of the newborn tiger's weight to the adult tiger's weight.

**4.** An adult blue whale weighs about 200 tons. A baby blue whale weighs about 3 tons at birth. Write the ratio of the newborn blue whale's weight to the adult blue whale's weight.

**1**

**5.** An adult male giraffe weighs about 3000 pounds. A baby giraffe weighs about 110 pounds at birth. Write the ratio of the newborn giraffe's weight to the adult male giraffe's weight.

**6.** An adult female polar bear weighs about 750 pounds. A baby polar bear cub weighs about 1.3 pounds at birth. Write the ratio of the newborn polar bear's weight to the adult female polar bear's weight.

Write the rate described by each problem situation.

**7.** Gina rode her bike 2 miles in 30 minutes.

2 miles per 30 minutes, or $\dfrac{2 \text{ miles}}{30 \text{ minutes}}$

**8.** Isabella drove 300 miles in 5 hours.

**9.** Marcus jogged 3 miles in 45 minutes.

**10.** In 1 hour, Monique made 4 bead necklaces.

**11.** In 3 hours, Jacob mowed 4 lawns.

**12.** In 25 minutes, Norton read 14 pages.

© Carnegie Learning

NAME_____ DATE _____

Convert each rate.

**13.** Convert the rate 5 feet per 3 seconds to yards per hour.

$$\frac{5 \text{ ft}}{3 \text{ sec}} \times \frac{3600 \text{ sec}}{1 \text{ hr}} = \frac{18,000 \text{ ft}}{3 \text{ hr}}$$

$$= \frac{6000 \text{ ft}}{1 \text{ hr}}$$

$$\frac{6000 \text{ ft}}{1 \text{ hr}} \times \frac{1 \text{ yd}}{3 \text{ ft}} = \frac{6000 \text{ yd}}{3 \text{ hr}}$$

$$= \frac{2000 \text{ yd}}{1 \text{ hr}}$$

The rate 5 feet per 3 seconds is equivalent to 2000 yards per hour.

**14.** Convert the rate 1000 fluid ounces per 2 hours to cups per minute.

1

**15.** Convert the rate of 10 yards per 5 minutes to feet per hour.

**16.** Convert the rate of 48 feet per hour to inches per minute.

**17.** Convert the rate of 12 pints per 15 minutes to quarts per hour.

NAME_____ DATE _____

**18.** Convert the rate of 48 ounces per 2 hours to pounds per day.

Scale each ratio up or down as needed to complete the proportion.

**19.** $\dfrac{16 \text{ oz}}{1 \text{ lb}} = \dfrac{?}{3 \text{ lb}}$

$\dfrac{16}{1} = \dfrac{48}{3}$

48 ounces

**20.** $\dfrac{4c}{1qt} = \dfrac{32 \text{ c}}{?}$

**21.** $\dfrac{6000 \text{ lb}}{3 \text{ t}} = \dfrac{?}{1 \text{ t}}$

**22.** $\dfrac{20 \text{ qt}}{5 \text{ gal}} = \dfrac{4 \text{ qt}}{?}$

**1**

**23.** $\dfrac{36 \text{ in.}}{1 \text{ yd}} = \dfrac{108 \text{ in.}}{?}$

**24.** $\dfrac{5280 \text{ ft}}{1 \text{ mi}} = \dfrac{?}{4 \text{ mi}}$

**25.** $\dfrac{10{,}800 \text{ sec}}{3 \text{ hrs}} = \dfrac{3600 \text{ sec}}{?}$

**26.** $\dfrac{216 \text{ in.}}{6 \text{ yd}} = \dfrac{?}{1 \text{ yd}}$

Convert each measurement using a rate.

**27.** How many pints are in 36 cups?

$36 \, c \times \dfrac{1 \text{ pt}}{2 \, c} = 18 \text{ pt}$

There are 18 pints in 36 cups.

**28.** How many feet are in 15 yards?

**29.** How many feet are in 96 inches?

**30.** How many seconds are in 4 hours?

**31.** How many ounces are in 7 pounds?

**32.** How many tons are in 18,000 pounds?

© Carnegie Learning

NAME_____ DATE _____

## Tutor Time!
## Using Tables to Solve Problems

## Problem Set

Complete each table.

**1.** The ratio of boys to girls participating in intramural basketball is 7 boys to 4 girls.

| Boys | 7 | 21 | 42 | 84 |
|------|---|----|----|----|
| Girls | 4 | 12 | 24 | 48 |

**2.** Perry is delivering newspapers. In 2 hours he delivers 60 newspapers.

| Newspapers | | 60 | 90 | 105 |
|------------|--|----|----|-----|
| Hours | 1 | 2 | | |

**3.** Joelle's new printer can print 10 photos in 5 minutes.

| Photos | | 10 | 25 | 50 |
|--------|--|----|----|----|
| Minutes | 1 | 5 | | |

**4.** Denisa is mixing blue paint and white paint to create a shade of light blue paint. She creates the shade she likes by mixing 12 ounces of blue paint with 8 ounces of white paint.

| Blue paint (oz) | | 12 | 18 | |
|-----------------|--|----|----|--|
| White paint (oz) | 1 | 8 | | 18 |

**1**

5. Belinda is making fruit salad. The recipe calls for 3 cups of sliced peaches to 2 cups of halved grapes.

| Peaches (c) |   | 3 |   | 6 |
|---|---|---|---|---|
| Grapes (c) | 1 | 2 | 3 |   |

6. Mattie is stuffing envelopes. She stuffs 100 envelopes in 1 hour.

| Envelopes |   |   | 100 |   |
|---|---|---|---|---|
| Hours | 0.25 | 0.5 | 1 | 2 |

Determine the unit rate to answer each question.

7. Luis mowed 8 lawns this week and earned $56. How much would Luis have earned if he had mowed 10 lawns?

$$\frac{\$56}{8 \text{ lawns}} = \frac{\$7}{1 \text{ lawn}}$$

The unit rate is $7 per lawn.

$$10 \text{ lawns} \times \frac{\$7}{1 \text{ lawn}} = \$70$$

If Luis had mowed 10 lawns, he would have earned $70.

NAME_____ DATE_____

8. Eva babysat for two families this weekend. She babysat 4 hours for the Rodgers family and 5 hours for the Mitchell family. She made a total of $58.50 for the weekend. Both families pay her the same amount per hour. How much did she earn from the Rodgers family?

9. Rita made 12 pairs of earrings in 2 hours. How many pairs of earrings could she make in 3 hours?

1

**10.** Pedro planted 12 plants in his garden in 45 minutes. How long did it take him to plant 5 plants?

**11.** Raul walked 2.5 miles in 1 hour and 15 minutes. How long did it take Raul to walk 0.5 mile?

**12.** Perry earned $96 shoveling snow from 8 driveways. How much would Perry have earned if he had shoveled 10 driveways?

**1**

## Looks Can Be Deceiving!
### Using Proportions to Solve Problems

## Vocabulary

Describe a situation in which you would use each of the following.

**1.** variable

**2.** means and extremes method

**3.** solve a proportion

**4.** inverse operations

## Problem Set

Tell which method (scaling, unit rate, or means and extremes) you would use to solve for each variable and explain why.

**1.** $\dfrac{2}{3} = \dfrac{20}{x}$

Use the scaling method because it is easy
to see that the numerator is multiplied by
10, so the denominator must also be
multiplied by 10.

**2.** $\dfrac{16}{4} = \dfrac{100}{x}$

**1**

**3.** $\dfrac{23}{48} = \dfrac{50}{x}$

**4.** $\dfrac{49}{7} = \dfrac{x}{5}$

**5.** $\dfrac{37}{15} = \dfrac{x}{8}$

**6.** $\dfrac{63}{36} = \dfrac{x}{4}$

Solve for each variable using the means and extremes method. Round to the nearest hundredth, if necessary.

**7.** $\dfrac{4}{28} = \dfrac{x}{35}$

$(28)(x) = (4)(35)$

$\dfrac{28x}{28} = \dfrac{140}{28}$

$x = 5$

**8.** $12 : 6 = 60 : x$

**9.** $560 : 80 = x : 300$

**10.** $\dfrac{41}{282} = \dfrac{7}{x}$

**NAME**_____ **DATE**_____

**11.** $\frac{39}{9} = \frac{x}{2}$

**12.** $74:31 = 2:x$

**13.** $\frac{x}{3} = \frac{1351}{7}$

**14.** $26:x = 117:9$

Use the given information to answer each question.

**15.** In the first quarter (3 months), a store sold 32 limited-edition action figures. If this quarter's sales represent a typical sales pattern, how many action figures should they expect to sell in a year?

$\frac{32}{3} = \frac{f}{12}$

$f = 128$

The store should expect to sell 128 action figures in a year.

**1**

16. A recipe calls for $3\frac{1}{2}$ cups of flour and $\frac{3}{4}$ cup of sugar. If you want to make the recipe with 6 cups of flour, about how much sugar will you need?

17. Marlene is planning a trip. She knows that her car gets 38 miles to the gallon on the highway. If her trip is going to be 274 miles and one gallon of gas is $2.30, about how much should she expect to pay for gas?

18. It takes Roger about 8 minutes to type a 500-word document. How long will it take him to type a 12-page essay with 275 words per page?

NAME_____ DATE _____

# The Price Is . . . Close
## Using Unit Rates in Real World Applications

## Problem Set

Calculate the unit rates for each item.

**1.** A bottle of fruit juice contains 63 ounces and costs $2.25. Calculate the unit rate showing ounces per dollar and the unit rate showing dollars per ounce.

$$\frac{63 \text{ oz}}{\$2.25} = \frac{28 \text{ oz}}{\$1}$$

$$\frac{\$2.25}{63 \text{ oz}} \approx \frac{\$0.04}{1 \text{ oz}}$$

The unit rate is 28 ounces per dollar or about $0.04 per ounce.

**2.** A dozen scones cost $5.95. Calculate the unit rate showing scones per dollar and the unit rate showing dollars per scone.

1

3. A 2.5 pound bag of apples costs $2.99. Calculate the unit rate showing pounds of apples per dollar and the unit rate showing dollars per pound of apples.

4. An 8 pound bag of oranges costs $4.95. Calculate the unit rate showing pounds of oranges per dollar and the unit rate showing dollars per pound of oranges.

5. A box of 40 envelopes costs $2.50. Calculate the unit rate showing number of envelopes per dollar and the unit rate showing dollars per envelope.

NAME_____ DATE _____

6. A package of 200 cotton balls costs $1.99. Calculate the unit rate showing cotton balls per dollar and the unit rate showing dollars per cotton ball.

Estimate the unit rates of each item to determine which is the better buy.

7. A 4 liter bottle of laundry detergent costs $7.99. A 6.5 liter bottle of laundry detergent costs $16.99. Which is the better buy?

$$\frac{\$7.99}{4\ L} \approx \frac{\$8}{4\ L}$$

$$= \frac{\$2}{1\ L}$$

$$\frac{\$16.99}{6.5\ L} \approx \frac{\$17}{6.5\ L}$$

$$\approx \frac{\$2.60}{1\ L}$$

Because $2 < $2.60, the 4 liter bottle is the better buy.

© Carnegie Learning

1

8. A 64 ounce bottle of apple juice costs $1.99. A 140 ounce bottle of apple juice costs $2.80. Which is the better buy?

9. A sleeve of 4 golf balls costs $6.99. A 20 pack of golf balls costs $24.95. Which is the better buy?

1

NAME_____ DATE _____

**10.** A 2.2 pound package of chicken costs $5.99. A 5.1 pound package of chicken costs $9.95. Which one is the better buy?

**11.** A 4 pack of dinner rolls costs $2.20. A 12 pack of dinner rolls costs $5.40. Which is the better buy?

**1**

**12.** An 18 ounce jar of peanut butter costs $1.29. A 64 ounce jar of peanut butter costs $3.80. Which is the better buy?

# Lesson 2.1   Skills Practice

NAME_____ DATE _____

## What Makes You Tap Your Feet?
### Introduction to Direct Variation

## Vocabulary

Define each term in your own words.

**1.** direct variation

**2.** origin

## Problem Set

Complete the table and use the table values to complete a graph for each problem situation.
For continuous data, connect the data points with a line or a curve.

1. Katherine makes $12 per hour at her job.

| Hours Worked | Pay (dollars) |
|:---:|:---:|
| 2 | 24 |
| 3 | 36 |
| 5 | 60 |
| 10 | 120 |
| 15 | 180 |
| 20 | 240 |

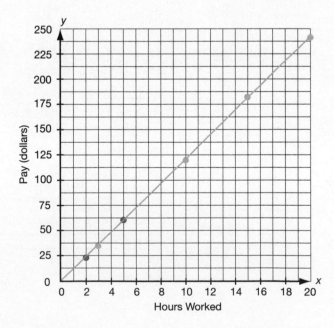

**NAME**_____ **DATE** _____

2. A patient receives an intravenous saline solution from a 1000-milliliter IV fluid bag. The solution is dispensed at a rate of 125 mL per hour.

| Time (hours) | Solution Left in Bag (mL) |
|:---:|:---:|
| 0 | |
| 1 | |
| | 750 |
| 3 | |
| 5 | |
| | 0 |

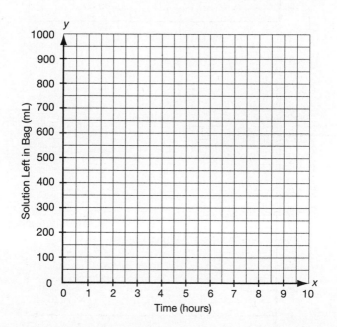

2

**3.** Vanessa and Michelle must decide how to divide 16 marbles among themselves.

| Number of Marbles Vanessa Takes | Number of Marbles Michelle Takes |
|:---:|:---:|
| 0 | 16 |
| 4 | |
| 6 | |
| | 7 |
| 13 | |
| | 0 |

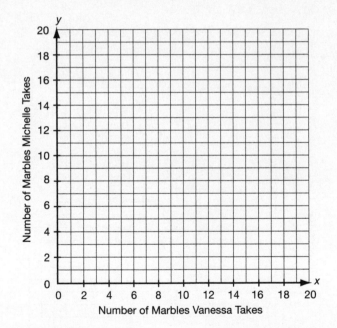

NAME_____ DATE_____

4. The perimeter of a square is 4 times the length of one side.

| Square Side Length (inches) | Perimeter (inches) |
|---|---|
|  | 4 |
| 2 |  |
|  | 16 |
| 8 |  |
| 12 |  |
|  | 64 |

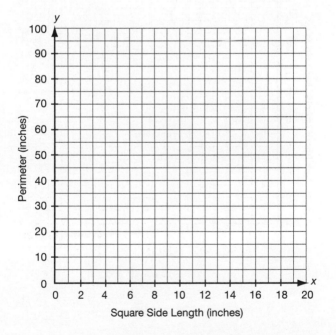

**5.** The area of a square is calculated by squaring the length of one side.

| Square Side Length (inches) | Area (square inches) |
|:---:|:---:|
| 1 | |
| | 4 |
| 3 | |
| | 25 |
| 7 | |
| 9 | |

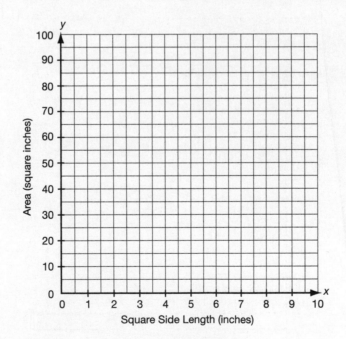

**NAME**_____ **DATE** _____

6. Preston attempts 20 basketball free throws at the end of practice each day.

| Free Throws Made | Free Throws Missed |
|:---:|:---:|
| 0 | |
| | 17 |
| 7 | |
| | 8 |
| 16 | |
| | 0 |

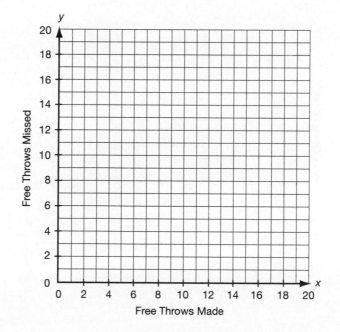

**7.** When Tara, a nurse at a local hospital, works on Saturdays, she is paid a $30 bonus plus $20 per hour worked.

| Hours Worked | Pay (dollars) |
|---|---|
| 1 | |
| 2 | |
| 3 | |
| | 110 |
| 6 | |
| | 190 |

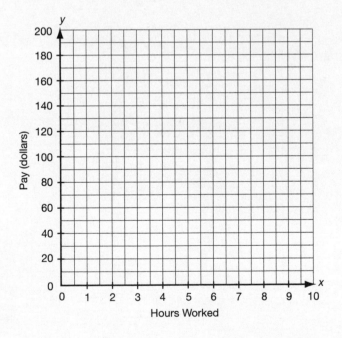

NAME_____ DATE _____

8. The actual volume (in decibels) of a particular stereo doubles with each increase of 1 on the volume setting. The volume settings on the stereo can only be whole numbers.

| Volume Setting | Actual Volume (decibels) |
|:---:|:---:|
| 0 | 1 |
| 1 | |
| 2 | |
| | 8 |
| 4 | |
| | 64 |

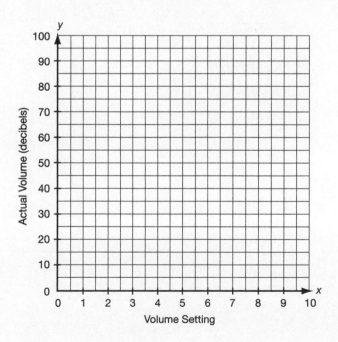

NAME_____  DATE _____

# Building Bird Feeders <u>Is</u> for the Birds!
## Determining Equivalent Ratios

## Problem Set

Calculate each ratio for the proportional relationship given.

**1.** The table shows the number of pounds of materials each class recycled. Calculate the ratio between the pounds of glass and pounds of paper.

| Grade | Glass (pounds) | Paper (pounds) |
|-------|----------------|----------------|
| Fifth | 42 | 63 |
| Sixth | 30 | 45 |

$\frac{42}{63} = \frac{2}{3}$ and $\frac{30}{45} = \frac{2}{3}$, so $\frac{\text{Glass}}{\text{Paper}} = \frac{2}{3}$

2. The table shows the number of votes each candidate received. Calculate the ratio between the votes from boys and the votes from girls.

| Candidate | Votes from Girls | Votes from Boys |
|---|---|---|
| Anita | 28 | 35 |
| Joey | 16 | 20 |

3. Ms. Kline drove at a steady rate for 40 minutes. She drove 30 miles during that time. Calculate the ratio between the number of miles and number of minutes she drove.

4. The table shows the costs for different numbers of pounds of peaches. Calculate the ratio between the total cost and the number of pounds.

| Number of Pounds | Total Cost |
|---|---|
| 3 | $3.75 |
| 7 | $8.75 |
| 8 | $10 |

5. Heather earns $13.50 for 3 hours of babysitting. Calculate the ratio between the amount Heather earns and the number of hours she babysits.

© Carnegie Learning

NAME_____ DATE _____

6. A store is having a going-out-of-business sale and every item is discounted by the same percent. A clock that was $60 is now $21. A chair that was $120 is now $42. Calculate the ratio between the sale price and the original price.

7. The table shows the heights of two white pine trees measured each of the past two summers. Calculate the ratio between the second year height and the first year height.

| Tree | First Year Height | Second Year Height |
|------|------|------|
| White Pine 1 | 5 | 6.5 |
| White Pine 2 | 3 | 3.9 |

8. The table shows the maximum heights achieved by a water propelled rocket when launched with different amounts of pressure. Calculate the ratio between the maximum height of the rocket and the rocket's launch pressure.

| Maximum Height (meters) | Launch Pressure (psi) |
|------|------|
| 90 | 75 |
| 108 | 90 |

**2**

9. The table shows the amount of power used by a light when the dimmer switch is placed at different settings. Calculate the ratio between the amount of power used and the switch setting.

| Power Used (watts) | Switch Setting |
|---|---|
| 58 | 4 |
| 87 | 6 |
| 130.5 | 9 |

10. A fruit stand sells 80 apples and 96 oranges every hour. Calculate the ratio between the number of apples sold and the number of oranges sold each hour.

Write and solve an equation using the constant of proportionality to answer each question.

11. The ratio between the number of children ($c$) on a field trip and the number of teachers ($t$) on the trip is $\frac{14}{3}$. There are 70 children on a field trip. How many teachers are on the trip?

$$\frac{14}{3} = \frac{c}{t}$$

$$\frac{14}{3} = \frac{70}{t}$$

$$14t = 3(70)$$

$$14t = 210$$

$$t = 15$$

There are 15 teachers on the trip.

NAME_____ DATE _____

12. The ratio between the number of junior varsity players ($j$) on the track team and the number of varsity players ($v$) on the team is $\frac{2}{5}$. There are 45 varsity players on the track team. How many junior varsity players are on the team?

13. The ratio between the number of cats ($c$) in a pet shelter and the number of dogs ($d$) in the shelter is 3. There are 27 cats in the shelter. How many dogs are in the shelter?

14. The ratio between the height of the water in a sink ($h$) in centimeters and the number of minutes it has been filling ($m$) is 0.95. The sink has been filling for 40 minutes. What is the height of the water in the sink?

15. The ratio between the number of fiction books ($f$) and the number of nonfiction books ($n$) in a library is $\frac{15}{22}$. There are 3498 nonfiction books in the library. How many fiction books are in the library?

NAME_____ DATE _____

2

16. The ratio between the number of markers ($m$) and the number of pencils ($p$) in an art room is $\frac{8}{3}$. There are 304 markers in the art room. How many pencils are in the art room?

17. The ratio between the number of catfish ($c$) in a farm pond and the number of bass ($b$) in the pond is $\frac{3}{7}$. There are 91 bass in the pond. How many catfish are in the pond?

**18.** The ratio between the number of red jelly beans (*r*) and the number of green jelly beans (*g*) in a bag is $\frac{8}{5}$. There are 200 red jelly beans in the bag. How many green jelly beans are in the bag?

**19.** The ratio between the number of pounds of nitrogen (*n*) and the number of pounds of phosphorus (*p*) in a bag of fertilizer is $\frac{4}{3}$. There are 50 pounds of nitrogen in the bag. How many pounds of phosphorus are in the bag of fertilizer?

NAME_____ DATE _____

20. The ratio between the number of green olive slices (g) and the number of black olive slices (b) on a pizza is $\frac{3}{2}$. There are 26 black olive slices on the pizza. How many green olive slices are on the pizza?

**2**

NAME_____ DATE _____

## Kids Just Wanna Have Fun!
**Determining and Applying the Constant of Proportionality**

### Vocabulary

Define the term in your own words.

**1.** constant of proportionality

### Problem Set

Write a proportion involving the two variables and solve it to determine each unknown table value.

**1.** All-Write Pencil factory produces graphite pencils.

| Time (seconds) | Number of Pencils Produced |
|:---:|:---:|
| 12 | 42 |
| 18 | 63 |
| 40 | 140 |

Let $t$ represent the time in seconds and let $p$ represent the number of pencils produced.

$\frac{12}{43} = \frac{t}{p}$ or $\frac{2}{7} = \frac{t}{p}$

$\frac{2}{7} = \frac{40}{p}$

$2p = 280$

$p = 140$

**2.** A bicyclist rides at a constant rate.

| Time (hours) | Distance Traveled (miles) |
|:---:|:---:|
| 2 | 25 |
| 5 | 62.5 |
| | 112.5 |

NAME_____ DATE _____

3. A professional jump rope competitor is trying to break the single rope speed record.

| Time (seconds) | Number of Jumps |
|:---:|:---:|
| 6 | |
| 14 | 63 |
| 32 | 144 |

2

**4.** A fishing tackle company produces tackle kits including hooks and sinkers.

| Number of Hooks | Number of Sinkers |
|---|---|
| 8 | 5 |
| 40 | |
| 72 | 45 |

NAME_____ DATE _____

5. Fruity Fruit Company sends out a proportional number of grapefruits and oranges in each of their gift boxes.

| Number of Grapefruits | Number of Oranges |
|:---:|:---:|
| 4 | 6 |
| 16 | 24 |
|  | 30 |

**6.** The blades on a wind turbine rotate at a constant rate.

| Time (seconds) | Number of Rotations |
|---|---|
| 14 | 5 |
| 35 | |
| 63 | 22.5 |

NAME_____ DATE _____

7. Telephone poles are spaced evenly along a length of road.

| Distance (miles) | Number of Telephone Poles |
| --- | --- |
| 3 | 105 |
| 5 | 175 |
|  | 300 |

© Carnegie Learning

8. Green Thumb Tree Nursery packages bundles of hickory tree and maple tree saplings to send to their distributors.

| Number of Hickory Saplings | Number of Maple Saplings |
|:---:|:---:|
| 10 | 4 |
| 15 | 6 |
| 35 | |

Use the equation for the constant of proportionality, $\frac{y}{x} = k$, to determine each unknown value.

9. $k = \frac{3}{2}$ and $y = 15$                    10. $k = \frac{1}{4}$ and $y = 5$

$\frac{y}{x} = k$

$\frac{15}{x} = \frac{3}{2}$

$3x = 15(2)$

$3x = 30$

$x = 10$

NAME_____ DATE _____

11. $k = \dfrac{7}{3}$ and $x = 21$                12.  $k = 6$ and $y = 2$

13. $k = 0.18$ and $y = 450$              14.  $k = \dfrac{5}{6}$ and $x = 126$

**2**

**15.** $k = 7$ and $y = 126$

**16.** $k = 0.22$ and $x = 550$

2

## Stop that Speeding Snail?
### Using the Constant of Proportionality to Solve Proportions

### Problem Set

Determine whether the relationship between the two data sets in each is proportional.

1.

| Data Set One | Data Set Two |
|:---:|:---:|
| 5 | 3 |
| 30 | 18 |

The relationship is proportional because $\frac{5}{3} = \frac{30}{18}$. The product of the means equals the product of the extremes.

$5(18) = (3)30$

$90 = 90$

2.

| Data Set One | Data Set Two |
|:---:|:---:|
| 25 | 35 |
| 45 | 50 |

© Carnegie Learning

2

3.

| Data Set One | Data Set Two |
|---|---|
| 18 | 45 |
| 28 | 70 |

4.

| Data Set One | Data Set Two |
|---|---|
| 279 | 45 |
| 434 | 70 |

NAME_____ DATE _____

**5.**

| Data Set One | Data Set Two |
|:---:|:---:|
| 7 | 18 |
| 11 | 26 |

**6.**

| Data Set One | Data Set Two |
|:---:|:---:|
| 33 | 4 |
| 110 | 13 |

2

7.

| Data Set One | Data Set Two |
|:---:|:---:|
| 8 | 6 |
| 44 | 33 |

8.

| Data Set One | Data Set Two |
|:---:|:---:|
| 15 | 108 |
| 20 | 144 |

# Lesson 2.5  Skills Practice

NAME_____  DATE _____

## The Man Who Ran from Marathon to Athens
### Graphing Direct Proportions

## Problem Set

Complete each table. Then, graph the values from the table on the coordinate plane shown. Connect the points if it is reasonable to do so.

1. The total cost of printing digital photos in dollars varies directly with the number of photos that are printed. The constant of proportionality is 0.1.

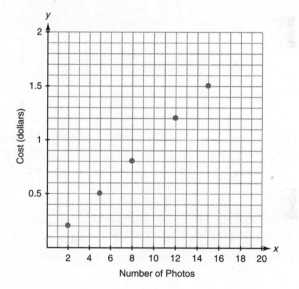

| Number of Photos | Cost (dollars) |
|:---:|:---:|
| 2 | 0.2 |
| 5 | 0.5 |
| 8 | 0.8 |
| 12 | 1.2 |
| 15 | 1.5 |

2. The total amount of rainfall in inches varies directly with the number of hours that it has been raining. The constant of proportionality is $\frac{1}{4}$.

| Number of Hours | Rain (inches) |
|---|---|
| 2 | |
| | 1 |
| | $1\frac{1}{2}$ |
| 8 | |
| 10 | |

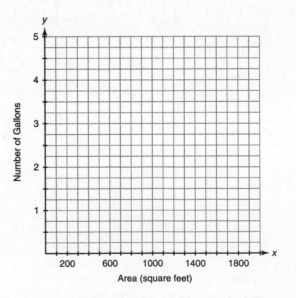

3. The number of gallons of paint needed to paint a room varies directly with the area to be painted in square feet. The constant of proportionality is $\frac{1}{350}$.

| Area (square feet) | Number of Gallons |
|---|---|
| 175 | |
| 700 | |
| 875 | |
| | 4 |
| 1750 | |

NAME_____ DATE _____

4. The number of drivers needed at a tour bus company each day varies directly with the number of tourists that come for a tour that day. The constant of proportionality is $\frac{1}{8}$.

| Number of Tourists | Number of Drivers |
|---|---|
|  | 3 |
|  | 5 |
| 48 |  |
| 64 |  |
| 80 |  |

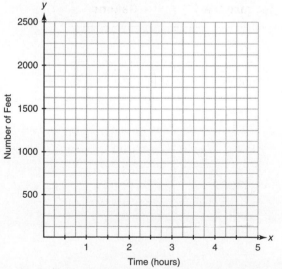

5. The total number of vertical feet that a climber has traveled varies directly with the number of hours she has been climbing. The constant of proportionality is 600.

| Time (hours) | Number of Feet |
|---|---|
| $\frac{1}{2}$ |  |
| 1 |  |
|  | 1800 |
|  | 2100 |
| 4 |  |

© Carnegie Learning

2

6. The amount of pay in dollars a worker earns during a week varies directly with the number of hours that he works. The constant of proportionality is 12.

| Number of Hours | Pay (dollars) |
|---|---|
| 8 | |
| | 162 |
| 20 | |
| 25 | |
| | 342 |

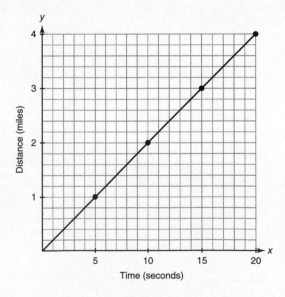

Determine the constant of proportionality *k* and interpret it in the context of each problem.

7. The graph shows the relationship between the distance in miles between you and a storm and the number of seconds between when you see lightning and when you hear thunder.

I chose a point on the graph and expressed the ratio formed by $\frac{y\text{-coordinate}}{x\text{-coordinate}}$.

$k = \frac{3}{15}$ or $\frac{1}{5}$ or 0.2

The constant of proportionality means the distance between you and the storm increases by 1 mile for every 5 seconds between the lightning and the thunder. Or, the distance increases by 0.2 miles for every second counted.

NAME_____ DATE _____

8. The graph shows the relationship between the number of Euros Jason received and the number of dollars Jason exchanged during his trip to Spain.

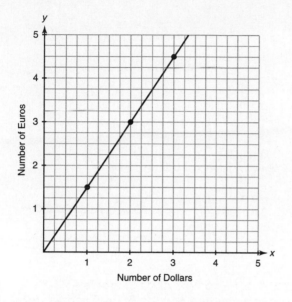

9. The graph shows the relationship between the weight of an object on Earth and the weight of the same object on Venus.

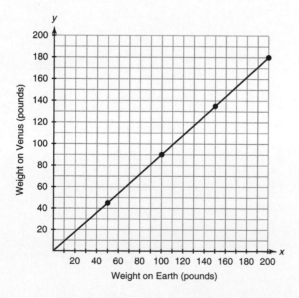

10. The graph shows the relationship between the area of a room in square feet and the cost of covering the floor with new tile.

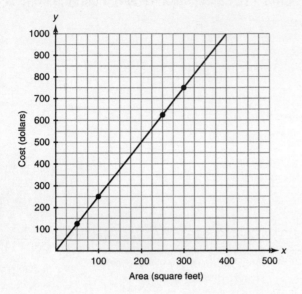

11. The graph shows the relationship between the cups of water and pounds of beef needed for a beef casserole.

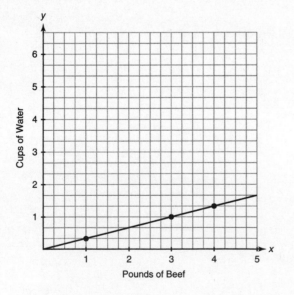

NAME_____ DATE _____

**12.** The graph shows the relationship between the number of posters in a classroom and the number of thumbtacks used to hold them up.

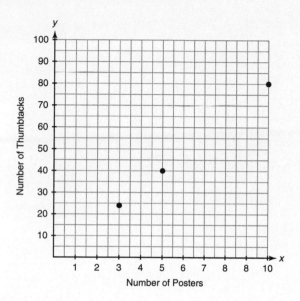

NAME_____   DATE _____

# Racing to the Finish Line!
## Using Direct Proportions

## Problem Set
Complete each table.

1. The number of pipes a construction crew can install is directly proportional to the number of hours they work.

| Hours Worked | Pipes Installed |
|:---:|:---:|
| $1\frac{1}{2}$ | 2 |
| 3 | 4 |
| 6 | 8 |

2. The number of meters Percy walks is directly proportional to the number of feet he walks.

| Meters | Feet |
|:---:|:---:|
| 825 | |
| | 450 |
| 1980 | 600 |
| 3300 | |

3. The distance Ms. Juarez drives is directly proportional to the length of time she drives.

| Time (in hours) | Distance (kilometers) |
|---|---|
|  | 164 |
| 5 |  |
| 6 | 492 |

4. The amount of water in a swimming pool is directly proportional to the length of time it has been filling up.

| Time (hours) | Number of Gallons |
|---|---|
|  | 39 |
| 2 | 104 |
|  | 312 |
| $6\frac{1}{2}$ |  |

5. The cost of freshly-crushed peanut butter is directly proportional to the number of ounces of peanuts that are crushed.

| Peanuts (ounces) | Cost of Peanut Butter (dollars) |
|---|---|
|  | 5.07 |
| 3 |  |
| 3.5 | 11.83 |
|  | 13.52 |

NAME _____ DATE _____

**6.** The cost of parking in a metered spot is directly proportional to the length of time parked.

| Time Parked (minutes) | Cost to Park (dollars) |
|---|---|
| 10 | |
| 60 | 1.50 |
| | 2.00 |
| 100 | |

Determine the constant of proportionality and tell what it represents in each situation.

**7.** The number of pages ($p$) Shirley reads is directly proportional to the time ($t$) she spends reading. Shirley reads 12 pages in 8 minutes.

$p = kt$

$12 = k(8)$

$12 = 8k$

$k = \dfrac{12}{8}$

$k = 1\dfrac{1}{2}$

The constant of proportionality is $1\dfrac{1}{2}$, and it represents the number of pages Shirley reads per minute.

2

8. The number of mini-muffins (*m*) Hector bakes is directly proportional to the number of cups (*c*) of mix that he uses. Hector uses 2.5 cups of mix to bake 45 mini-muffins.

9. The score (*s*) on a test is directly proportional to the number of questions (*q*) that the test taker answers correctly. Cindy scores 73.5 points by answering 21 questions correctly.

NAME_____ DATE _____

10. The number of calories (*c*) in a bottle of juice is directly proportional to the number of servings (*s*) in the bottle. A bottle containing 6 servings of juice contains 390 calories.

11. The distance (*d*) a spring stretches is directly proportional to the weight (*w*) attached to the end of it. A spring stretches 8 centimeters when an object weighing 40 pounds is attached to it.

**2**

**12.** The number of tokens (*t*) game players receive is directly proportional to the number of dollars (*d*) that they pay. Hailey pays $5 for 30 tokens.

NAME_____ DATE _____

Write and solve a direct variation equation to answer each question.

**13.** The number of words Lynne types is directly proportional to the number of minutes she types. Lynne types 320 words in 5 minutes. How long would it take her to type a document with 544 words?

Let $w$ represent the number of words and $m$ represent the number of minutes.
First calculate $k$.

$w = km$

$320 = k(5)$

$320 = 5k$

$k = \dfrac{320}{5}$

$k = 64$

Then, write and solve the equation with $k = 64$.

$w = 64m$

$544 = 64m$

$m = \dfrac{544}{64}$

$m = 8.5$

It would take her 8.5 minutes to type 544 words.

**14.** The relationship between Mexican pesos and American dollars is a direct proportional relationship. During Kevin's vacation, Kevin exchanged 20 American dollars for 250 Mexican pesos. How many pesos would he receive for 50 dollars?

NAME_____ DATE _____

**15.** The length of a segment on a blueprint is directly proportional to the corresponding length in a house. A segment that is 15.75 centimeters on the blueprint corresponds to a beam that is 21 feet long in the house. If the length of a segment on the blueprint is 20.25 centimeters, what is the corresponding length in the house?

**16.** The cost of a car rental is directly proportional to the number of days the car is rented. Mr. Thompson paid $602 to rent a car for 2 weeks. How much would he pay to rent a car for 5 days?

2

NAME_____ DATE _____

**17.** The number of bags of grass seed needed for a lawn is directly proportional to the size of the lawn. Ms. Carpenter needed 7 bags to cover 2800 square feet. How many bags does Mr. Larson need to buy if his lawn measures 3900 square feet?

**18.** The weight of an object on Earth is directly proportional to the weight of the object on the Moon. An astronaut who weighs 180 pounds on Earth would weigh 30 pounds on the Moon. If an object weighs 7 pounds on the Moon, how much would it weigh on Earth?

NAME_____ DATE _____

# Connecting Representations of Proportional Relationships
## Interpreting Multiple Representations of Direct Proportions

## Problem Set

Determine whether the relationship is directly proportional. Explain your reasoning.

1. The table shows the relationship between the numbers of hours that a plumber works on a job and the amount the plumber charges for the job.

| Number of Hours | Amount Charged (dollars) |
|---|---|
| 3 | $220 |
| 5 | $340 |
| 6 | $400 |

I set up the ratio $\dfrac{\text{amount charged}}{\text{number of hours}}$ for each pair of values.

$$\frac{220}{3} = 73\frac{1}{3} \qquad \frac{340}{5} = 68 \qquad \frac{400}{6} = 66\frac{2}{3}$$

The ratios are not constant, so the relationship between the number of hours and the amount charged is not directly proportional.

2. The equation $c = 0.45p$ shows the relationship between the cost ($c$) of printing a yearbook and the number of pages ($p$) in the book.

**2**

3. The table shows the relationship between the size of a painting and the cost of the painting.

| Size (square centimeters) | Cost (dollars) |
|---|---|
| 240 | $7.20 |
| 610 | $18.30 |
| 900 | $27.00 |

4. Emilio bought $\frac{1}{2}$ pound of raisins for $1.07, while Tory bought $1\frac{1}{2}$ pounds of raisins for $3.21.

NAME_____ DATE _____

5. The graph shows the relationship between the age of a cat and its corresponding age in "human years."

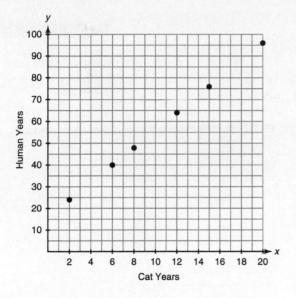

6. The graph shows the relationship between the number of clowns and number of jugglers needed for a performance.

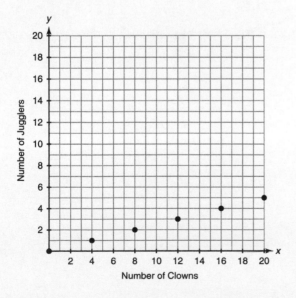

**2**

Determine the constant of proportionality and interpret it in the context of each problem.

7. The distance (d) Mr. Benson can drive is directly proportional to the number of gallons (g) of gas in his car. He needs 15 gallons of gas to drive 480 miles.

   The equation for the relationship is $d = 32g$, so $k = 32$. It is the number of miles Mr. Benson can drive on 1 gallon of gas.

8. The table shows the relationship between the number of minutes customers use the Internet at an Internet café and the amount they are charged for using it.

| Number of Minutes | Cost (dollars) |
|---|---|
| 8 | $1.20 |
| 15 | $2.25 |
| 40 | $6.00 |

9. The equation $t = 25p$ shows the relationship between the time (t) to deliver newspapers in seconds and the number of papers (p) delivered.

NAME_____ DATE _____

10. The graph shows the relationship between the number of tickets Ricky buys and the number of rides he can ride.

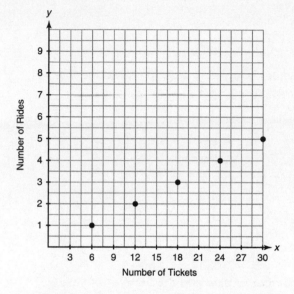

11. The equation $a = \dfrac{4}{15}m$ shows the relationship between the number of advertisements ($a$) during a television program and the number of minutes ($m$) the program lasts.

12. The number of buttons ($b$) Sally needs to make shirts for a dance team is directly proportional to the number of shirts ($s$) she needs to make. She needs 36 buttons to make 3 shirts.

© Carnegie Learning

Use the given information to answer each question.

**13.** The equation $g = 3b$ shows the relationship between the number of girls ($g$) and number of boys ($b$) needed for a musical. How many boys are needed if 21 girls are in the musical?

$g = 3b$

$21 = 3b$

$\dfrac{21}{3} = b$

$7 = b$

Seven boys are needed.

**14.** The graph shows the relationship between the number of blue and the number of yellow tablespoons of paint an artist needs to make a shade of green. How many tablespoons of yellow paint does the artist need to mix with 44 tablespoons of blue paint?

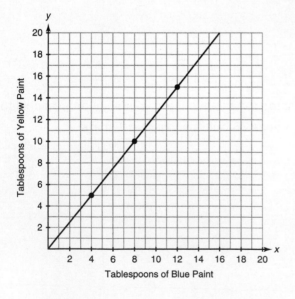

NAME_____ DATE _____

15. The equation $r = \frac{2}{7}p$ shows the relationship between the number of rocks ($r$) and plants ($p$) in a garden design. How many rocks does a homeowner following this design need if he has 35 plants?

16. Maryanne redeemed 4000 gift points for a $20 gift card and 10,000 gift points for a $50 gift card. How many gift points does she need to get a $75 gift card?

**2**

**17.** The table shows the relationship between the height of a custom-built fence to enclose a given area and the cost of the fence. What would be the cost of a fence that is 8 feet high?

| Height (feet) | Cost (dollars) |
|---|---|
| 3 | $225 |
| 5 | $375 |
| 6 | $450 |

**18.** The equation $a = 1.2p$ shows the relationship between the number of apples ($a$) and the number of pears ($p$) in a fruit basket. How many pears are in a basket if there are 12 apples?

# Lesson 3.1  Skills Practice

NAME_____ DATE _____

## Give Me a Ballpark Figure of the Cost
### Estimating and Calculating with Percents and Rates

## Problem Set

Calculate the value of each expression.

**1.** $\frac{1}{4}$ of 80

$$\frac{1}{4}(80) = \frac{80}{4}$$

$$= 20$$

**2.** $\frac{1}{8}$ of 96

**3.** $\frac{1}{6}$ of 4200

**4.** $\frac{1}{5}$ of 300

**5.** $\frac{2}{5}$ of 120

**6.** $\frac{3}{8}$ of 200

7. $\frac{3}{4}$ of 160

8. $\frac{7}{10}$ of 500

9. $\frac{3}{10}$ of 90

10. $\frac{7}{8}$ of 104

Calculate the value of each expression.

11. 5% of 80

(0.05)(80) = 4

12. 8% of 300

13. 10% of 200

14. 22% of 250

15. 15% of 160

16. 55% of 90

17. 20% of 160

18. 85% of 400

19. 25% of 176

20. 95% of 600

© Carnegie Learning

NAME_____ DATE _____

Estimate the value of each expression.

**21.** $\frac{1}{10}$ of 99.9

The value 99.9 is about 100 and 100 divided by 10 is 10. The estimated value is 10.

**22.** $\frac{1}{5}$ of 24.8

**23.** $\frac{1}{20}$ of 40.2

**24.** $\frac{1}{2}$ of 199.59

**25.** $\frac{1}{4}$ of 81.09

**26.** $\frac{1}{3}$ of 29.99

**27.** $\frac{2}{10}$ of 49.8

**28.** $\frac{2}{5}$ of 30.29

**29.** $\frac{3}{10}$ of 199.95

**30.** $\frac{3}{4}$ of 100.99

Estimate the value of each expression.

**31.** 10% of 29.99

The value 29.99 is about 30 and 10% or one-tenth of 30 is 3. The estimated value is 3.

**32.** 5% of 79.95

**33.** 15% of 49.5

**34.** 20% of 119.99

**35.** 25% of 399

**36.** 30% of 150.49

NAME_____ DATE _____

**37.** 40% of 495

**38.** 60% of 89.95

**39.** 15% of 201.25

**40.** 90% of 199.99

Estimate the sale price of each item. Then, calculate the actual sale price of the item.

**41.** A clock is on sale for 10% off the original price of $39.90.

The amount $39.90 is about $40 and 10% or one-tenth of $40 is $4. The estimated sale price is $40 − $4 or $36.

The actual discount is $(0.10)(39.90) = \$3.99$. The actual sale price is $39.90 − $3.99 = $35.91.

**42.** A desk is on sale for 5% off the original price of $99.

**43.** A microwave oven is on sale for 20% off the original price of $79.50.

**44.** A computer is on sale for 15% off the original price of $399.

**45.** A cell phone is on sale for 25% off the original price of $199.

**46.** A bicycle is on sale for 30% off the original price of $149.50.

NAME_____ DATE _____

**47.** A jacket is on sale for 40% off the original price of $59.75.

**48.** A lawnmower is on sale for 15% off the original price of $118.

**49.** A skateboard is on sale for 25% off the original price of $159.

**50.** A couch is on sale for 60% off the original price of $499.

NAME_____ DATE _____

## One Size Fits All?
### Solving Percent Problems

## Problem Set

Solve each percent problem using the percent formula.

**1.** Fifteen is what percent of 50?

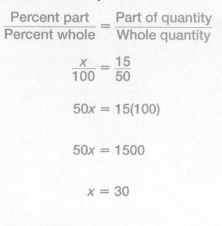

$$\frac{\text{Percent part}}{\text{Percent whole}} = \frac{\text{Part of quantity}}{\text{Whole quantity}}$$

$$\frac{x}{100} = \frac{15}{50}$$

$$50x = 15(100)$$

$$50x = 1500$$

$$x = 30$$

Fifteen is 30% of 50.

**2.** Sixty is 30% of what number?

© Carnegie Learning

3

**3.** What number is 60% of 70?

**4.** Eighty-four is 70% of what number?

NAME_____ DATE _____

5. What number is 75% of 150?

6. Thirty is what percent of 240?

3

7. Eighteen is 12% of what number?

8. What number is 95% of 350?

NAME_____ DATE _____

9.  Seventy-eight is 26% of what number?

10.  What number is 58% of 420?

The table shows the results of a survey given to the students in Ms. Williams' homeroom class. Use the data to solve the percent problem.

| Name | Transportation to School | Birth Month | Number of Siblings |
|---|---|---|---|
| Juan | Bus | September | 2 |
| Elizabeth | Car | July | 1 |
| Steven | Bus | January | 0 |
| Marcy | Walk | February | 1 |
| Rosa | Bike | April | 3 |
| Antonio | Bus | November | 0 |
| Mei | Bus | September | 1 |
| Casey | Car | November | 3 |
| Eric | Walk | October | 2 |
| Roger | Bus | October | 2 |
| Asna | Bus | April | 1 |
| Quentin | Bus | October | 5 |
| Victoria | Car | April | 0 |
| Gerald | Bus | September | 3 |
| Zane | Car | June | 1 |
| Deidre | Bus | March | 3 |

NAME _____ DATE _____

11. What percent of the students in the class ride in a car to school?

$$\frac{\text{Percent part}}{\text{Percent whole}} = \frac{\text{Part of quantity}}{\text{Whole quantity}}$$

$$\frac{x}{100} = \frac{4}{16}$$

$$16x = 4(100)$$

$$16x = 400$$

$$x = 25$$

Twenty-five percent of the students in the class ride in a car to school.

12. What percent of the students in the class walk to school?

**13.** What percent of the students in the class ride the bus to school?

**14.** What percent of the students in the class ride a bike to school?

NAME_____ DATE _____

**15.** What percent of the students in the class were born in September?

**16.** What percent of the students in the class have a birthday in the calendar year before July?

**17.** What percent of the students in the class were born in either April or October?

**18.** What percent of the students in the class have 3 or more siblings?

NAME_____ DATE _____

**19.** What percent of the students in the class have no siblings?

**20.** What percent of the students in the class have at least one sibling?

A furniture store is running a going-out-of-business sale. On Friday, every item in the store is 25% off. Every item is 35% off on Saturday. On Sunday, every item is 45% off. Use this information to solve each problem.

**21.** Joseph buys a table and chairs for $300 on Friday. What was the original price?

$100\% - 25\% = 75\%$

$$\frac{\text{Percent part}}{\text{Percent whole}} = \frac{\text{Part of quantity}}{\text{Whole quantity}}$$

$$\frac{75}{100} = \frac{300}{x}$$

$$75x = 300(100)$$

$$75x = 30,000$$

$$x = 400$$

The original price of the table and chairs was $400.

**22.** How much does Sakura pay for a sofa on Friday if the original price is $440?

**NAME**_____ **DATE**_____

23. Terrence buys a grandfather clock on Friday. If the original price is $180, how much does he get off the original price?

24. Beverly buys a desk for $234 on Saturday. What was the original price?

3

25. Rich buys an entertainment center on Saturday. How much does he pay for the entertainment center if the original price is $250?

26. Kato buys a recliner on Saturday. If the original price is $350, how much does he get off the original price?

NAME_____ DATE _____

**27.** Trisha buys a nightstand for $78 on Saturday. What was the original price?

**28.** Jackie buys an armoire on Sunday. How much does she pay for the armoire if the original price is $130?

**29.** Julian buys a mattress on Sunday. If the original price is $900, how much does he get off the original price?

**30.** Shanise buys a dresser for $302.50 on Sunday. What was the original price?

**NAME**_____  **DATE** _____

# Mathematics and Nutrition
## Using Proportions and Percent Equations

## Vocabulary

Define the term in your own words.

**1.** percent equation

## Problem Set

Answer each question by solving both a percent equation and a proportion in the table shown.

**1.** What number is 20% of 160?

| Use a Percent Equation | Use a Proportion |
|---|---|
| $(0.20)(160) = p$ <br> $32 = p$ | $\dfrac{20}{100} = \dfrac{p}{160}$ <br> $100p = (20)(160)$ <br> $\dfrac{100p}{100} = \dfrac{3200}{100}$ <br> $p = 32$ |

Thirty-two is 20% of 160.

**2.** Forty is what percent of 180?

| Use a Percent Equation | Use a Proportion |
| --- | --- |
|  |  |

**3.** Fifty is 30% of what number?

| Use a Percent Equation | Use a Proportion |
| --- | --- |
|  |  |

NAME_____ DATE _____

4. What number is 85% of 300?

| Use a Percent Equation | Use a Proportion |
|---|---|
|  |  |

5. Forty-eight is what percent of 160?

| Use a Percent Equation | Use a Proportion |
|---|---|
|  |  |

**6.** Seventy-seven is 22% of what number?

| Use a Percent Equation | Use a Proportion |
|---|---|
|  |  |

Answer each question by solving both a percent equation and a proportion in the table shown. Write your answer in a complete sentence.

**7.** You want to buy a sweater that is 25% off. If the original price of the sweater is $38, how much will your discount be?

| Use a Percent Equation | Use a Proportion |
|---|---|
| $(0.25)(38) = d$<br>$9.50 = d$ | $\frac{25}{100} = \frac{d}{38}$<br>$100d = (25)(38)$<br>$\frac{100d}{100} = \frac{950}{100}$<br>$d = 9.50$ |

The discount will be $9.50.

NAME_____ DATE _____

8. If you ate a 315-calorie meal, and 95 calories are from fat, about what percent of the meal is fat?

| Use a Percent Equation | Use a Proportion |
| --- | --- |
|  |  |

9. You want to leave a tip for a meal that costs $17.95. If all you have is $3.00, what percentage tip will you be able to leave?

| Use a Percent Equation | Use a Proportion |
| --- | --- |
|  |  |

10. If the 481 children's books represent 13% of the books in the library, how many total books are in the library?

| Use a Percent Equation | Use a Proportion |
|---|---|
|  |  |

11. Jeremy bought a souvenir while on vacation. The item cost $22.00, but the total bill was $23.43. What percent was sales tax?

| Use a Percent Equation | Use a Proportion |
|---|---|
|  |  |

NAME_____   DATE _____

12. A town's population is 760 in one year and 798 the next year. By what percent did the population grow?

| Use a Percent Equation | Use a Proportion |
| --- | --- |
|  |  |

13. Nina gets a $50 allowance each month (4 weeks). She spends $5 per week and saves the rest. What percentage of her allowance does she save?

| Use a Percent Equation | Use a Proportion |
| --- | --- |
|  |  |

**14.** If you deposit $800 into a savings account with an interest rate of 3.8%, what will be your balance at the end of one year?

| Use a Percent Equation | Use a Proportion |
|---|---|
|  |  |

**15.** A solution is 45% saline. If 27 mL of saline was added to make the solution, what is the total amount of the solution?

| Use a Percent Equation | Use a Proportion |
|---|---|
|  |  |

NAME_____ DATE _____

**16.** Luis read 166 pages of a 415-page novel. What percentage of the book does he have left to read?

| Use a Percent Equation | Use a Proportion |
|---|---|
| | |

# Lesson 3.4  Skills Practice

NAME_____  DATE_____

## Be Mindful of the Fees!
### Using Percents

## Vocabulary

Choose the term from the box that best completes the statement.

| interest | principal | percent increase | percent decrease | depreciate | simple interest |

1. The amount of money in a bank account is called the _____.

2. _____ is the money added to a bank account by the bank in return for borrowing the principal.

3. _____ is a fixed percentage of the principal paid over a specific period of time.

4. A(n) _____ occurs when a new amount of a quantity is less than the original amount.

5. A(n) _____ occurs when a new amount of a quantity is greater than the original amount.

6. When an item loses value over time, it is said to _____.

## Problem Set

Calculate simple interest for each given principal, interest rate, and time period.

1. Principal: $225, Interest Rate: 6%, Time: 2 years

$$I = P \cdot r \cdot t$$

$$= 225 \cdot 0.06 \cdot 2$$

$$= 27$$

The simple interest is $27.

3

**2.** Principal: $1500, Interest Rate: 4%, Time: 3 years

**3.** Principal: $300, Interest Rate: 7%, Time: 5 years

**4.** Principal: $624, Interest Rate: 5%, Time: 4 years

NAME_____ DATE _____

5. Principal: $739, Interest Rate: 6%, Time: 3 years

6. Principal: $213, Interest Rate: 7%, Time: 2 years

Use the given information to answer each question.

7. Ronna earned $235 babysitting. She decides to deposit the money into a bank account that earns 3% interest. If she leaves the money in the account for 2 years, how much interest will she earn?

$I = P \cdot r \cdot t$

$= 235 \cdot 0.03 \cdot 2$

$= 14.1$

Ronna will earn $14.10 in interest.

8. Pablo earned $752 cutting grass this summer. He decides to deposit the money into a bank account that earns 4% interest. If he leaves the money in the account for 2 years, what is the total amount that Pablo will have in the account?

NAME_____ DATE _____

9. Carmen borrows $115 from her parents for a new cell phone. She agrees to pay her parents back the original amount plus 2% interest in 2 years. How much interest will Carmen pay?

10. Lucas borrows $5629 from the bank to purchase a motorcycle. He agrees to pay the bank back the original amount plus 6% interest in 5 years. What is the total amount that Lucas will pay the bank?

Calculate each percent increase or percent decrease. Round to the nearest whole percent if necessary.

**11.** original amount: 30, new amount: 45

amount of increase = new amount − original amount

$$= 45 - 30$$

$$= 15$$

percent increase = $\dfrac{\text{amount of increase}}{\text{original amount}}$

$$= \dfrac{15}{30}$$

$$= 0.5$$

$$= 50\%$$

**12.** original amount: 12, new amount: 16

NAME_____ DATE _____

**13.** original amount: 17, new amount: 21

**14.** original amount: 85, new amount: 56

© Carnegie Learning

3

**15.** original amount: 48, new amount: 37

**16.** original amount: 124, new amount: 76

NAME_____ DATE _____

Use the given information to answer each question.

**17.** Carlos purchased an antique chair at a garage sale for $15. He later sold the chair for $27 to an antique dealer. What was the percent increase of the price of the chair?

amount of increase = new amount − original amount

$$= 27 - 15$$

$$= 12$$

percent increase = $\dfrac{\text{amount of increase}}{\text{original amount}}$

$$= \dfrac{12}{15}$$

$$= 0.8$$

$$= 80\%$$

The price of the chair increased by 80%.

**18.** Lamar purchased a comic book at a garage sale for $3. He later sold the comic book to a comic book dealer for $5. What was the percent increase of the price of the comic book?

**19.** Eva purchased a car for $21,000. One year later the value of the car had dropped to $16,000. What is the percent decrease in the value of the car?

NAME_____ DATE _____

**20.** Fernando purchased a motorcycle for $7840. One year later the value of the motorcycle was $6640. What is the percent decrease in the value of the motorcycle?

Calculate the depreciation of each given item.

**21.** A motorcycle which costs $15,000 depreciates at a rate of 9% per year. How much does the motorcycle depreciate in the first year?

(0.09)(15,000) = 1350

The motorcycle depreciates $1350 in the first year.

**22.** A new car which costs $25,000 depreciates at a rate of 12% per year. How much does the car depreciate in the first year?

**23.** A new boat which costs $18,000 depreciates at a rate of 8% per year. How much does the boat depreciate in the first year?

**24.** A Jet Ski which costs $12,000 depreciates at a rate of 6% per year. What is the value of the Jet Ski after one year?

**25.** A new car which costs $24,000 depreciates at a rate of 12% per year. What is the value of the car after one year?

**26.** A new car which costs $32,000 depreciates at a rate of 12% the first year. The car depreciates at a rate of 10% the second year. What is the value of the car after two years?

NAME_____ DATE _____

## Shoe Super Store
### Solving Percent Problems Involving Proportions

## Vocabulary

Define the term in your own words.

**1.** commission

## Problem Set

Use the direct variation equation to solve each problem.

**1.** The equation $d = 0.2p$ shows the relationship between the discount ($d$) an employee receives and the regular purchase price ($p$) of an item at the store where he works. Tell what percent discount the employee receives and determine the regular price of a jacket if the employee's discount is $14.

The employee receives a 20% discount.

$d = 0.2p$

$14 = 0.2p$

$\dfrac{14}{0.2} = p$

$70 = p$

The regular cost of the jacket is $70.

2. The equation $s = 0.1p$ shows the relationship between the amount George saves ($s$) from each paycheck and the amount of his paycheck ($p$). Tell what percent of each paycheck George saves and determine how much of a $128 paycheck George saves.

3. The equation $s = 0.35m$ shows the relationship between the amount of salt ($s$) in a mixture and the total amount of the mixture ($m$) in grams. Tell what percent of the mixture is salt and determine how much mixture a scientist made if the mixture contains 14 grams of salt.

NAME_____ DATE _____

4. The equation $c = 0.55p$ shows the relationship between the clearance price ($c$) of an item and the original price ($p$) of the item. Tell what percent the clearance price is of the original price and determine the clearance price on a picture frame that originally sold for $13.

5. The equation $r = 0.25t$ shows the relationship between the number of red pens ($r$) and the total number of pens ($t$) a school secretary orders every year. Tell what percent of the pens the secretary orders are red pens and determine the total number of pens she ordered if she ordered 75 red pens.

**6.** The equation $g = 0.18f$ shows the relationship between the number of goldfish ($g$) in an aquarium and the total number of fish ($f$) in the aquarium. Tell what percent of the fish in the aquarium are goldfish and determine the number of goldfish in the aquarium if there are 50 fish in all.

Use the given information to answer each question.

**7.** The Reinholds always devote the same percent of space in their vegetable garden to corn. The table shows the relationship between the total area ($t$) of the garden and the corn area ($c$). How much space will they devote to corn if their total garden space is 60 square feet?

| Total Area (square feet) | Corn Area (square feet) |
|---|---|
| 40 | 16 |
| 75 | 30 |
| 90 | 36 |

I used the ratio $\frac{16}{40} = 0.4$ to write the equation $c = 0.4t$.

$c = 0.4t$

$c = 0.4(60)$

$c = 24$

They will devote 24 square feet to corn.

NAME_____ DATE _____

8. The table shows the relationship between the amount Ms. Hashimoto sells (s) and the commission (c) she earns for it. How much did she sell if she earned a commission of $188?

| Amount Sold (dollars) | Commission Earned (dollars) |
|---|---|
| $980 | $78.40 |
| $1350 | $108 |
| $1475 | $118 |

**9.** A flower shop's most popular style of bouquet is called the ultimate bouquet. In the ultimate bouquet, 35% of the flowers are roses. How many roses are in an ultimate bouquet if there are a total of 40 flowers in the bouquet?

**10.** The table shows the relationship between the number of dance songs (*d*) on Gloria's MP3 player and the total (*t*) number of songs on it. How many songs does she now have on her MP3 player if 72 are dance songs?

| Total Number of Songs | Number of Dance Songs |
| --- | --- |
| 40 | 24 |
| 75 | 45 |
| 80 | 48 |

NAME_____ DATE _____

**11.** Forty-two percent of the students in the sixth grade at Lincoln Middle School play sports. How many students are in the sixth grade if 84 of them play sports?

**12.** A car is worth 72% of its original value. What is the value of the car if it was originally worth $18,200?

13. The table shows the relationship between the number of birdcages (*f*) Fred can paint and the number of birdcages (*t*) Tonya can paint during the same time. How many birdcages can Tonya paint in the same time that Fred can paint 12 birdcages?

| Birdcages Fred Painted | Birdcages Tonya Painted |
|:---:|:---:|
| 4 | 3 |
| 9 | 6.75 |
| 15 | 11.25 |

14. A company charges a 12% late fee on bills not paid within 30 days. What is the amount of a bill if the late fee is $8.04?

# Lesson 4.1 Skills Practice

NAME_____ DATE _____

## Math Football
### Using Models to Understand Integers

## Problem Set

Determine the ending position by adding and subtracting the indicated steps from each starting position.

|     | Starting Position | Steps Backward | Steps Forward | Ending Position |
| --- | --- | --- | --- | --- |
| 1. | +3 | 4 | 5 | +4 |
| 2. | +7 | 6 | 2 | |
| 3. | +5 | 2 | 4 | |
| 4. | 0 | 5 | 8 | |
| 5. | −4 | 3 | 7 | |
| 6. | +1 | 7 | 9 | |
| 7. | −6 | 1 | 5 | |
| 8. | −2 | 5 | 6 | |
| 9. | 8 | 3 | 1 | |
| 10. | −9 | 2 | 4 | |

Write a number sentence to describe each set of steps forward and backward.

|      | Starting Position | Steps Backward | Steps Forward | Number Sentence |
|------|:-----------------:|:--------------:|:-------------:|-----------------|
| 11.  | +2 | 4 | 7 | +2 + (−4) + 7 = +5 |
| 12.  | −7 | 3 | 5 |  |
| 13.  | +6 | 9 | 4 |  |
| 14.  | +4 | 6 | 1 |  |
| 15.  | −5 | 2 | 9 |  |
| 16.  | 0  | 5 | 3 |  |
| 17.  | −3 | 1 | 4 |  |
| 18.  | −8 | 2 | 6 |  |
| 19.  | 0  | 8 | 2 |  |
| 20.  | +9 | 7 | 8 |  |

Calculate each sum.

**21.** $+9 + (−4) + 3 = +8$

**22.** $−2 + (−5) + 8 =$

**23.** $+6 + (−8) + 5 =$

**24.** $0 + (−2) + 7 =$

**25.** $−9 + (−1) + 6 =$

**26.** $+3 + (−6) + 5 =$

**27.** $0 + (−7) + 9 =$

**28.** $+1 + (−1) + 9 =$

**29.** $−5 + (−3) + 4 =$

**30.** $−3 + (−2) + 8 =$

© Carnegie Learning

NAME_____ DATE _____

Write a number sentence to describe the results of each roll of two number cubes (numbered 1 through 6). The result of the red number cube represents a negative number and the result of the black number cube represents a positive number.

**31.** Your score starts at 0. You roll a red 5 and a black 3.

$0 + (-5) + 3 = -2$

**32.** Your score is 4. You roll a red 3 and a black 6.

**33.** Your score is $-2$. You roll a red 4 and a black 1.

**34.** Your score is 7. You roll a red 6 and a black 2.

**35.** Your score is $-5$. You roll a red 2 and a black 4.

**36.** Your score is 1. You roll a red 5 and a black 3.

**37.** Your score starts at 0. You roll a red 6 and a black 1.

**38.** Your score is $-3$. You roll a red 1 and a black 5.

Determine a roll of two number cubes (numbered 1 through 6) that will result in a final score of 10. Write a number sentence to describe the results of each roll. The result of the red number cube represents a negative number and the result of the black number cube represents a positive number.

Sample answers.

| | Starting Score | Roll of the Red Number Cube | Roll of the Black Number Cube | Number Sentence |
|---|---|---|---|---|
| 39. | +7 | 3 | 6 | +7 + (−3) + 6 = +10 |
| 40. | +8 | | | |
| 41. | +5 | | | |
| 42. | +9 | | | |
| 43. | +12 | | | |
| 44. | +6 | | | |
| 45. | +14 | | | |
| 46. | +10 | | | |

# Lesson 4.2 Skills Practice

**NAME** _____ **DATE** _____

## Walk the Line
### Adding Integers, Part I

## Problem Set

Use the number line to determine the number described by each statement. Explain your reasoning.

1. Determine the number that is 3 more than −5.

   The number that is 3 more than −5 is −2. Go to −5 on the number line and then move 3 units to the right.

2. Determine the number that is 9 more than −4.

3. Determine the number that is 12 more than −8.

4. Determine the number that is 10 more than −1.

5. Determine the number that is 7 less than 3.

6. Determine the number that is 13 less than 6.

7. Determine the number that is 10 less than 2.

8. Determine the number that is 4 less than 1.

Use the number line to determine each sum.

**4**

9. $-3 + 8 =$ ___5___

$3 + (-8) =$ ___-5___

$-3 + (-8) =$ ___-11___

$3 + 8 =$ ___11___

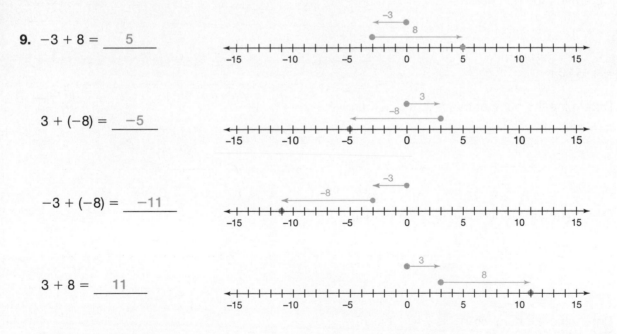

NAME_____ DATE_____

**10.** 9 + (−2) = _____

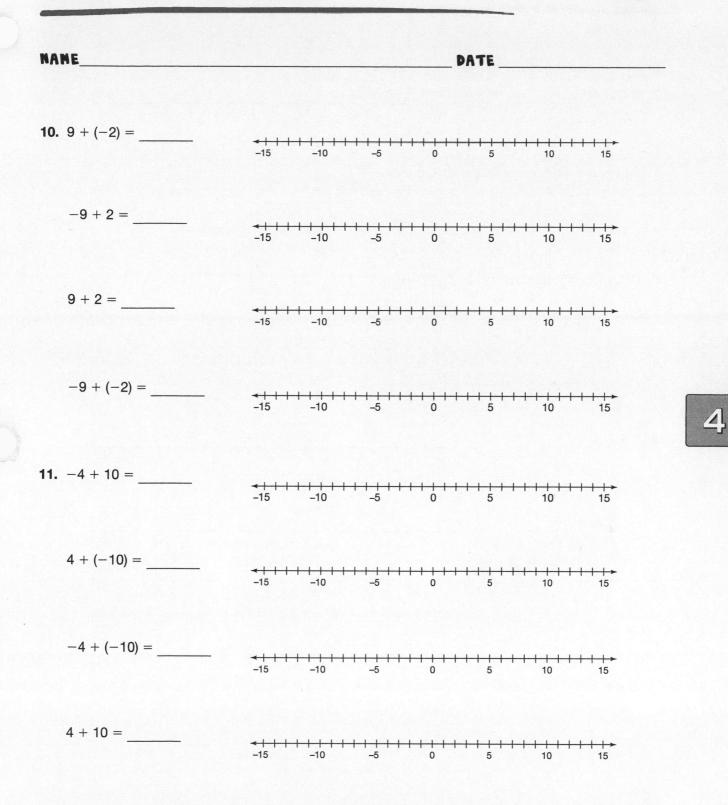

−9 + 2 = _____

9 + 2 = _____

−9 + (−2) = _____

**11.** −4 + 10 = _____

4 + (−10) = _____

−4 + (−10) = _____

4 + 10 = _____

4

**12.** $5 + (-7) =$ _____

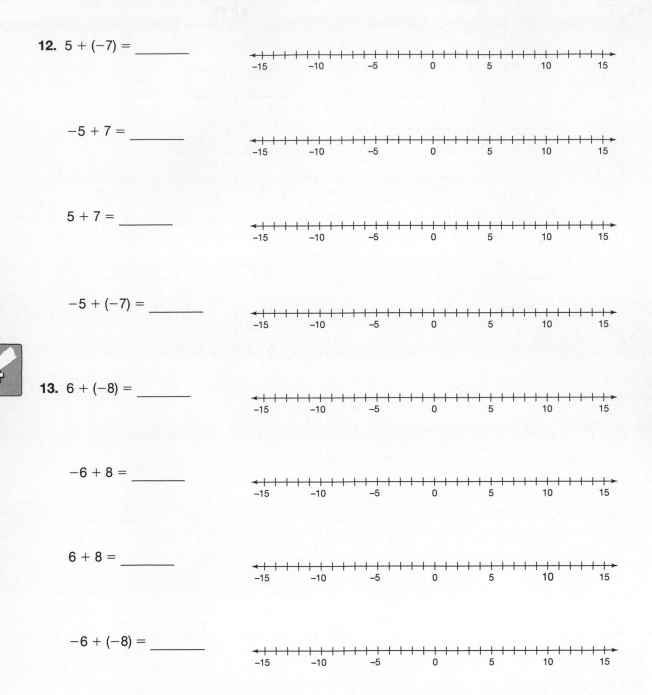

$-5 + 7 =$ _____

$5 + 7 =$ _____

$-5 + (-7) =$ _____

**13.** $6 + (-8) =$ _____

$-6 + 8 =$ _____

$6 + 8 =$ _____

$-6 + (-8) =$ _____

NAME_____ DATE_____

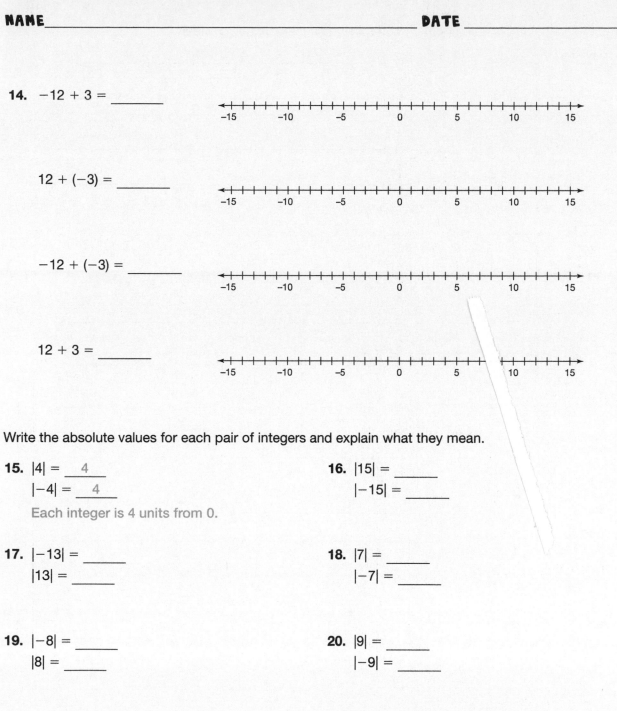

14. $-12 + 3 =$ _____

$12 + (-3) =$ _____

$-12 + (-3) =$ _____

$12 + 3 =$ _____

Write the absolute values for each pair of integers and explain what they mean.

15. $|4| =$ __4__
    $|-4| =$ __4__
    Each integer is 4 units from 0.

16. $|15| =$ _____
    $|-15| =$ _____

17. $|-13| =$ _____
    $|13| =$ _____

18. $|7| =$ _____
    $|-7| =$ _____

19. $|-8| =$ _____
    $|8| =$ _____

20. $|9| =$ _____
    $|-9| =$ _____

Complete each number line model and then determine the unknown addend.

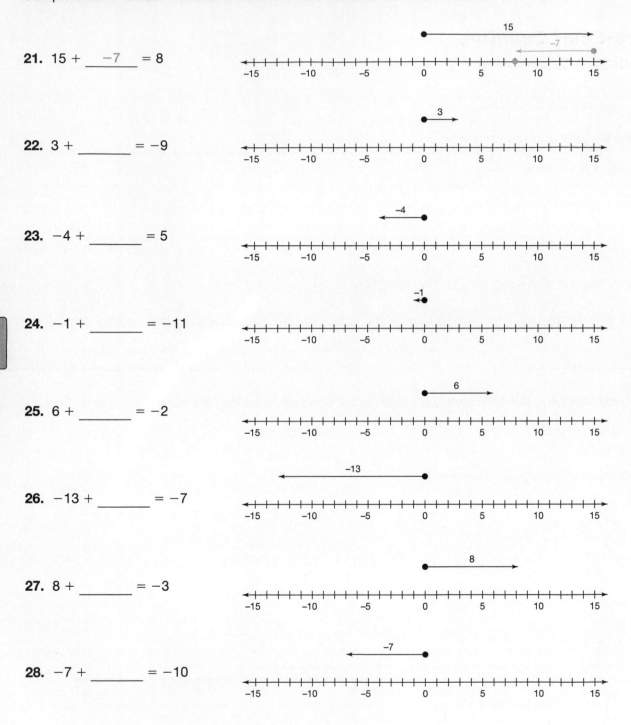

**21.** 15 + ___−7___ = 8

**22.** 3 + _____ = −9

**23.** −4 + _____ = 5

**24.** −1 + _____ = −11

**25.** 6 + _____ = −2

**26.** −13 + _____ = −7

**27.** 8 + _____ = −3

**28.** −7 + _____ = −10

# Lesson 4.3 Skills Practice

NAME _____ DATE _____

## Two-Color Counters
### Adding Integers, Part II

## Vocabulary

Define the term in your own words.

**1.** additive inverses

## Problem Set

Determine each sum using the number line model or two-color counters.

**1.** $5 + (-5) =$ ___0___

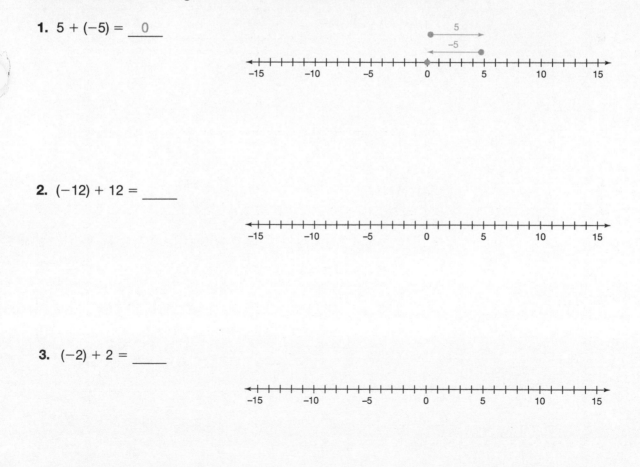

**2.** $(-12) + 12 =$ _____

**3.** $(-2) + 2 =$ _____

**4.** $9 + (-9) =$ _____

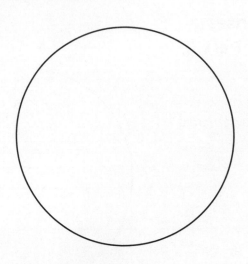

**5.** $4 + (-4) =$ _____

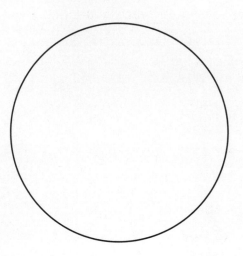

NAME_____ DATE _____

**6.** (−6) + 6 = ____

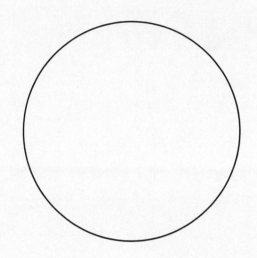

Write a number sentence to represent each model. Cancel out the pairs of counters to show the answer.

**7.** 2 + (−9) = −7 or −9 + 2 = −7

**8.**

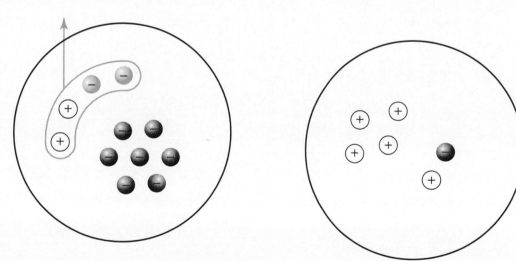

**9.**

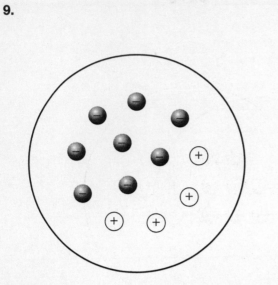

**10.**

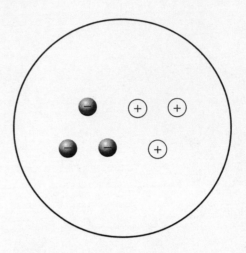

**11.**

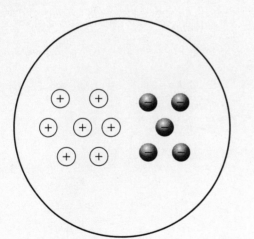

**12.**

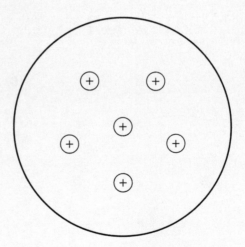

**NAME**_____ **DATE**_____

13.                                                    14.

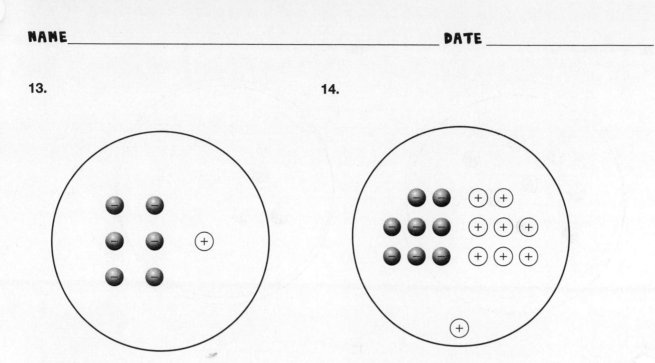

Draw a picture with two-color counters to represent and solve each number sentence. Cancel out the pairs of counters to show the answer.

**15.** $-9 + 3 =$ ___−6___                    **16.** $-3 + 9 =$ _____

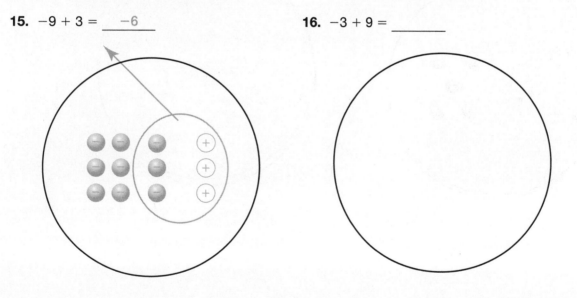

**17.** $-9 + (-3) =$ _____

**18.** $2 + (-5) =$ _____

**19.** $5 + (-2) =$ _____

**20.** $2 + 5 =$ _____

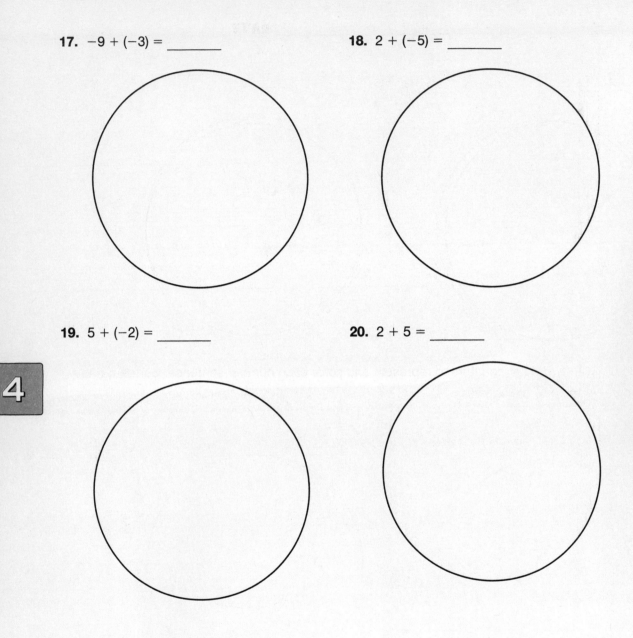

4

NAME_____ DATE_____

**21.** −11 + 7 = _____

**22.** −7 + 11 = _____

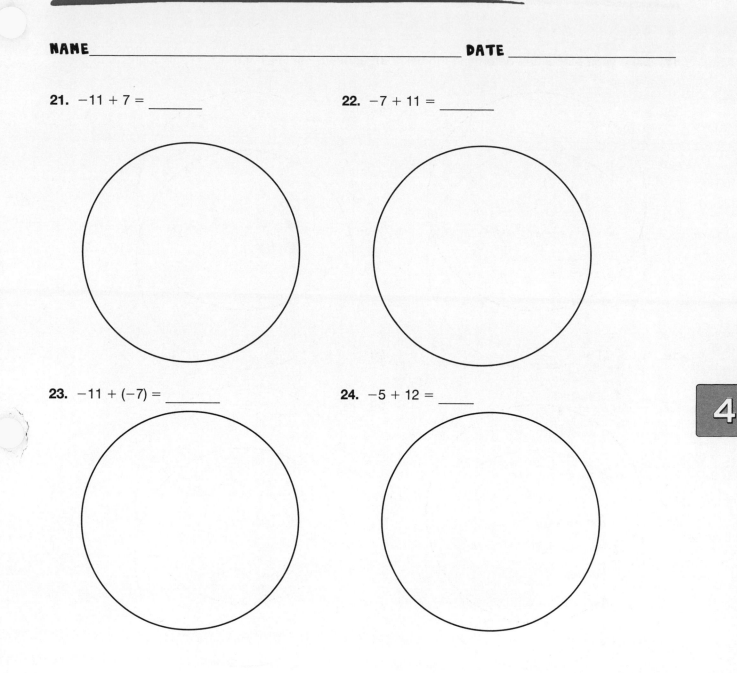

**23.** −11 + (−7) = _____

**24.** −5 + 12 = _____

Complete each model and determine the unknown addend. Circle all of the zero pair counters to show the answer.

**25.** $8 + \underline{\ -2\ } = 6$

**26.** $-4 + \underline{\hspace{2cm}} = 3$

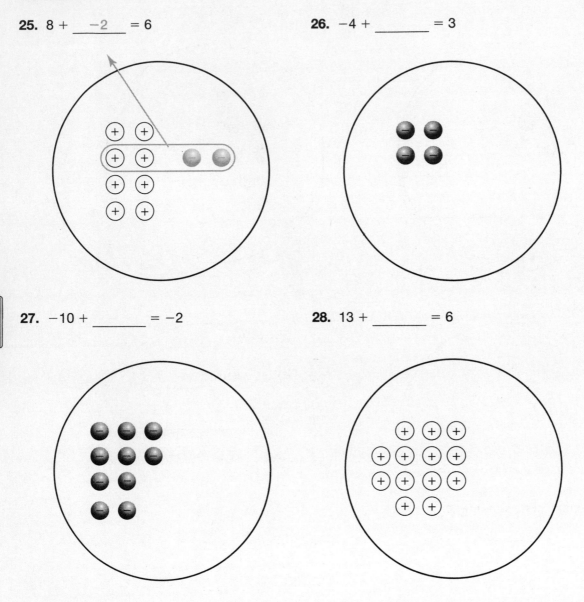

**27.** $-10 + \underline{\hspace{2cm}} = -2$

**28.** $13 + \underline{\hspace{2cm}} = 6$

NAME_____ DATE _____

**29.** $-3 +$ _____ $= -8$

**30.** $-5 +$ _____ $= 0$

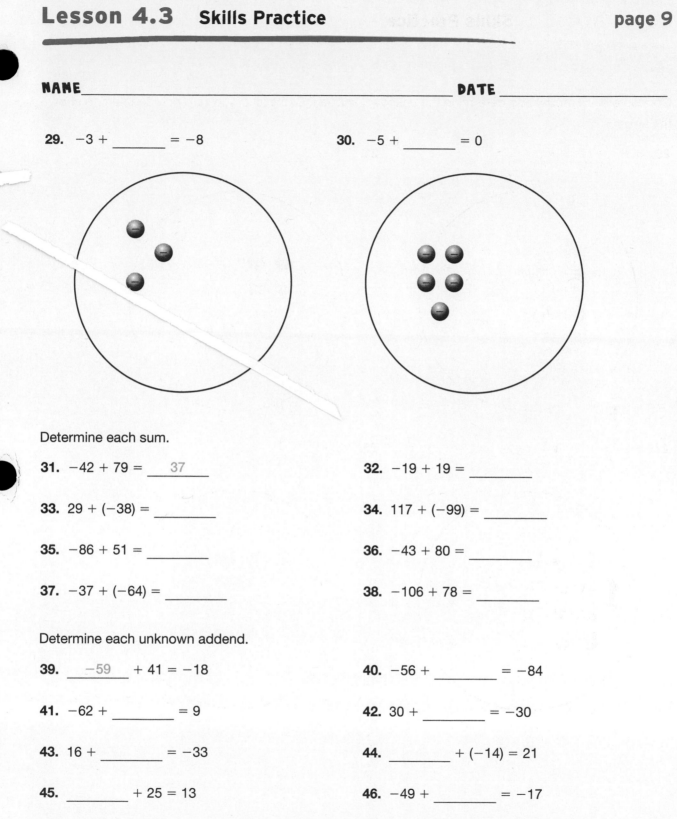

Determine each sum.

**31.** $-42 + 79 =$ ___37___

**32.** $-19 + 19 =$ _____

**33.** $29 + (-38) =$ _____

**34.** $117 + (-99) =$ _____

**35.** $-86 + 51 =$ _____

**36.** $-43 + 80 =$ _____

**37.** $-37 + (-64) =$ _____

**38.** $-106 + 78 =$ _____

Determine each unknown addend.

**39.** ___$-59$___ $+ 41 = -18$

**40.** $-56 +$ _____ $= -84$

**41.** $-62 +$ _____ $= 9$

**42.** $30 +$ _____ $= -30$

**43.** $16 +$ _____ $= -33$

**44.** _____ $+ (-14) = 21$

**45.** _____ $+ 25 = 13$

**46.** $-49 +$ _____ $= -17$

4

NAME_____ DATE _____

## What's the Difference?
### Subtracting Integers

## Vocabulary

Define the term in your own words.

**1.** zero pair

## Problem Set

Draw two other models to represent each integer.

**1.** −3

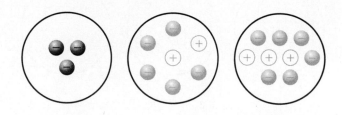

**2.** 4

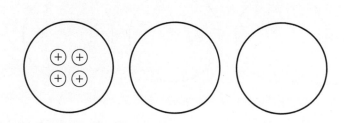

**3.** 2

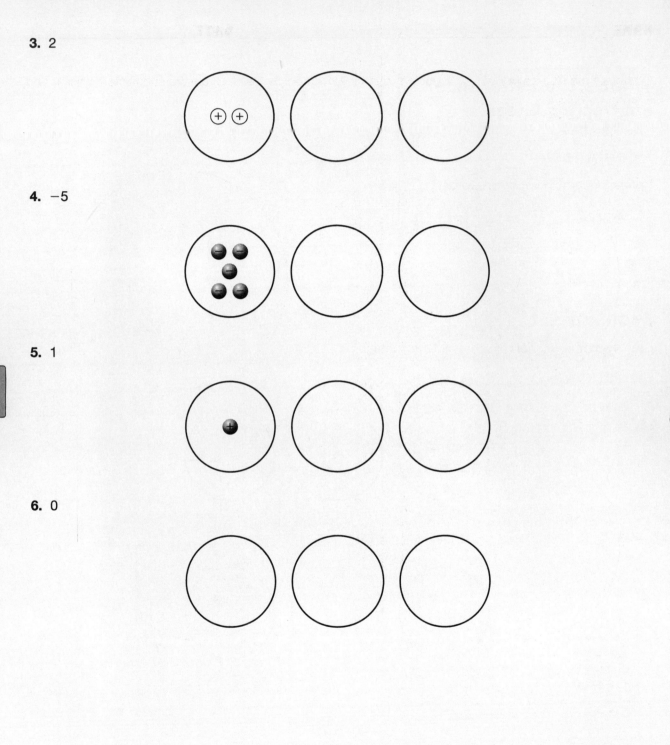

**4.** −5

**5.** 1

**6.** 0

NAME_____ DATE _____

Complete the two-color counter model for each subtraction problem. Circle the subtracted portion and write the difference.

**7.** −3 − 6 = ____−9____

**8.** −3 − (−6) = _____

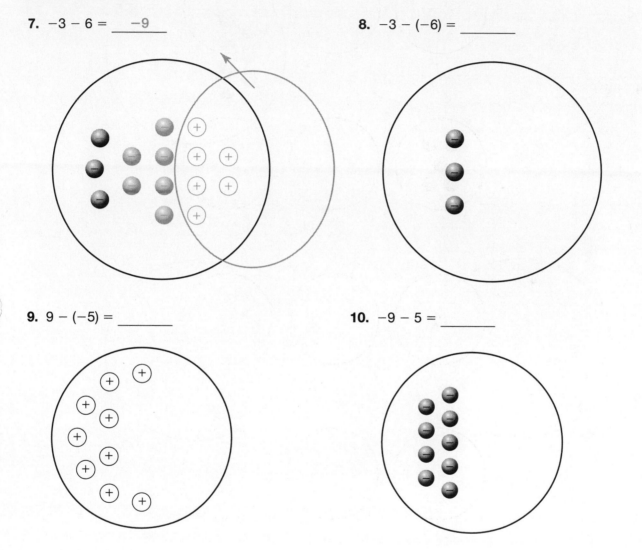

**9.** 9 − (−5) = _____

**10.** −9 − 5 = _____

**11.** 7 − (−2) = _____

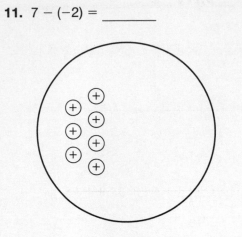

**12.** −7 − 2 = _____

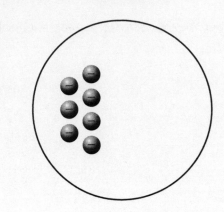

**13.** 4 − 8 = _____

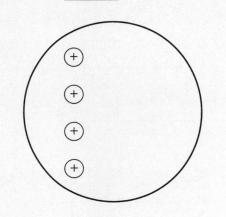

**14.** 4 − (−8) = _____

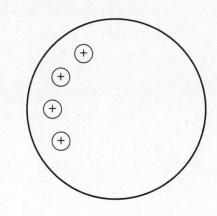

**NAME**_____ **DATE**_____

Draw a number line model to solve each subtraction problem.

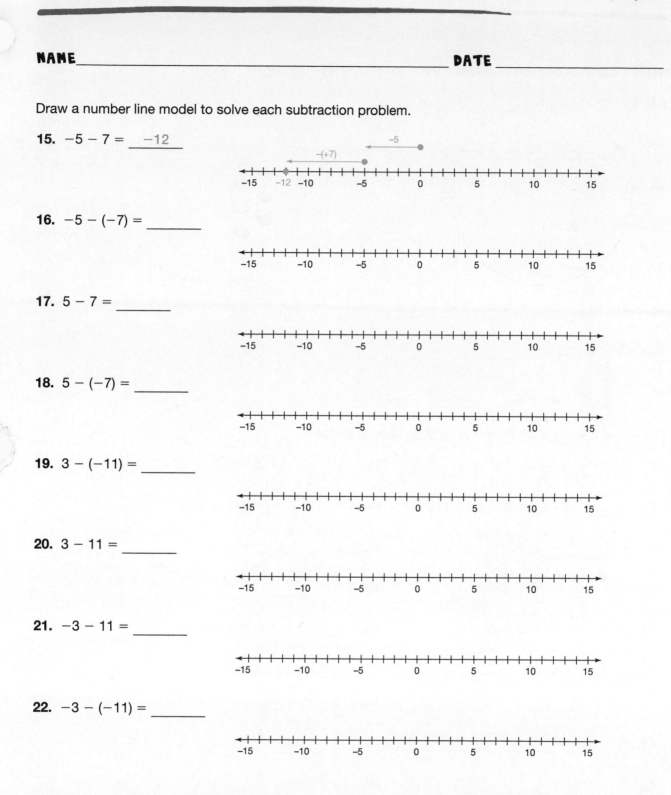

**15.** $-5 - 7 =$ ___−12___

**16.** $-5 - (-7) =$ _____

**17.** $5 - 7 =$ _____

**18.** $5 - (-7) =$ _____

**19.** $3 - (-11) =$ _____

**20.** $3 - 11 =$ _____

**21.** $-3 - 11 =$ _____

**22.** $-3 - (-11) =$ _____

Rewrite each subtraction expression using addition. Then calculate the result.

**23.** $13 - (-9) = \underline{\phantom{13}13\phantom{13}} + \underline{\phantom{9}9\phantom{9}} = \underline{\phantom{22}22\phantom{22}}$

**24.** $-22 - 15 = \underline{\phantom{xxx}} + \underline{\phantom{xxx}} = \underline{\phantom{xxx}}$

**25.** $31 - 17 = \underline{\phantom{xxx}} + \underline{\phantom{xxx}} = \underline{\phantom{xxx}}$

**26.** $-10 - (-8) = \underline{\phantom{xxx}} + \underline{\phantom{xxx}} = \underline{\phantom{xxx}}$

**27.** $5 - (-16) = \underline{\phantom{xxx}} + \underline{\phantom{xxx}} = \underline{\phantom{xxx}}$

**28.** $14 - 23 = \underline{\phantom{xxx}} + \underline{\phantom{xxx}} = \underline{\phantom{xxx}}$

**29.** $-20 - (-32) = \underline{\phantom{xxx}} + \underline{\phantom{xxx}} = \underline{\phantom{xxx}}$

**30.** $-2 - 19 = \underline{\phantom{xxx}} + \underline{\phantom{xxx}} = \underline{\phantom{xxx}}$

Determine the unknown integer in each number sentence.

**31.** $\underline{\phantom{xx}21\phantom{xx}} - (-6) = 27$

**32.** $\underline{\phantom{xxxx}} + (-6) = 27$

**33.** $\underline{\phantom{xxxx}} - 6 = -27$

**34.** $4 - \underline{\phantom{xxxx}} = 31$

**35.** $4 - \underline{\phantom{xxxx}} = -31$

**36.** $-8 + \underline{\phantom{xxxx}} = -38$

**37.** $8 - \underline{\phantom{xxxx}} = -38$

**38.** $-8 + \underline{\phantom{xxxx}} = 38$

**39.** $\underline{\phantom{xxxx}} + (-12) = 50$

**40.** $\underline{\phantom{xxxx}} - (-12) = 50$

Determine each absolute value.

**41.** $|5 - 9| = \underline{\phantom{x}4\phantom{x}}$

**42.** $|-5 - 9| = \underline{\phantom{xxx}}$

**43.** $|5 - (-9)| = \underline{\phantom{xxx}}$

**44.** $|-5 - (-9)| = \underline{\phantom{xxx}}$

**45.** $|-7 - 15| = \underline{\phantom{xxx}}$

**46.** $|7 - (-15)| = \underline{\phantom{xxx}}$

**47.** $|-7 - (-15)| = \underline{\phantom{xxx}}$

**48.** $|7 - 15| = \underline{\phantom{xxx}}$

NAME _____ DATE _____

## What Do We Do Now?
### Adding and Subtracting Rational Numbers

## Problem Set

Calculate each sum.

**1.** $2\frac{3}{8} + 5\frac{1}{4} =$

$2\frac{3}{8} + 5\frac{1}{4} = 7\frac{5}{8}$

$2\frac{3}{8} = 2\frac{3}{8}$

$+5\frac{1}{4} = 5\frac{2}{8}$

$\overline{\phantom{xxxx} 7\frac{5}{8}}$

**2.** $7\frac{1}{6} + 4\frac{2}{3} =$

**3.** $12\frac{2}{5} + \left(-3\frac{1}{4}\right) =$

**4.** $5.3 + (-7.45) =$

© Carnegie Learning

**5.** $-\dfrac{5}{8} + 8\dfrac{3}{8} =$

**6.** $-9.21 + 10.39 =$

**7.** $-3\dfrac{2}{5} + \left(-2\dfrac{3}{5}\right) =$

**8.** $-18.76 + (-11.23) =$

**9.** $14\dfrac{1}{4} + \left(-5\dfrac{2}{3}\right) =$

**10.** $-20.245 + 15.12 =$

NAME_____ DATE _____

Calculate each difference.

**11.** $2\frac{3}{8} - 5\frac{1}{4} =$

**12.** $-8.38 - 11.29 =$

**13.** $7\frac{2}{3} - \left(-4\frac{1}{4}\right) =$

**14.** $32.85 - (-10.65) =$

**15.** $-4\frac{5}{6} - 6\frac{2}{3} =$

**16.** $-19.01 - 10.91 =$

**17.** $-3\frac{1}{5} - \left(-5\frac{1}{10}\right) =$

**18.** $-6.2 - (-3.82) =$

**19.** $10\frac{5}{6} - \left(-2\frac{1}{3}\right) =$

**20.** $-17.538 - 12.371 =$

4

NAME_____ DATE _____

Add or subtract using your algorithms.

**21.** $4.76 - (-2.91) =$ ___7.67___

**22.** $-\dfrac{3}{8} + \left(-\dfrac{5}{6}\right) =$ _____

**23.** $-0.108 - (-4.3) =$ _____

**24.** $-719 - (-698) =$ _____

**25.** $-2\dfrac{4}{7} - 1\dfrac{1}{4} =$ _____

**26.** $-824 + 970 =$ _____

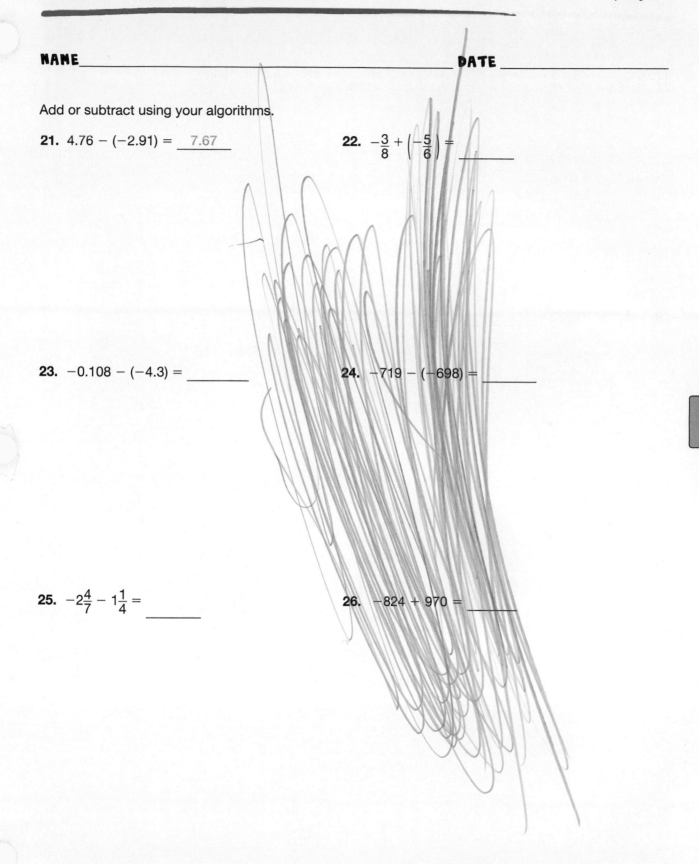

**27.** $3.862 + (-7.4) =$ _____

**28.** $4\frac{7}{11} - 6\frac{2}{3} =$ _____

**29.** $-5.5 + 18.002 =$ _____

**30.** $\frac{13}{15} + \left(-\frac{7}{9}\right) =$ _____

4

# Lesson 5.1 Skills Practice

NAME_____ DATE _____

## Equal Groups
### Multiplying and Dividing Integers

## Problem Set

Draw a two-color counter model to determine each product. Describe the expression in words.

**1.** $2 \times (-6) =$ ___−12___

The expression $2 \times (-6)$ means 2 groups of $(-6)$.

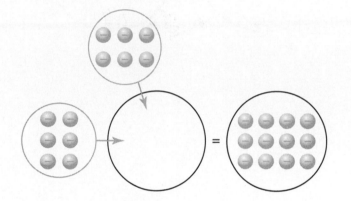

**2.** $-4 \times (-2) =$ _____

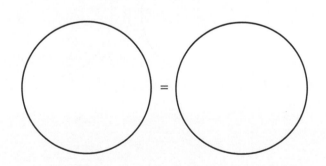

© Carnegie Learning

**3.** $7 \times 3 =$ _____

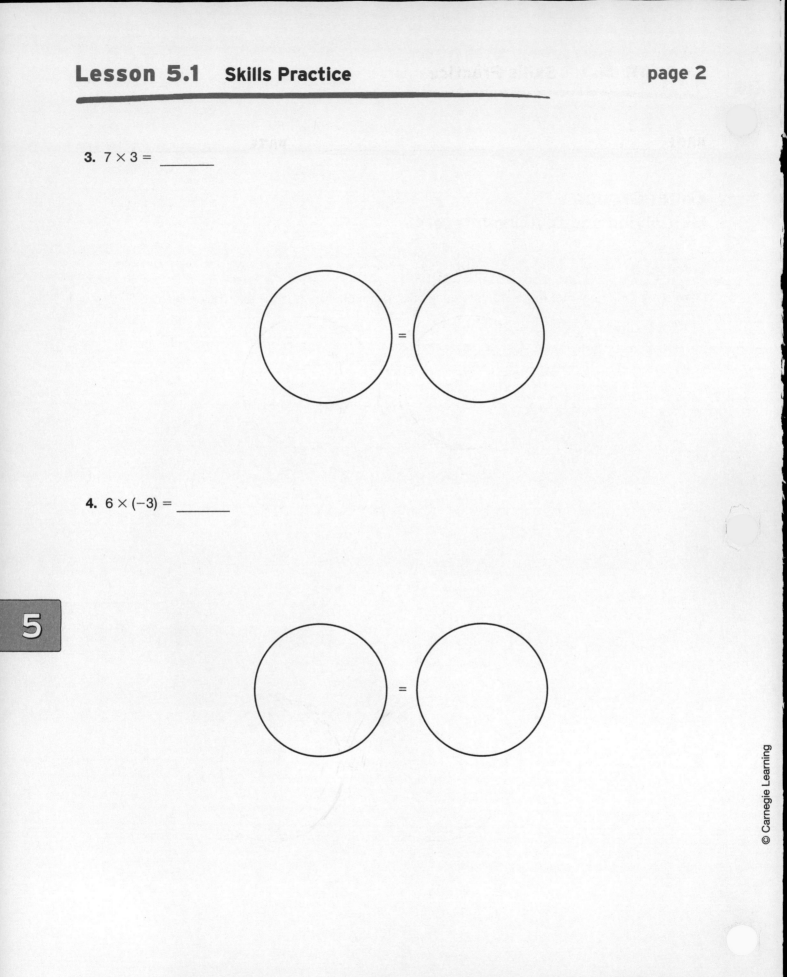

**4.** $6 \times (-3) =$ _____

NAME_____ DATE _____

**5.** $-2 \times 5 =$ _____

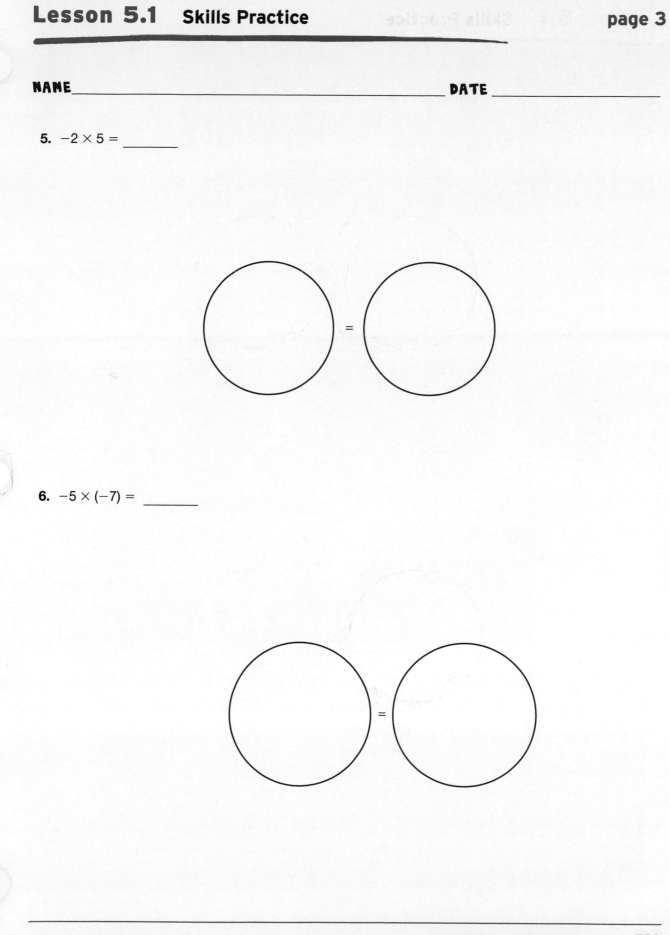

**6.** $-5 \times (-7) =$ _____

© Carnegie Learning

Complete a number line representation to determine each product.

**7.** $2 \times (-7) = $ ___−14___

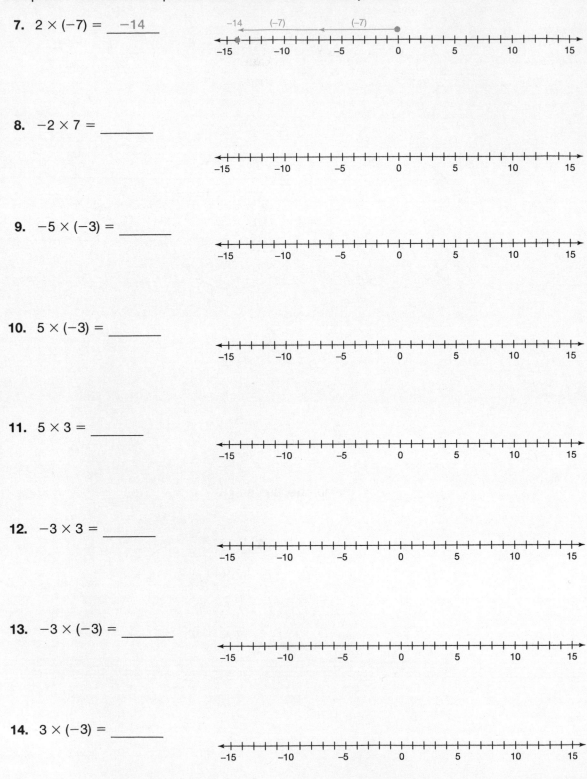

**8.** $-2 \times 7 = $ _____

**9.** $-5 \times (-3) = $ _____

**10.** $5 \times (-3) = $ _____

**11.** $5 \times 3 = $ _____

**12.** $-3 \times 3 = $ _____

**13.** $-3 \times (-3) = $ _____

**14.** $3 \times (-3) = $ _____

NAME_____ DATE _____

Write each expression as a repeated addition **sentence**.

**15.** $6 \times (-7) = (-7) + (-7) + (-7) + (-7) + (-7) + (-7) = -42$

**16.** $-4 \times 8 =$

**17.** $-3 \times 9 =$

**18.** $-5 \times (-4) =$

**19.** $10 \times (-2) =$

**20.** $11 \times 6 =$

Determine each product and write the next three number sentences that extend the pattern. Then tell whether the pattern is increasing or decreasing.

**21.** $-4 \times 4 = \underline{\ -16\ }$

$-4 \times 3 = \underline{\ -12\ }$

$-4 \times 2 = \underline{\ -8\ }$

$-4 \times 1 = \underline{\ -4\ }$

$\underline{\ -4\ } \times \underline{\ 0\ } = \underline{\ 0\ }$

$\underline{\ -4\ } \times \underline{\ -1\ } = \underline{\ 4\ }$

$\underline{\ -4\ } \times \underline{\ -2\ } = \underline{\ 8\ }$

increasing

**22.** $7 \times (-1) = \underline{\hspace{1cm}}$

$7 \times (-2) = \underline{\hspace{1cm}}$

$7 \times (-3) = \underline{\hspace{1cm}}$

$7 \times (-4) = \underline{\hspace{1cm}}$

$\underline{\hspace{1cm}} \times \underline{\hspace{1cm}} = \underline{\hspace{1cm}}$

$\underline{\hspace{1cm}} \times \underline{\hspace{1cm}} = \underline{\hspace{1cm}}$

$\underline{\hspace{1cm}} \times \underline{\hspace{1cm}} = \underline{\hspace{1cm}}$

**23.** $-6 \times (-3) =$ _____

$-6 \times (-2) =$ _____

$-6 \times (-1) =$ _____

$-6 \times 0 =$ _____

_____ $\times$ _____ $=$ _____

_____ $\times$ _____ $=$ _____

_____ $\times$ _____ $=$ _____

**24.** $-9 \times 3 =$ _____

$-9 \times 4 =$ _____

$-9 \times 5 =$ _____

$-9 \times 6 =$ _____

_____ $\times$ _____ $=$ _____

_____ $\times$ _____ $=$ _____

_____ $\times$ _____ $=$ _____

Determine each product.

**25.** $12 \times 8 =$ ___96___

$12 \times (-8) =$ ___−96___

$-12 \times 8 =$ ___−96___

$-12 \times (-8) =$ ___96___

**26.** $5 \times 11 =$ _____

$5 \times (-11) =$ _____

$-5 \times 11 =$ _____

$-5 \times (-11) =$ _____

**27.** $6 \times 9 =$ _____

$6 \times (-9) =$ _____

$-6 \times 9 =$ _____

$-6 \times (-9) =$ _____

**28.** $3 \times 4 \times 5 =$ _____

$-3 \times (-4) \times 5 =$ _____

$-3 \times 4 \times 5 =$ _____

$-3 \times (-4) \times (-5) =$ _____

$3 \times 4 \times (-5) =$ _____

$3 \times (-4) \times (-5) =$ _____

NAME_____ DATE _____

Determine the integers that make each number sentence true.

**29.** _____ × _____ = −49    7, −7 or −7, 7

**30.** _____ × _____ = 27    _____

**31.** _____ × (−9) = −36    _____

**32.** 3 × _____ = −24    _____

**33.** 14 × _____ = 56    _____

**34.** _____ × (−6) = 30    _____

Write a fact family for each set of integers.

**35.** 3, −4, −12

  3 × (−4) = −12

  (−4) × 3 = −12

  −12 ÷ 3 = −4

  −12 ÷ (−4) = 3

**36.** −6, −8, 48

**37.** −2, 9, −18

**38.** 4, 5, 20

**39.** 7, −3, −21

**40.** −9, −8, 72

Determine the unknown integer that will make each number sentence true.

**41.** 81 ÷ (−9) = ___−9___

**42.** 9 = (−63) ÷ _____

**43.** −40 ÷ _____ = −8

**44.** 16 ÷ _____ = −8

**45.** _____ ÷ (−6) = −4

**46.** 0 ÷ (−12) = _____

**47.** _____ ÷ 4 = −7

**48.** −13 ÷ _____ = −1

NAME_____ DATE _____

## What's My Product or Quotient?
**Multiplying and Dividing Rational Numbers**

## Problem Set

Calculate each product.

**1.** $3\frac{1}{5} \times -2\frac{2}{3} =$

$3\frac{1}{5} \times -2\frac{2}{3} = -8\frac{8}{15}$

$3\frac{1}{5} \times -2\frac{2}{3} =$

$\frac{16}{5} \times -\frac{8}{3} =$

$-\frac{128}{15} = -8\frac{8}{15}$

**2.** $-1\frac{3}{4} \times 5\frac{1}{7} =$

**3.** $-4.25 \times -7.8 =$

**4.** $-2\frac{5}{7} \times -4\frac{2}{3} =$

**5.** $5.5 \times -3.26 =$

**6.** $-10\frac{2}{3} \times 4\frac{3}{8} =$

**7.** $-9.2 \times 4.5 \times -2.1 =$

**8.** $-2\frac{3}{4} \times -2\frac{3}{4} =$

**9.** $-1.9 \times -4.5 \times -5.2 =$

**10.** $10\frac{1}{5} \times -5\frac{2}{3} =$

NAME_____ DATE_____

Calculate each quotient.

**11.** $6\frac{2}{3} \div -\frac{2}{3} =$

$6\frac{2}{3} \div -\frac{2}{3} = -10$

$6\frac{2}{3} \div -\frac{2}{3} =$

$\frac{20}{3} \div -\frac{2}{3} =$

$\frac{20}{3} \times -\frac{3}{2} = -10$

**12.** $-12\frac{3}{4} \div -2\frac{1}{4} =$

**13.** $-144.15 \div 15.5 =$

**14.** $-12\frac{2}{5} \div 15\frac{1}{2} =$

5

**15.** $-79.54 \div -9.7 =$

**16.** $7\frac{1}{2} \div -\frac{5}{6} =$

**17.** $33.33 \div -6.06 =$

**18.** $-16\frac{1}{2} \div -24\frac{3}{4} =$

**5**

**19.** $(-33.28 \div -5.2) \div -1.6 =$

**20.** $\left(-14\frac{7}{8} \div 1\frac{3}{4}\right) \div -\frac{1}{2} =$

NAME_____ DATE _____

## Properties Schmoperties
### Simplifying Arithmetic Expressions with Rational Numbers

## Problem Set

For each step of the simplification of the expression, identify the operation or property applied.

**1.** $3\frac{1}{2} + 6\frac{1}{2} - 4\frac{1}{3} =$

Number Property/Operation

$10 - 4\frac{1}{3} =$

_____Addition_____

$5\frac{2}{3}$

_____Subtraction_____

**2.** $\left(7\frac{3}{4} + 6\frac{2}{3}\right) + 5\frac{2}{3} =$

Number Property/Operation

$7\frac{3}{4} + \left(6\frac{2}{3} + 5\frac{2}{3}\right) =$

_____

$7\frac{3}{4} + 12\frac{1}{3} =$

_____

$20\frac{1}{12}$

_____

**3.** $2\frac{1}{5}\left(17\frac{1}{3}\right) - 2\frac{1}{5}\left(2\frac{1}{3}\right) =$

Number Property/Operation

$2\frac{1}{5}\left(17\frac{1}{3} - 2\frac{1}{3}\right) =$

_____

$2\frac{1}{5}(15) =$

_____

$33$

_____

**4.** $8\frac{1}{4} + 3\frac{2}{3} + 2\frac{1}{4} =$

$3\frac{2}{3} + 8\frac{1}{4} + 2\frac{1}{4} =$

$3\frac{2}{3} + 10\frac{1}{2} =$

$14\frac{1}{6}$

Number Property/Operation

_____

_____

**5.** $-3\frac{1}{2}\left(4\frac{3}{5} - 2\frac{1}{5}\right) =$

$-3\frac{1}{2}\left(2\frac{2}{5}\right) =$

$-8\frac{2}{5}$

Number Property/Operation

_____

_____

**6.** $5\frac{1}{3} + 9\frac{1}{6} + \left(-2\frac{1}{3}\right) =$

$5\frac{1}{3} + \left(-2\frac{1}{3}\right) + 9\frac{1}{6} =$

$3 + 9\frac{1}{6} =$

$12\frac{1}{6}$

Number Property/Operation

_____

_____

_____

**7.** $1.5 \times 5.2 \times 3.5 =$

$1.5 \times 3.5 \times 5.2 =$

$5.25 \times 5.2 =$

$27.3$

Number Property/Operation

_____

_____

_____

NAME_____ DATE _____

**8.** $1\frac{1}{4}(3\frac{1}{2} + 2\frac{1}{4}) =$                     Number Property/Operation

$\quad 1\frac{1}{4}\left(3\frac{1}{2}\right) + 1\frac{1}{4}\left(2\frac{1}{4}\right) =$                    _____

$\quad\quad\quad \frac{35}{8} + \frac{45}{16} =$                      _____

$\quad\quad\quad\quad 7\frac{3}{16}$                        _____

Supply the next step in the simplification using the operation or property provided.

**9.** $\left(9\frac{3}{5} + 3\frac{1}{4}\right) + 2\frac{3}{4} =$                  Number Property/Operation

$\quad 9\frac{3}{5} + \left(3\frac{1}{4} + 2\frac{3}{4}\right) =$              Associative Property of Addition

$\quad\quad\quad 9\frac{3}{5} + 6 =$                       Addition

$\quad\quad\quad\quad 15\frac{3}{5}$                        Addition

**10.** $1\frac{1}{3}\left(12\frac{1}{2}\right) - 1\frac{1}{3}\left(5\frac{1}{2}\right) =$             Number Property/Operation

Distributive Property of
Multiplication over Subtraction

Subtraction

Multiplication

**11.** $-5.2(20-5.05) =$

Number Property/Operation

_____
Subtraction

_____
Multiplication

**12.** $\dfrac{3\frac{3}{4}}{5} - \dfrac{2\frac{1}{4}}{5} =$

Number Property/Operation

_____
Distributive Property of
Division over Subtraction

_____
Subtraction

_____
Division

**13.** $\left(-4\frac{2}{3}\right) + 5\frac{1}{4} + 8\frac{2}{3} =$

Number Property/Operation

_____
Commutative Property of Addition

_____
Addition

_____
Addition

NAME_____ DATE _____

**14.** $9.5(12.9) - 9.5(6.7) =$

Number Property/Operation

Distributive Property of
Multiplication over Subtraction
_____

Subtraction
_____

Multiplication
_____

**15.** $-\dfrac{12}{5} \times \left(\dfrac{5}{12} \times 4\dfrac{4}{5}\right) =$

Number Property/Operation

Associative Property
of Multiplication
_____

Multiplication
_____

Multiplication
_____

**16.** $\left(-2\dfrac{1}{2}\right)\left(7\dfrac{1}{4}\right) + \left(-2\dfrac{1}{2}\right)\left(2\dfrac{3}{4}\right) =$

Number Property/Operation

Distributive Property of
Multiplication over Addition
_____

Addition
_____

Multiplication
_____

© Carnegie Learning

# Lesson 5.3   Skills Practice

Simplify the expression step by step, listing the property or operation used at each step.

**17.** $\left(1\frac{3}{4} + 2\frac{1}{3}\right) + 4\frac{2}{3} =$

Number Property/Operation

$1\frac{3}{4} + \left(2\frac{1}{3} + 4\frac{2}{3}\right) =$

Associative Property of Addition

$1\frac{3}{4} + 7 =$

Addition

$8\frac{3}{4}$

Addition

**18.** $1\frac{1}{2}\left(2\frac{1}{4} - 5\frac{3}{4}\right) =$

Number Property/Operation

**19.** $3.2(10.8) - 3.2(8.3) =$

Number Property/Operation

538 • **Chapter 5**   Skills Practice

© Carnegie Learning

© Carnegie Learning

NAME_____ DATE _____

**20.** $6\frac{3}{4} + 2\frac{1}{3} + \left(-3\frac{1}{4}\right) =$

Number Property/Operation

_____

_____

_____

**21.** $\left(-\frac{5}{9}\right) \times \left(-\frac{3}{11}\right) \times \left(-\frac{9}{5}\right) =$

Number Property/Operation

_____

_____

_____

**22.** $\dfrac{7\frac{3}{5}}{3} + \dfrac{1\frac{2}{5}}{3} =$

Number Property/Operation

_____

_____

_____

5

NAME_____ DATE _____

## Building a Wright Brothers' Flyer
### Evaluating Expressions with Rational Numbers

## Problem Set

Solve each problem.

1. Edith is baking cookies. She has $6\frac{7}{8}$ cups of sugar. Each batch of cookies requires $\frac{3}{4}$ cup of sugar. How many full batches of cookies can Edith make? How much sugar will she have left over?

$$6\frac{7}{8} \div \frac{3}{4} = \frac{55}{8} \times \frac{4}{3}$$

$$= \frac{55}{6}$$

$$= 9\frac{1}{6}$$

Edith can make 9 full batches.

$$\frac{1}{6}\left(\frac{3}{4}\right) = \frac{1}{8}$$

Edith will have $\frac{1}{8}$ cup of sugar left over.

5

2. A construction company is building concrete pillars at the entrance of an auditorium. Each pillar requires $5\frac{3}{4}$ cubic yards of concrete. How many cubic yards will be required to construct 9 pillars?

3. Tomas needs to cut a 15-foot steel pipe into $2\frac{1}{3}$-foot pieces. How many $2\frac{1}{3}$-foot pieces can h  cut from the pipe?

NAME_____ DATE _____

4. Mizuki is sowing a large field with alfalfa. Each acre requires $12\frac{2}{5}$ pounds of alfalfa seed. How many pounds of alfalfa will Mizuki use if she sows 7 acres?

5. A veterinarian is vaccinating cattle. One bottle of vaccine is 8 ounces. How many $\frac{2}{3}$-ounce doses can the veterinarian get out of one bottle of vaccine? How many ounces of vaccine will be left in the bottle after she draws the maximum number of doses out?

6. A nightlight uses $8\frac{1}{3}$ watts of power every hour. How many watts will the nightlight use every $6\frac{1}{2}$ hours?

7. Lamar feeds $21\frac{3}{4}$ ounces of milk to 6 kittens. If each kitten drinks an equal amount, how many ounces of milk does each kitten drink?

**NAME**_____ **DATE** _____

8. Eight divers recover $18\frac{1}{3}$ ounces of gold from a sunken ship. How many ounces of gold will each diver get if they divide the gold equally?

9. Abigail's car uses $3\frac{2}{3}$ gallons of gas every hour on a long distance trip. How many gallons does the car use in $8\frac{1}{2}$ hours?

**10.** Devin is cutting $5\frac{1}{2}$-foot strips of ribbon from a 60-foot roll. How many full strips can he cut from the roll? Once he cuts the maximum number of full strips from the roll, how many feet of ribbon will be left over?

5

NAME_____ DATE _____

Evaluate each expression for the given value.

**11.** Evaluate $\frac{5}{6}x$ for $x = -8$.

$$\frac{5}{6}(-8) = \frac{5}{6} \times \frac{-8}{1}$$

$$= \frac{-20}{3}$$

$$= -6\frac{2}{3}$$

**12.** Evaluate $9\frac{1}{3} - m$ for $m = -1\frac{2}{3}$.

**13.** Evaluate $t \div \frac{3}{4}$ for $t = 9\frac{3}{4}$.

**14.** Evaluate $\frac{2}{5}k - 3\frac{1}{2}$ for $k = 15$.

5

**15.** Evaluate $-3\frac{1}{4} - 2\frac{3}{4}z$ for $z = -4$.

**16.** Evaluate $\frac{3}{4}\left(x - 1\frac{1}{5}\right)$ for $x = 2$.

**17.** Evaluate $12 \div v$ for $v = -\frac{3}{5}$.

**18.** Evaluate $\left(-3\frac{1}{2}\right)n - 2\frac{2}{3}$ for $n = -3$.

NAME_____ DATE _____

**19.** Evaluate $x \div \left(-1\frac{1}{5}\right)$ for $x = 6\frac{3}{4}$.

**20.** Evaluate $2\frac{1}{4}\left(7\frac{5}{6} - m\right)$ for $m = 4\frac{2}{3}$.

**NAME** _____ **DATE** _____

# Repeat or Not? That Is the Question!
## Exact Decimal Representations of Fractions

## Vocabulary

Write the term that best completes each statement.

1. A _____ neither terminates nor repeats.

2. A _____ has a finite number of digits, meaning that the decimal will end, or terminate.

3. _____ can be used to signify the repeating digits in a repeating decimal.

4. A _____ is a decimal in which a digit, or a group of digits, repeats without end.

5. A _____ is a decimal that continues without end.

## Problem Set

Convert each fraction to a decimal. Classify the decimal as terminating, non-terminating, repeating, or non-repeating. If the decimal repeats, rewrite it using bar notation.

1. $\frac{6}{40}$

   The decimal equivalent is 0.15. The decimal is terminating.

2. $\frac{3}{8}$

3. $\frac{5}{6}$

4. $\frac{7}{25}$

5. $\frac{2}{11}$

6. $\frac{5}{12}$

7. $\frac{2}{15}$

8. $\frac{5}{16}$

9. $\frac{11}{30}$

10. $\frac{4}{37}$

**5**

Convert the fractions and mixed numbers to decimals and evaluate each expression. Round the answer to the nearest hundredth.

11. $3\frac{1}{4} + 2\frac{1}{2} + 6\frac{1}{5}$

$3\frac{1}{4} + 2\frac{1}{2} + 6\frac{1}{5} = 3.25 + 2.5 + 6.2$

$= 11.95$

12. $5\frac{7}{10} + \left(-6\frac{1}{4}\right) + 1\frac{2}{5}$

13. $\left(-\frac{3}{5}\right) + 3\frac{3}{4} + \left(-5\frac{1}{2}\right)$

14. $\frac{4}{5}\left(8\frac{1}{4} - 4\frac{3}{5}\right)$

NAME_____ DATE _____

**15.** $\left(-9\frac{1}{2}\right)\left(-5\frac{7}{10}\right)$

**16.** $12\frac{3}{4} \div 1\frac{1}{5}$

**17.** $\left(-2\frac{1}{2}\right)\left(-4\frac{1}{4} - 5\frac{3}{4}\right)$

**18.** $\left(-3\frac{4}{5}\right) + 8\frac{1}{4} + 3\frac{3}{4} + \left(-5\frac{9}{10}\right)$

**19.** $15\frac{2}{5} - 3\frac{1}{2}\left(3\frac{3}{5}\right)$

**20.** $6\frac{1}{4}\left(2\frac{1}{2}\right) - 4\frac{2}{5}\left(1\frac{7}{10}\right)$

# Lesson 6.1 Skills Practice

NAME _____ DATE _____

## What's It Really Saying?
### Evaluating Algebraic Expressions

## Vocabulary

Write an example for each term.

1. variable

2. algebraic expression

3. evaluate an algebraic expression

## Problem Set

Define a variable and write an algebraic expression for each problem. Evaluate the expression for the given values.

1. The charge for ice skating is $3 for the skate rental and $2 per hour to skate. How much will you pay if you skate for:

   **a.** 2 hours?

   **b.** 4 hours?

   **c.** $3\frac{1}{2}$ hours?

   Let $h$ represent the number of hours you skate; $3 + 2h$

   a. You will pay $7 to skate for 2 hours. $3 + 2(2) = 7$

   b. You will pay $11 to skate for 4 hours. $3 + 2(4) = 11$

   c. You will pay $10 to skate for $3\frac{1}{2}$ hours. $3 + 2\left(3\frac{1}{2}\right) = 10$

2. A birthday party at the skating rink costs $45 to reserve a party area and $4.50 per guest for skating and skate rental. How much will a party cost if you invite:

   a. 5 guests?

   b. 9 guests?

   c. 25 guests?

3. You have $15 to spend at the snack bar. All of the snacks at the snack bar cost $1.75. How much money will you have left if you buy:

   a. 3 snacks?

   b. 5 snacks?

   c. 8 snacks?

NAME_____ DATE _____

4. The zamboni can resurface 1050 square feet per minute. How many minutes will it take the zamboni to resurface the entire rink if its dimensions are:

   a. 70 ft × 150 ft?

   b. 84 ft × 100 ft?

   c. 90 ft × 175 ft?

5. The skating rink is running a promotion on skating lessons. For every ten lessons you take, you get one free lesson. If you have already taken 4 lessons, how many free lessons will you get if you take:

   a. 6 more lessons?

   b. 16 more lessons?

   c. 26 more lessons?

6

6. One lap around the skating rink is about 400 feet and the length is 150 feet. How far will you skate if you skate:

   a. the length 3 times plus 20 laps?

   b. the length 5 times plus 35 laps?

   c. the length 2 times plus 48 laps?

Evaluate each algebraic expression.

7. $20x$

   a. for $x = 2$

     $20x = 20(2) = 40$

   b. for $x = -8$

     $20x = 20(-8) = -160$

   c. for $x = 0$

     $20x = 20(0) = 0$

8. $3c + 17$

   a. for $c = 5$

   b. for $c = -2$

   c. for $c = -15$

NAME_____ DATE _____

9. $64 - 9p$

   **a.** for $p = 4$

   **b.** for $p = 9$

   **c.** for $p = -3$

10. $-w + 8.5$

    **a.** for $w = 12$

    **b.** for $w = -1.5$

    **c.** for $w = 5.3$

11. $46 + (-2k)$

    **a.** for $k = 3$

    **b.** for $k = 23$

    **c.** for $k = -2$

**12.** $n^2 - 25$

  **a.** for $n = -10$

  **b.** for $n = -5$

  **c.** for $n = 3$

**13.** $\dfrac{-7d + 14}{2}$

  **a.** for $d = 2$

  **b.** for $d = -2$

  **c.** for $d = 4$

**14.** $32.68 - 4.15q$

  **a.** for $q = 0$

  **b.** for $q = 10$

  **c.** for $q = -3$

6

NAME_____ DATE _____

Complete each table.

**15.**

| b | 3b + 14 |
|----|---------|
| −5 | −1 |
| −3 | 5 |
| 0 | 14 |
| 4 | 26 |

**16.**

| t | $-(t^2 - 6)$ |
|----|---------|
| 2 | |
| −5 | |
| 6 | |
| 1 | |

**17.**

| v | 1 | 2 | 5 | −3.25 |
|----------|---|---|---|-------|
| 6.75 − 6v | | | | |

**18.**

| f | 4 | 8 | −12 | −1 |
|-----------|---|---|-----|----|
| $\frac{f}{4} + 3f$ | | | | |

**19.**

| s | $34 - 6s^3$ |
|---|---|
| 3 | |
| −1 | |
| 2 | |
| −3 | |

**20.**

| z | 1 | 2 | 4 | 9 |
|---|---|---|---|---|
| $-\sqrt{z}$ | | | | |

Evaluate each algebraic expression for the given quantity.

**21.** $4.9x - 6.8x$, $x = 1.5$

$4.9x - 6.8x = 4.9(1.5) - 6.8(1.5)$

$= 7.35 - 10.2$

$= -2.85$

**22.** $-7.4x + 8.1x$, $x = 5.2$

NAME_____ DATE _____

**23.** $-6.2x + 1.4x, x = -9.3$

**24.** $3\frac{1}{2}x - 5\frac{1}{3}x, x = \frac{2}{5}$

**25.** $-6\frac{1}{6}x + 2\frac{2}{3}x, x = -\frac{3}{4}$

**26.** $-7\frac{1}{5}x - 8\frac{1}{5}x, x = \frac{3}{8}$

6

6

# Lesson 6.2 Skills Practice

## Express Math
### Simplifying Expressions Using Distributive Properties

## Vocabulary

Match each property to the correct example.

1. Distributive Property of Multiplication over Addition

   a. $5(10 - 3) = 5(10) - 5(3)$

2. Distributive Property of Multiplication over Subtraction

   b. $\frac{4 + 8}{2} = \frac{4}{2} + \frac{8}{2}$

3. Distributive Property of Division over Addition

   c. $3(6 + 2) = 3(6) + 3(2)$

4. Distributive Property of Division over Subtraction

   d. $\frac{12 - 9}{3} = \frac{12}{3} - \frac{9}{3}$

## Problem Set

Draw a model for each expression and calculate or simplify.

1. $7(54)$

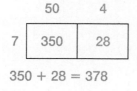

$350 + 28 = 378$

2. $-6(870)$

3. $9(560)$

4. $3(x - 11)$

**5.** $-4(2x + 5)$

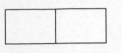

**6.** $\dfrac{a + 9}{3}$

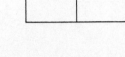

**7.** $8(-4b - 9)$

**8.** $-5(12x - 7)$

**9.** $\dfrac{12a - 28}{4}$

**10.** $\dfrac{-2b + 25}{-5}$

Use the Distributive Property to rewrite each expression in its equivalent form.

**11.** $4(x + 3)$

$4x + 12$

**12.** $-7y(4 - y)$

**13.** $6x(3x + 5y - 4)$

**14.** $\dfrac{9a - 3}{3}$

**15.** $\dfrac{-5x + 20}{5}$

**16.** $\dfrac{500n + 300m - 100}{-100}$

NAME_____ DATE _____

**17.** $\dfrac{60x - 3x^2}{3x}$

**18.** $-y^2(27y - 9z + z^2 - 30)$

**19.** $\dfrac{0.4(0.3m + 0.6n)}{1.2}$

**20.** $-9\frac{2}{3}(-2\frac{1}{4}a + b + 8\frac{1}{4})$

Evaluate each expression for the given value. Choose whether to simplify before evaluating or not. Show your work.

**21.** $5(-4a + (-13))$ for $a = 2.7$

$5(-4a + (-13)) = 5(-4a) + 5(-13)$

$= -20a + (-65)$

$= -20(2.7) - 65$

$= -54 - 65$

$= -119$

**22.** $\dfrac{8x + 3x}{11} - 9$ for $x = -2$

6

**23.** $-3x(2x - 14)$ for $x = 1\frac{1}{6}$

**24.** $\dfrac{5.2(4a + 3.8)}{1.3}$ for $a = 4.3$

**25.** $\dfrac{3.2x - 5.6}{0.4x}$ for $x = 7$

**26.** $-4\frac{3}{8}a\left(-1\frac{3}{4} + \frac{7}{12}a\right) - \frac{19}{24}$ for $a = -\frac{4}{7}$

**6**

© Carnegie Learning

NAME_____ DATE _____

## Reverse Distribution
### Factoring Algebraic Expressions

## Vocabulary

Match each term to the correct example.

1. factoring

2. common factor

3. coefficient

4. like terms

5. combining like terms

**a.** $6(7) + 6(3) = 6(7 + 3)$

**b.** the 6 in $6(7) + 6(3)$

**c.** $7x$ and $2x$

**d.** $7x + 2x = 9x$

**e.** the 4 in $4x$

## Problem Set

Rewrite each expression by factoring out the greatest common factor.

1. $64x + 24$

   $8(8x) + 8(3) = 8(8x + 3)$

2. $-5y - 35$

3. $36 - 8z$

4. $54n - 81$

5. $-36a^2 + 18a$

6. $7b^2 - 21ab$

7. $42mn + 27m$

8. $-17x^3 + 12x^2 - 3x$

© Carnegie Learning

6

**9.** $30c^2 - 15cd + 45c$

**10.** $28a + 14b$

Simplify each expression by combining like terms. If the expression is already simplified, state how you know.

**11.** $6x + 4x$

$10x$

**12.** $-5y + 2y$

**13.** $-3m - 8m$

**14.** $4a + 8b$

**15.** $-qr + 7qr$

**16.** $9m - 7m + 13$

**17.** $12a^2 + 5a$

**18.** $3s^2 - 5s^2 + s - 6s$

**19.** $-20x^2y + 4x^2 + 16x$

**20.** $11m^2 - 15m^2$

NAME_____ DATE _____

Evaluate each expression for the given value. Choose whether or not to factor before evaluating.

**21.** $-27x + 18$ for $x = \dfrac{1}{3}$

$$-27\left(\dfrac{1}{3}\right) + 18 = -9 + 18$$

$$= 9$$

**22.** $6.4 - 9.6x$ for $x = 0.5$

**23.** $15x + 60$ for $x = -4$

**24.** $\dfrac{1}{3} + \left(-\dfrac{5}{6}x\right)$ for $x = 4$

**25.** $8x^2 - 20x$ for $x = -3\dfrac{1}{2}$

**26.** $35x + 63x^3$ for $x = \dfrac{2}{3}$

6

Evaluate each expression for the given value. Choose whether or not to combine like terms before evaluating.

**27.** $(2y - 1) + (4y + 8)$ for $y = \dfrac{1}{2}$

$\left(2\left(\dfrac{1}{2}\right) - 1\right) + \left(4\left(\dfrac{1}{2}\right) + 8\right) = (1 - 1) + (2 + 8)$

$= 10$

**28.** $(5 + 4y) + (3 - 3y)$ for $y = -2$

**29.** $3x - 12x + 4$ for $x = -\dfrac{7}{9}$

**30.** $4.5x + 6 + (-3.5x) + 7$ for $x = 7$

**31.** $\left(\dfrac{2}{3} + \dfrac{3}{8}x + \dfrac{1}{4}\right) + \left(\dfrac{1}{4}x + \dfrac{1}{2}\right)$ for $x = -8$

NAME_____ DATE _____

**32.** $(5.3 - 8.2y) + (13.3y - 4.1)$ for $x = 3$

6

NAME_____ DATE _____

## Are They the Same or Different?
### Verifying That Expressions Are Equivalent

## Problem Set

Determine whether the two expressions in each may be equivalent by evaluating for the given value.

1. $\frac{1}{3}(9x + 12) = \frac{1}{4}(8x + 4) + x$ for $x = 3$

$$\frac{1}{3}(9x + 12) = \frac{1}{3}(9 \cdot 3 + 12)$$

$$= \frac{1}{3}(27 + 12)$$

$$= \frac{1}{3}(39)$$

$$= 13$$

$$\frac{1}{4}(8x + 4) + x = \frac{1}{4}(8 \cdot 3 + 4) + 3$$

$$= \frac{1}{4}(24 + 4) + 3$$

$$= \frac{1}{4}(28) + 3$$

$$= 7 + 3$$

$$= 10$$

$13 \neq 10$. The expressions are not equivalent.

6

2. $0.4(6x + 0.8) + 0.18 = 0.5 + 2.4x$ for $x = 0.5$

3. $-9\left(\dfrac{2}{5}x + \dfrac{4}{9}\right) = \dfrac{9}{10}x - 17\dfrac{1}{2}$ for $x = -5$

NAME_____ DATE _____

4. $-3(1.8x - 10.8) + 1.2x = 9.3x + 5.6$ for $x = 2$

5. $4\frac{1}{2}\left(-6x + 3\frac{5}{9}\right) = -8\left(1\frac{1}{2}x - \frac{3}{4}\right) + 15x$ for $x = \frac{1}{3}$

6. $5.4(3.3x - 7.1) + 2.2(1.6x + 1.8) = 2(2.5x + 7.5) + 0.8(10x + 11.25)$ for $x = 7$

NAME_____ DATE _____

Determine whether the two expressions in each are equivalent by simplifying.

**7.** $-5\left(5 + \frac{4}{5}x\right) = 2\left(-12\frac{1}{2} - 2x\right)$

$$-5\left(5 + \frac{4}{5}x\right) = -5(5) + (-5)\left(\frac{4}{5}x\right)$$

$$= -25 - 4x$$

$$2\left(-12\frac{1}{2} - 2x\right) = 2\left(-12\frac{1}{2}\right) + 2(-2x)$$

$$= -25 - 4x$$

$-25 - 4x = -25 - 4x.$ The expressions are equivalent.

**8.** $(6.3x - 1.4) + (3.7x - 1.6) = 4(2.5x - 0.75)$

9. $0.9(-3x + 5) + 0.6(9x - 7.5) = 18(1.5x - 0.2) + 3.6$

10. $-\dfrac{2}{10}(-x - 40) = 2\left(\dfrac{1}{10}x - 4\right)$

NAME_____ DATE _____

**11.**  $15(-0.2 - 2x) + 4.8 = 7.4 - 5.5(5.4x + 1)$

**12.**  $\frac{1}{3}\left(\frac{6}{10}x - 4\frac{4}{5}\right) - 2\frac{1}{2}x - \frac{2}{5} = 2\left(\frac{1}{10}x - 9\right) + 16 + 2\frac{1}{2}x$

Determine whether the two expressions in each are equivalent by using graphing technology.

**13.** $-2(7x - 3) = 6 + 14x$

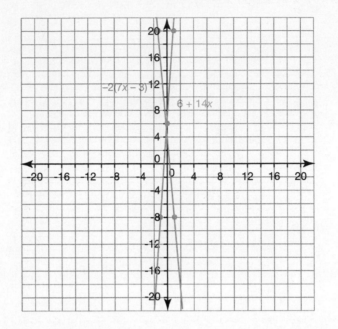

The expressions are not equivalent.

**14.** $0.4(5x + 10) - 1 = 6(0.25x + 1) + 0.5x - 3$

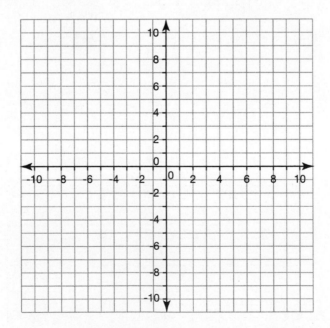

© Carnegie Learning

NAME_____ DATE _____

**15.** $-\dfrac{3}{10}\left(\dfrac{2}{3}x - \dfrac{5}{6}\right) + 2\left(\dfrac{1}{10}x + \dfrac{5}{8}\right) = 12\left(\dfrac{4}{9}x - \dfrac{3}{8}\right) - 5\dfrac{1}{3}x + 6$

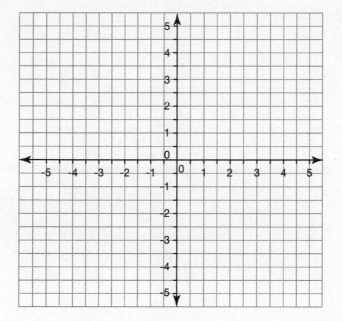

**16.** $-14 - 5(1.8x - 2.6) + 7x = -2(2x + 4) + 30(0.2x + 0.3)$

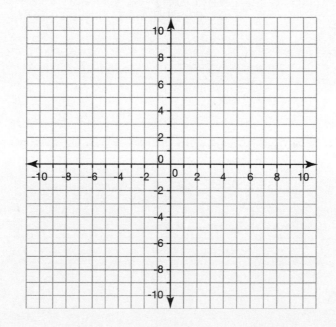

**17.** $\frac{1}{5}\left(1\frac{2}{3}x + 10\right) + 2 = -2 + \frac{1}{7}\left(2\frac{1}{3}x + 14\right)$

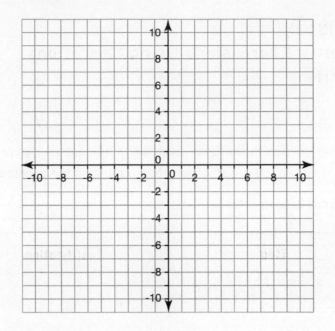

**18.** $5x + 4(x - 2) - 8\frac{1}{2} = 3\left(x - 4\frac{1}{2}\right) + 1\frac{1}{2}(4x - 2)$

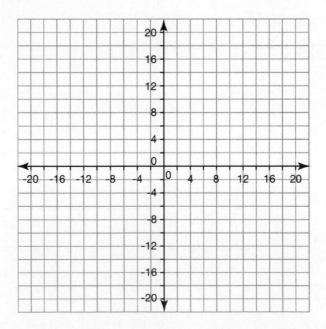

NAME_____  DATE _____

## It Is Time to Justify!
### Simplifying Algebraic Expressions Using Operations and Their Properties

## Problem Set

Complete each table. Either simplify the left side using the given operation or property, or use an operation or a property to justify each simplification step. Indicate if the expressions are equivalent.

1. $-4(-2x + 5) + 2(0.5x + 2) = 9x - 16$

| Step | Justification |
|---|---|
| $-4(-2x + 5) + 2(0.5x + 2) =$ | Given |
| $8x + (-20) + x + 4 =$ | Distributive Property of Multiplication over Addition |
| $8x + x + (-20) + 4 =$ | Commutative Property of Addition |
| $9x - 16$ | Addition of Like Terms Yes, they are equivalent. |

6

**2.** $\dfrac{5x - 4}{6} + 2x - \dfrac{2}{3} = \dfrac{17}{6}x - \dfrac{8}{6}$

| Step | Justification |
|---|---|
| $\dfrac{5x - 4}{6} + 2x - \dfrac{2}{3} =$ | |
| $\dfrac{5x}{6} - \dfrac{4}{6} + 2x - \dfrac{2}{3} =$ | |
| $\dfrac{5}{6}x + \dfrac{12}{6}x + \left(-\dfrac{4}{6}\right) + \left(-\dfrac{4}{6}\right) =$ | |
| $\dfrac{17}{6}x - \dfrac{8}{6}$ | |

**3.** $4.1(3.2x - 5.3) + 12.7(5.8x - 3.6) = 86x - 67$

| Step | Justification |
|---|---|
| $4.1(3.2x - 5.3) + 12.7(5.8x - 3.6) =$ | |
| $13.12x - 21.73 + 73.66x - 45.72 =$ | |
| $13.12x + 73.66x + (-21.73) + (-45.72) =$ | |
| $86.78x - 67.45$ | |

NAME_____  DATE _____

**4.** $7(2 - 3x) - 5(6 + x) + 4x = -16 - 22x$

| Step | Justification |
|---|---|
|  | Given |
|  | Distributive Property of Multiplication over Addition and Subtraction |
|  | Commutative Property of Addition |
|  | Addition of Like Terms |

**5.** $\dfrac{12x + 7}{4} - \dfrac{30 - 18x}{6} = x - \dfrac{13}{4}$

| Step | Justification |
|---|---|
|  | Given |
|  | Distributive Property of Division over Addition and Subtraction |
|  | Divide |
|  | Commutative Property of Addition |
|  | Addition of Like Terms |

6.  $-3[7x + 2(5 + x)] = -24x - 30$

| Step | Justification |
|---|---|
| $-3[7x + 2(5 + x)] =$ | |
| $-3[7x + 10 + 2x] =$ | |
| $-3[7x + 2x + 10] =$ | |
| $-3[9x + 10] =$ | |
| $-27x - 30$ | |

NAME_____ DATE _____

**7.** $\dfrac{8x + 3(7 + x)}{10} + \dfrac{(9x - 1)}{10} = 2x + 2$

| Step | Justification |
|---|---|
|  | Given |
|  | Distributive Property of Multiplication over Addition |
|  | Commutative Property of Addition |
|  | Addition of Like Terms |
|  | Distribution of Division over Addition and Subtraction |
|  | Commutative Property of Addition |
|  | Addition of Like Terms |
|  | Division<br>Yes, they are equivalent. |

6

**8.** $6(1.3 - 0.2x) + 0.5[3.2 - 4(0.3 + 2.1x) - 3.6 = 5.2 - 5.4x$

| Step | Justification |
|---|---|
| $6(1.3 - 0.2x) + 0.5[3.2 - 4(0.3 + 2.1x) - 3.6 =$ | |
| $7.8 - 1.2x + 0.5[3.2 - 1.2 - 8.4x) - 3.6 =$ | |
| $7.8 - 1.2x + 0.5(2 - 8.4x) - 3.6 =$ | |
| $7.8 - 1.2x + 1 - 4.2x - 3.6 =$ | |
| $7.8 + 1 + (-3.6) + (-1.2x) + (-4.2x) =$ | |
| $5.2 - 5.4x$ | |

Simplify the left side and/or right side completely to determine if the two expressions are equivalent. Use an operation or a property to justify each step and indicate if the expressions are equivalent.

**9.** $-6(-4x + 8) + 10 + 3(-5x + 7) = 9x - 17$

| Step | Justification |
|---|---|
| $-6(-4x + 8) + 10 + 3(-5x + 7) =$ | Given |
| $24x + (-48) + 10 + (-15x) + 21 =$ | Distributive Property of Multiplication over Addition |
| $24x + (-15x) + (-48) + 10 + 21 =$ | Commutative Property of Addition |
| $9x - 17$ | Addition of Like Terms |
| | Yes, they are equivalent. |

NAME_____ DATE_____

**10.** $9(0.3x - 2.2) + 6(0.3x - 2.2) = 3(1.5x - 11)$

Step                                                         Justification

**11.** $\dfrac{5 - 4(6x + 2)}{3} + \dfrac{7(12 + 8x)}{4} = 6x - 20$

Step                                                         Justification

**12.** $8 - 4(-x - 11) - 5(x + 9) + 13x = x - 7(x + 2) + 2(9x + 10) + 1$

Left Side

Step                                                      Justification

Right Side

Step                                                      Justification

NAME_____ DATE _____

**13.** $0.5(-3.2x + 2.4) + 6[1.7 + 4(0.9x + 0.8)] = 3.8(2x - 7) + 1.4(6 + 3x)$

Left Side

| Step | Justification |
|------|---------------|

Right Side

| Step | Justification |
|------|---------------|

6

**14.** $2\frac{1}{2} + 1\frac{3}{4}(16x - 8) - 4\frac{1}{2}x + \frac{1}{8} = -19\frac{1}{2}x - 2\frac{1}{3}(-9x - 12) + 5\frac{1}{2}(-12 + 4x) + 26\frac{5}{8}$

Left Side

| Step | Justification |
|------|---------------|
|      |               |

Right Side

| Step | Justification |
|------|---------------|
|      |               |

# Lesson 7.1 Skills Practice

## Picture This
### Picture Algebra

## Vocabulary

1. Write a definition for **equation** in your own words.

## Problem Set

Draw a picture to represent each situation. Label the unknown parts with variables and the known parts with their values. Solve the problem and write an equation to represent the situation.

1. The ages of three siblings total 21 years. The middle child is one year older than the youngest, and the eldest is three times as old as the youngest. How old is each child?

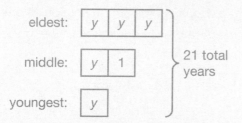

$3y + y + 1 + y = 21$ or $5y + 1 = 21$

The youngest child is 4 years old, the middle child is 5 years old, and the eldest child is 12 years old.

2. Carly is making three cakes for the bake sale. The second cake requires $\frac{1}{2}$ cup more flour than the first cake. The third cake requires twice the amount of flour as the first cake. The two-pound bag of flour she bought has $8\frac{1}{2}$ cups—exactly the amount she needs. How much flour is needed for each cake?

3. Of the 1850 books in the library, there are four times as many books in the fiction section as are in the nonfiction section. Also, there are 650 more books in the reference section than are in the nonfiction section. How many books are in each section?

NAME_____ DATE _____

4. Two friends pooled the tickets they won from playing video games to get a prize that requires 500 tickets. If one friend won 80 more tickets than the other friend, how many tickets did each friend win?

5. There are 3900 workers in the three main buildings downtown. Twice as many people work in the largest building as in the smallest of the three. There are 500 more workers in the second-largest building than in the smallest building. How many workers are in each building?

6. Lamar, Harris, and Tyler ran a 15-mile relay race as a team. Tyler ran 3 miles farther than Harris, and Lamar ran twice as far as Harris. How many miles was each boy's leg of the race?

7. The Petersons set aside $500 to donate to their three favorite charities: the children's home, the food bank, and the animal shelter. They gave twice as much to the food bank as to the animal shelter. Their donation to the children's home was $50 more than the donation to the food bank. How much did each charity receive from the Petersons?

NAME_____ DATE _____

8. There are 7000 middle-school students in the four middle schools in a city. There are three times as many students at Hill Middle School than at Bell Middle School. There are twice as many students at Ware Middle School than at Bell. Cane Middle School has 176 more students than Ware. How many students are in each school?

# Lesson 7.2  Skills Practice

NAME_____  DATE _____

## Maintaining a Balance
### Solving Equations

## Vocabulary

Match the property of equality with its definition.

1. Addition Property of Equality

    **a.** if $a = b$, then $a + c = b + c$

2. Subtraction Property of Equality

    **b.** if $a = b$, then $ac = bc$

3. Multiplication Property of Equality

    **c.** if $a = b$, and $c \neq 0$, then $\frac{a}{c} = \frac{b}{c}$

4. Division Property of Equality

    **d.** if $a = b$, then $a - c = b - c$

## Problem Set

Determine what will balance one rectangle. Explain your solution. Then rewrite each representation as an equation.

1.

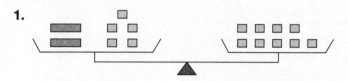

I subtracted 5 squares from each side which left 2 rectangles on one side and 4 squares on the other side. Then I divided each side by 2 which left 1 rectangle on one side and 2 squares on the other side.

1 rectangle = 2 squares

$2x + 5 = 9$

2.

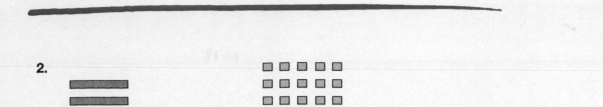

3.

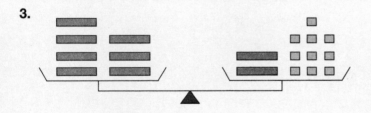

7

NAME_____ DATE _____

4.

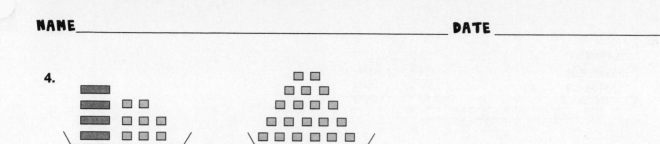

5.

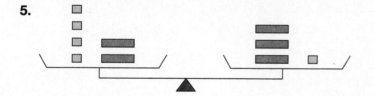

© Carnegie Learning

7

**6.**

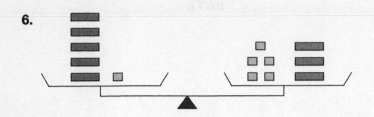

Solve each two-step equation. State the inverse operations, in the correct order of operations, you used to isolate the variable. Check your solution.

**7.** $3w - 17 = 4$

Add first, and then divide.

$3w - 17 = 4$

$3w - 17 + 17 = 4 + 17$

$3w = 21$

$\dfrac{3w}{3} = \dfrac{21}{3}$

$w = 7$

Check:

$3(7) - 17 = 4$

$21 - 17 = 4$

$4 = 4$

**7**

NAME_____ DATE _____

8. $25 + 8x = 65$

9. $94 = \dfrac{y}{4} - 18$

7

10. $\dfrac{g}{9} + 47 = 64$

11. $72 = 5h + 22$

7

NAME_____ DATE _____

**12.** $\dfrac{c}{20} - 41 = 59$

**13.** $138 = 7h + 5$

7

**14.** $16 = 8 + \dfrac{p}{2}$

Solve each riddle using equations.

**15.** What is a number that when you multiply it by 3 and subtract 12 from the product, you get 12?

$3x - 12 = 12$

$3x = 24$

$x = 8$

The number is 8.

NAME_____ DATE _____

16. What is a number that when you multiply it by 7 and add 25 to the product, you get 46?

17. What is a number that when you multiply it by 4 and add 74 to the product, you get 90?

18. What is a number that when you multiply it by 11 and subtract 30 from the product, you get 91?

7

**19.** What is a number that when you multiply it by 5 and add 19 to the product, you get 54?

**20.** What is a number that when you multiply it by 9 and subtract 63 from the product, you get 45?

NAME_____ DATE _____

## Planning a Graduation Party
### Solving Two-Step Equations

## Vocabulary

1. Give an example of a two-step equation and describe the steps you would use to solve it.

## Problem Set

Write a sentence to describe how to apply inverse operations to solve each equation. Then, solve the equation and verify your solution.

**1.** $4x + 12 = 24$

First subtract 12 from each side, then divide each side by 4.

$$4x + 12 = 24$$

$$4x + 12 - 12 = 24 - 12$$

$$\frac{4x}{4} = \frac{12}{4}$$

$$x = 3$$

Verify the solution by substituting 3 for $x$ in the equation.

$$4(3) + 12 \overset{?}{=} 24$$

$$24 = 24$$

7

**2.** $25 - 8x = -15$

**3.** $13 - \dfrac{x}{7} = 6$

7

NAME_____ DATE _____

4.  $-5x - 12 = 18$

5.  $\frac{x}{9} + 29 = 41$

7

**6.** $42 = -7x + 35$

**7.** $-8 = 2x - 14$

7

NAME_____ DATE _____

**8.** $21 = 36 - \dfrac{x}{30}$

**9.** $-19 = 35 + 9x$

7

**10.** $11x + 13 = -9$

7

**NAME**_____ **DATE** _____

Write an equation to represent each situation. Define your variables, solve the equation, and verify your solution.

**11.** Ms. Moderelli charges her piano students $40 per lesson plus a semester recital fee of $55. How many lessons did Jerry take if he paid a total of $695 for lessons this semester?

$40p + 55 = 695$

Let $p$ represent the number of lessons taken during the semester.

$$40p + 55 = 695$$

$$40p + 55 - 55 = 695 - 55$$

$$\frac{40p}{40} = \frac{640}{40}$$

$$p = 16$$

Jerry took 16 lessons.

Verify the solution by substituting 16 for $p$ in the equation.

$$40(16) + 55 \stackrel{?}{=} 695$$

$$695 = 695$$

**12.** The Sunshine Nursery offers a spring flower deal. If a customer purchases at least one flat of 6 annuals, they will receive 3 free perennials. How many flats of annuals must you buy to get a total of 21 plants?

NAME_____ DATE _____

13. The student council ordered 1000 pencils embossed with the school name to give to honor roll students. If they give each honor roll student two pencils and they have 840 pencils left after the first quarter, how many students are on the honor roll in the first quarter?

**14.** Craig and four of his friends had a car wash to earn some extra money. They split the profits and Craig got an extra $18 to repay his parents for the car wash supplies. If Craig got $32, how much total money did they split among themselves?

NAME_____ DATE _____

**15.** Javier has a collection of 125 comic books. He gives each of his 3 friends the same number of comic books and keeps his favorite 38 comic books for himself. How many comic books did he give to each of his friends?

7

**16.** Tyler is planning a party at a restaurant. There is a flat fee of $250 to reserve the restaurant for the evening and a charge of $20 per person for food and drink. If Tyler has $500 to spend, what is the maximum number of people that can attend the party?

NAME_____ DATE _____

## Solving in Big-Time Style
### Using Two-Step Equations

## Problem Set

Solve each equation using the Distributive Property.

**1.** $6(x + 1) + 5 = 35$

$6(x + 1) + 5 = 35$

$6x + 6 + 5 = 35$

$6x + 11 = 35$

$6x + 11 - 11 = 35 - 11$

$\dfrac{6x}{6} = \dfrac{24}{6}$

$x = 4$

**2.** $-14 = -2(5 - x) + 16$

**3.** $3(2x + 7) - 3x = 18$

**4.** $0.7(x - 2) = 0.3$

**5.** $1.95(6.2 - 3x) - 4.81 = -18.46$

**6.** $28 = 14 + 7(x - 6)$

**7.** $78 = -9x - 3(-56 + 12x)$

**8.** $0.20x - 0.08(x - 10) = 24.80$

NAME_____ DATE _____

**9.** $7(4x + 9) - 13 = -87$

**10.** $0.25(3 - x) = 0.375$

7

Write an equation to represent each situation. Define your variables and solve the equation.

**11.** At the Namaste Yoga Studio, the first two yoga classes you take are free with your registration fee of $15. Each class after that is $45. How many classes can you take for $1185?

$$1185 = 15 + 45(x - 2)$$

Let $y$ represent the total amount paid and $x$ represent the number of classes taken.

$$1185 = 15 + 45x - 90$$

$$1185 = 45x - 75$$

$$1185 + 75 = 45x - 75 + 75$$

$$\frac{1260}{45} = \frac{45x}{45}$$

$$28 = x$$

You can take 28 yoga classes for $1185 dollars.

**12.** Clara has a coupon for $10 off at her favorite clothing store. The coupon is applied before any discounts are taken. The store is having a sale, and offering 15% off everything. If Clara has $50 to spend, how much can her purchases total before applying the discount and her coupon? Round to the nearest cent.

NAME_____ DATE _____

**13.** Nico bought groceries for the week. He used his debit card to pay for the groceries, including sales tax, and added $25 cash back. If the groceries totaled $138.24 before tax, and the total debited from his account was $173.61, what percentage was the sales tax? Round to the nearest tenth of a percent.

**14.** A party store uses 20% of a tank of helium a day and fills 80 balloons. Each balloon takes 0.5 cubic feet of helium to fill. How many cubic feet of helium are in a full tank?

**15.** Susana bought a laptop for $500. It was marked $50 off because it was out of the box and slightly scratched. She also got a 25% student discount, which was taken off of the original price. What was the original price of the laptop?

NAME_____ DATE _____

**16.** A dog kennel charges $40 to board a dog for one night and $35 per night each night after that. Henry paid a total of $215 for dog boarding. For how many nights did Henry board his dog?

NAME _____ DATE _____

## We're Shipping Out!
### Solving and Graphing Inequalities in One Variable

## Vocabulary

Use the words "graph," "solve," or "reverse" to best complete each sentence.

1. You _____ an inequality when you determine the values of the variable that make the inequality true.

2. You _____ the inequality symbol when you multiply or divide each side of an inequality by a negative value.

3. You _____ an inequality on a number line with an open or closed circle and a ray.

## Problem Set

Write an inequality for each situation.

1. Tyler needs to buy a book for school that costs $13. He also wants to get a book for each of his two sisters and he wants to be sure he spends the same amount on each of their books. He only has $27 to spend. Let $b$ represent the amount he can spend on each additional book.

   $13 + 2b \leq 27$

2. Ming rents a cart for her bike to carry tools and wood to school for her science project. Her toolbox weighs 20 pounds and the cart can carry a maximum of 50 pounds. Each wood board weighs 3 pounds. Let $w$ represent the number of wood boards she can carry.

3. There must be less than 36 people on one bus. There are already 17 people on the bus. Let $p$ represent the additional number of people that can ride the bus.

4. A family of three has a coupon for $5 off their total bill when everyone orders the same meal. The family has $40 to spend on dinner. Let $m$ represent the cost of the meal they can order.

7

5. Vijay wants to keep the cost per person of his party under $15. The Party Place charges a flat fee of $250 for an all-inclusive party. Let $g$ represent the number of guests, including himself, he can invite.

6. The temperature of the liquid starts at 72°F and drops 2 degrees per second. The liquid is not to go below 40°F. Let $s$ represent the number of seconds.

A list of possible solutions for each inequality is shown. Choose the solutions that make the inequality true. Then, list three additional solutions to the inequality.

7. $x > 2$

   $-2, -1, 0, 1, 2, 3, 4, 5, 6, 7$

   The numbers 3, 4, 5, 6, and 7 make the inequality true.

   Answers will vary. Three additional solutions for the inequality are 8, 9, and 10.

8. $5x < 30$

   $-2, -1, 0, 1, 2, 3, 4, 5, 6, 7$

9. $2x + 7 \geq 5$

   $-2, -1, 0, 1, 2, 3, 4, 5, 6, 7$

10. $8 \leq -4x$

    $-2, -1, 0, 1, 2, 3, 4, 5, 6, 7$

NAME_____ DATE _____

**11.** $3x - 1 \leq 14$

$-2, -1, 0, 1, 2, 3, 4, 5, 6, 7$

**12.** $4 < \frac{x}{3} + 2$

$-2, -1, 0, 1, 2, 3, 4, 5, 6, 7$

Solve each inequality and then graph the solution.

**13.** $8x > 56$

$8x > 56$

$\frac{8x}{8} > \frac{56}{8}$

$x > 7$

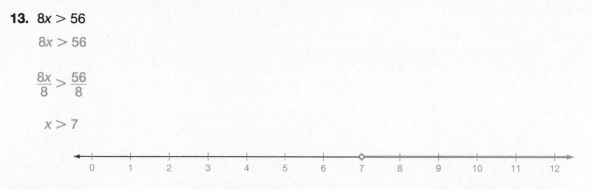

**14.** $144 \geq -12x$

**15.**  $2x + 4 \leq 20$

**16.**  $-17 < 3 - 5x$

7

NAME_____ DATE _____

**17.**  $21 - 9x \geq -6$

**18.**  $78 > 4x + 6$

**19.** $-500 \leq 11x - 60$

**20.** $-x + 38 < 59$

NAME_____ DATE _____

## Some Places are Expensive; Some Places are More Affordable
### Multiple Representations of Problem Situations

## Problem Set

Complete each table and then create a graph from the table of values.

**1.** The library charges $1 to use the copier and $0.50 for each page copied.

| Number of Pages | Copier Use Charge (dollars) | Total Cost (dollars) |
|:---:|:---:|:---:|
| 1 | $1 | $1.50 |
| 2 | $1 | $2.00 |
| 5 | $1 | $3.50 |
| 8 | $1 | $5.00 |
| 10 | $1 | $6.00 |

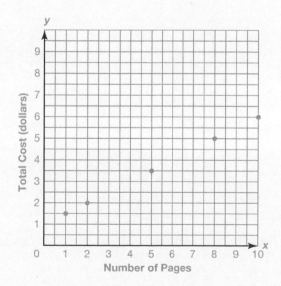

8

**2.** The bakery charges $7.50 for one dozen bagels and $0.50 for each additional bagel.

| Number of Bagels | Cost of First Dozen (dollars) | Total Cost (dollars) |
|---|---|---|
| | | $7.50 |
| | | $8.00 |
| 14 | | $8.50 |
| 15 | | |
| 16 | | |

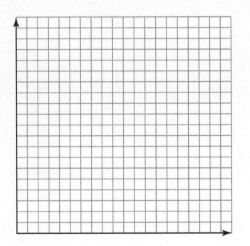

NAME_____ DATE _____

**3.** At a local farm it costs $5 to pick your own peck of apples. It costs $3 for each additional peck.

| Number of Pecks | Cost of First Peck (dollars) | Total Cost (dollars) |
|---|---|---|
| 1 | | |
| 2 | | $8 |
| 3 | | $11 |
| 4 | | |
| | | $17 |

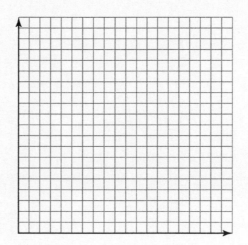

8

4. A children's museum charges $10 admission for the first visitor and $5 for each additional visitor in a group.

| Number of Visitors | Cost of First Visitor (dollars) | Total Cost (dollars) |
|---|---|---|
| 1 | | |
| 3 | | |
| 7 | | |
| | | $60 |
| | | $75 |

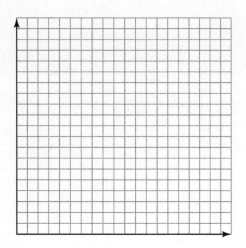

NAME_____ DATE_____

5. A party store charges $18 for 6 foil balloons and $2 for each additional foil balloon.

| Number of Balloons | Cost of First Six Balloons (dollars) | Total Cost (dollars) |
|---|---|---|
| 6 | | $18 |
| | | $20 |
| 8 | | |
| | | $24 |
| 10 | | |

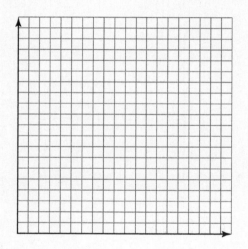

8

6. The bakery charges $4.50 for one dozen muffins and $0.25 for each additional muffin.

| Number of Muffins | Cost of First Dozen (dollars) | Total Cost (dollars) |
|---|---|---|
| 12 | | |
| 13 | | |
| 14 | | |
| | | $5.25 |
| | | $5.50 |

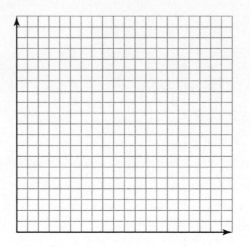

NAME_____ DATE _____

Write an equation that represents each problem situation. Then use the equation to answer the question.

7. The daycare center charges $120 for one week of care. Families with multiple children pay $95 for each additional child per week. Write an equation for the total cost for one week of care in terms of the number of children. Define your variables. How much will one week of care cost a family with 3 children?

   Let $t$ represent the total cost for one week of care.

   Let $c$ represent the number of children.

   $t = 120 + 95(c - 1)$

   $\phantom{t} = 120 + 95(3 - 1)$

   $\phantom{t} = 120 + 95(2)$

   $\phantom{t} = 310$

   One week of care for a family with 3 children will cost $310.

8. The zoo offers special admission rates for large groups of visitors. The zoo charges $7.50 admission for the first visitor and $5.50 for each additional visitor in the group. Write an equation for the total cost of admission in terms of the number of visitors. Define your variables. How much is admission for a group of 6 visitors?

8

**9.** The local farm is advertising a special on fresh picked peaches. The farm charges $4.25 to pick your own peck of peaches and $3.50 for each additional peck you pick. Write an equation for the total cost of peaches in terms of the number of pecks. Define your variables. How much does it cost to pick 3 pecks of peaches?

**10.** A restaurant charges $100 to rent its banquet room for an event. It also charges $15 to serve dinner to each guest. Write an equation for the total cost of the banquet room in terms of the number of guests. Define your variables. What is the total cost of the banquet room for 20 guests?

NAME_____ DATE _____

11. The party store has a special on greeting cards. It charges $14 for 4 greeting cards and $1.50 for each additional card. Write an equation for the total cost of greeting cards in terms of the number of cards. Define your variables. What is the total cost for 9 greeting cards?

12. The jewelry store has a special on earrings. If you purchase 2 pairs of earrings for $65, each additional pair of earrings is $24.99. Write an equation that represents the total cost of earrings based on the number of pairs of earrings purchased. Define your variables. What is the total cost of 4 pairs of earrings?

**8**

Solve the equation.

**13.** $27 = 6x + 9$

$$27 = 6x + 9$$

$$27 - 9 = 6x + 9 - 9$$

$$18 = 6x$$

$$\frac{18}{6} = \frac{6x}{6}$$

$$3 = x$$

**14.** $41 = 4x - 7$

**15.** $15x + 26 = 146$

**16.** $3.7x - 28 = 30.46$

**17.** $12.15 = 1.9x + 3.6$

**18.** $5.1x - 2.6 = 11.68$

NAME_____ DATE _____

# Plastic Containers
## Using Two-Step Equations

## Problem Set

Write an equation that represents each problem situation.

1. The table shows the total cost for dinner in the banquet room of Anthony's Bistro.

| Number of Guests | Total Cost |
| --- | --- |
| | Anthony's Bistro |
| 10 | $169.90 |
| 11 | $185.89 |
| 12 | $201.88 |
| 13 | $217.87 |
| 14 | $233.86 |
| 15 | $249.85 |

Write an equation that represents the total cost for dinner at Anthony's Bistro, $t$, in terms of the number of guests, $g$.

$185.89 - 169.90 = 15.99$

$201.88 - 185.89 = 15.99$

$217.87 - 201.88 = 15.99$

The difference in the total cost between consecutive numbers of guests is $15.99.

$t = 169.90 + 15.99(g - 10)$

8

**2.** The table shows the total cost for dinner in the banquet room of Emilio's Ristorante.

| Number of Guests | Total Cost |
|---|---|
| | Emilio's Ristorante |
| 10 | $214.90 |
| 11 | $227.89 |
| 12 | $240.88 |
| 13 | $253.87 |
| 14 | $266.86 |
| 15 | $279.85 |

Write an equation that represents the total cost for dinner at Emilio's Ristorante, $t$, in terms of the number of guests, $g$.

NAME_____ DATE _____

3. The table shows the total cost of admission for large groups to Ocean World.

| Number of Students | Total Cost |
|---|---|
| | Ocean World |
| 20 | $330.00 |
| 21 | $341.50 |
| 22 | $353.00 |
| 23 | $364.50 |
| 24 | $376.00 |

Write an equation that represents the total cost of admission to Ocean World, $t$, in terms of the number of students, $s$.

**8**

4. The table shows the total cost of admission for large groups to Safari Land.

| Number of Students | Total Cost |
|---|---|
| | Safari Land |
| 20 | $370.00 |
| 21 | $379.50 |
| 22 | $389.00 |
| 23 | $398.50 |
| 24 | $408.00 |

Write an equation that represents the total cost of admission to Safari Land, *t*, in terms of the number of students, *s*.

5. The Gladiolus plants at the garden center are 4 inches tall and grow at a rate of 3 inches per week. Write an equation that represents the height of the Gladiolus plants, *h*, in terms of the number of weeks, *w*.

6. The Dahlia plants at the garden center are 6 inches tall and grow at a rate of 2.5 inches per week. Write an equation that represents the height of the Dahlia plants, *h*, in terms of the number of weeks, *w*.

NAME_____   DATE_____

7. Hector is choosing vegetable plants from a garden center. The plum tomato plants at the garden center are 6 inches tall and grow at a rate of 5 inches per week. The height of the plum tomato plants, $h$, in terms of the number of weeks, $w$, is represented by the equation $h = 6 + 5w$. Calculate how many weeks Hector will have to wait until the plum tomato plants are at least 5 feet tall and begin to produce ripe tomatoes.

8. Denise is choosing vegetable plants from a garden center. The cherry tomato plants at the garden center are 5 inches tall and grow at a rate of 4 inches per week. The height of the cherry tomato plants, $h$, in terms of the number of weeks, $w$, is represented by the equation $h = 5 + 4w$. Calculate how many weeks Denise will have to wait until the cherry tomato plants are at least 3.5 feet tall and begin to produce ripe tomatoes.

**8**

Evaluate the two equations given in each problem situation to make a decision.

9. Manuel is planning an anniversary dinner party for his parents. He is comparing restaurants to find the most affordable location. The total cost for dinner at Luigi's, $t$, in terms of the number of guests, $g$, is represented by the equation $t = 245 + 17.5(g - 10)$. The total cost for dinner at Mario's, $t$, in terms of the number of guests, $g$, is represented by the equation $t = 265 + 14.5(g - 10)$. Calculate the total cost at each restaurant if Manuel invites 20 guests. Which restaurant is the most affordable for 20 guests?

Total Cost at Luigi's

$t = 245 + 17.5(g - 10)$

$\phantom{t} = 245 + 17.5(20 - 10)$

$\phantom{t} = 245 + 17.5(10)$

$\phantom{t} = \$420$

Total Cost at Mario's

$t = 265 + 14.5(g - 10)$

$\phantom{t} = 265 + 14.5(20 - 10)$

$\phantom{t} = 265 + 14.5(10)$

$\phantom{t} = \$410$

For 20 guests, Mario's is the most affordable.

NAME_____ DATE _____

**10.** Nami is deciding which online photo sharing service to subscribe to. Photo World charges an initial membership fee of $35 for the first month, and $4 for each additional month. Picture Palace charges an initial membership fee of $15 for the first month, and $6 for each additional month. The total cost of the Photo World membership, $t$, in terms of months, $m$, is represented by the equation $t = 35 + 4(m - 1)$. The total cost of the Picture Palace membership, $t$, in terms of months, $m$, is represented by the equation $t = 15 + 6(m - 1)$. Calculate the total cost of a membership to each online photo sharing service if Nami joins for 1 year. Which service is the least expensive?

**8**

**11.** Jamal is deciding which fitness center to join. Joe's Gym charges an initial membership fee of $120 for the first month, and $24 for each additional month. King Gym charges an initial membership fee of $89 for the first month, and $26 for each additional month. The total cost of a Joe's Gym membership, $t$, in terms of months, $m$, is represented by the equation $t = 120 + 24(m - 1)$. The total cost of a King Gym membership, $t$, in terms of months, $m$, is represented by the equation $t = 89 + 26(m - 1)$. Calculate the total cost of a membership to each fitness center if Jamal joins for 1 year. Which fitness center is the least expensive?

NAME_____ DATE _____

## Just Another Saturday
### Solving More Complicated Equations

## Vocabulary

Determine the multiplicative inverse for each value.

**1.** 2       **2.** $\frac{3}{4}$       **3.** $\frac{1}{5}$       **4.** 100

## Problem Set

Solve each equation and verify your solution.

**1.** $\frac{3}{8}x = 6$                           **2.** $10 = -\frac{5}{6}x$

$$\frac{3}{8}x = 6$$

$$\frac{8}{3}\left(\frac{3}{8}x\right) = \frac{8}{3}(6)$$

$$x = 16$$

Verify the solution by substituting
16 for $x$ in the equation.

$$\frac{3}{8}(16) \stackrel{?}{=} 6$$

$$6 = 6$$

**8**

**3.** $\frac{1}{2}(x + 3) = \frac{5}{2}$

**4.** $\frac{3}{5}x - \frac{7}{10} = -\frac{2}{5}$

**5.** $14 = 22 - \frac{2}{3}x$

**6.** $\frac{3}{4}(5x - 4) = 12$

NAME_____ DATE _____

7. $-\dfrac{7}{8}x + 13 = -29$

8. $-\dfrac{43}{5} = -\dfrac{2}{7}\left(\dfrac{7}{10} - 3x\right)$

**8**

**9.** $3x = 7x - 4$

**10.** $5x - 2 = 8x + 1$

**11.** $4(x + 9) = 6x$

**12.** $20 - 7x = 12x - 3$

NAME_____ DATE _____

**13.** $8(12 - 2x) = 5x + 12$

**14.** $-3x + 5 = -3(9x + 1)$

**15.** $7(-5 - x) = 8(-x + 13)$

**16.** $\frac{2}{3}x = 15 - \frac{1}{3}x$

**8**

Write an equation for each situation, define your variable, and solve the equation.
Then verify your solution.

**17.** Petit Chat cat salon charges $35 for each cat-grooming session. Pretty Kitty cat salon charges a one-time fee of $20 and $25 for each cat-grooming session. How many grooming sessions would make their fees equal?

$35x = 20 + 25x$

Let $x$ represent the number of grooming sessions.

$$35x = 20 + 25x$$

$$35x - 25x = 20 + 25x - 25x$$

$$\frac{10x}{10} = \frac{20}{10}$$

$$x = 2$$

The fees would be equal at 2 grooming sessions.

Verify the solution by substituting 2 for $x$ in the equation.

$$35(2) \stackrel{?}{=} 20 + 25(2)$$

$$70 = 70$$

NAME_____ DATE _____

**18.** Francis earns $3.50 an hour mowing lawns. He also gets $10 a week allowance. Bella earns $5.25 an hour babysitting and spends $11 a week on books. If Francis and Bella work the same number of hours a week and have the same amount of money at the end of each week, for how many hours a week do they each work?

**8**

19. David is making a bookshelf. Each shelf needs to be $3\frac{1}{2}$ feet long. Each side of the bookshelf needs to be $5\frac{1}{2}$ feet tall. He has a 25-foot board that will be exactly enough wood if he cuts precisely. How many shelves will be on the bookshelf?

**NAME**_____ **DATE** _____

20. There are two candy machines in a restaurant. One is filled with 200 gumballs and the other is filled with 900 chocolate candies. The gumballs are dispensed 1 at a time and the chocolate candies are dispensed 8 candies at a time. How many dispenses from each machine will make the number of candies in the machines equal?

8

**21.** Tim and George are the same height. Tim is $\frac{5}{6}$ the height of their friend Peter, and George is $\frac{7}{8}$ the height of Peter minus $2\frac{1}{4}$ inches. How tall are Peter, Tim, and George?

NAME_____ DATE _____

**22.** The Beach Shack rents boats for $60 the first hour and $30 each hour after that. The Surf Shop rents boats for $40 an hour. At what number of hours are the rental fees for a boat from each shop equal?

NAME_____ DATE _____

## Climbing El Capitan
### Making Sense of Negative Solutions

## Problem Set

Evaluate each expression for the given quantity.

**1.** $25 + 14t$, for $t = 8$

$25 + 14t = 25 + 14(8)$

$= 25 + 112$

$= 137$

**2.** $56 + 3y$, for $y = 11$

**3.** $23n - 17$, for $n = 5$

**4.** $12b + 18$, for $b = -24$

**5.** $34 - 19t$, for $t = 4$

**6.** $5d - 98$, for $d = 4$

**8**

Solve each equation for the given quantity.

**7.** $h = 130 + 35t$, for $h = 445$

$h = 130 + 35t$

$445 = 130 + 35t$

$315 = 35t$

$9 = t$

**8.** $m = 78 + 16n$, for $m = 46$

**9.** $a = 37 - 12b$, for $a = -35$

**10.** $x = 14 - 31y$, for $x = 231$

**11.** $h = 12t - 85$, for $h = -37$

**12.** $c = 3d - 56$, for $c = -101$

**NAME**_____ **DATE** _____

Use the given information to answer each question.

13. Lea is considering a new cell phone contract. She is currently halfway through her existing 1-year contract. She has already paid $354 for the first 6 months of her contract. Her bills average $59 per month. Define the independent and dependent variables. Write an equation that represents the total cost of her cell phone in terms of months from today. How much will Lea have paid for her cell phone contract 6 months from today when it expires?

Dependent variable: $c$ = total cost in dollars

Independent variable: $m$ = time in months from today

$c = 354 + 59m$

$c = 354 + 59(6)$

$c = 354 + 354$

$c = 708$

Lea will have paid a total of $708 for her cell phone contract.

8

**14.** Nelson is traveling with his family from the northern border of West Virginia to the southern border of West Virginia. The total distance of the trip is 180 miles. They begin their trip at 9:00 AM and travel at an average speed of 65 miles per hour. Nelson falls asleep at the beginning of the trip and wakes up at 10:30 AM. When he wakes up they are halfway through the total distance of their journey. Define the independent and dependent variables. Write an equation that represents the total distance Nelson's family has traveled in terms of hours from the time Nelson woke up. When were Nelson and his family 38 miles into their journey?

NAME_____ DATE _____

15. Tanya is competing in a 3-mile race that starts at 10:00 AM. She hopes to run at an average rate of 6 miles per hour. At 10:15 AM her mother arrives at the finish line and is told that Tanya is exactly halfway through the race. Define the independent and dependent variables. Write an equation that represents the total distance Tanya has run in terms of minutes from the time her mother arrives. How long will Tanya's mother have to wait at the finish line for Tanya to arrive? Assume Tanya continues to run at the same speed.

**16.** Raul is considering a new internet service provider. He has been using his current provider for
4 months and has already paid $160 for the service. His bills average $40 per month. Define the
independent and dependent variables. Write an equation that represents the total cost of his internet
service in terms of months from today. When did the cost of Raul's internet service exceed $100?

NAME_____ DATE _____

17. Haru is competing in a 400-mile stock car race. His average speed is 125 miles per hour. It is now two hours after the race began and Haru is 250 miles into the race. Define the independent and dependent variables. Write an equation that represents the total distance Haru has raced in terms of hours from now. How much longer will it take Haru to finish the race?

**18.** Miguel is competing in a cross-country mountain bike race. His average speed is 18 kilometers per hour. After 30 minutes, Miguel is 9 kilometers into the 36-kilometer race. Define the independent and dependent variables. Write an equation that represents the total distance Miguel has raced in terms of hours from now. How much longer will it take Miguel to finish the race?

NAME_____ DATE _____

## Flying in the Ocean
### Rate of Change

## Vocabulary

Define the term in your own words.

1. unit rate of change

## Problem Set

Define the independent and dependent variables and write an equation to represent each problem situation. Use the equation to complete the table.

1. A hot air balloon is rising at a rate of 10 meters per second. Write an equation that represents the height of the balloon as it takes off from the ground.

Independent variable:

$t$ = time in seconds

Dependent variable:

$h$ = height in meters

$h = 10t$

| | Independent Quantity | Dependent Quantity |
|---|---|---|
| Label | Time | Height |
| Units | seconds | meters |
| | 0 | 0 |
| | 1 | 10 |
| | 2 | 20 |
| | 3 | 30 |
| | 4 | 40 |

**8**

**2.** A helium balloon is rising at a rate of 6 feet per second. Write an equation that represents the height of the balloon as it floats up from the ground.

|  | Independent Quantity | Dependent Quantity |
|---|---|---|
| Label | | |
| Units | | |
| | 0 | |
| | 1 | |
| | 2 | |
| | 3 | |
| | 4 | |

**3.** A submarine is diving at a rate of 0.25 meter per second. Write an equation that represents the depth of the submarine as it dives below the surface.

|  | Independent Quantity | Dependent Quantity |
|---|---|---|
| Label | | |
| Units | | |
| | 0 | |
| | 30 | |
| | 60 | |
| | 90 | |
| | 120 | |

© Carnegie Learning

NAME_____ DATE _____

**4.** A submarine is diving at a rate of 0.7 foot per second. Write an equation that represents the depth of the submarine as it dives below the surface.

|  | Independent Quantity | Dependent Quantity |
|---|---|---|
| Label |  |  |
| Units |  |  |
|  | 0 |  |
|  | 30 |  |
|  | 60 |  |
|  | 90 |  |
|  | 120 |  |

**5.** A submarine is rising from a depth of −50 meters at a speed of 0.2 meter per second. Write an equation that represents the depth of the submarine as it rises to the surface.

|  | Independent Quantity | Dependent Quantity |
|---|---|---|
| Label |  |  |
| Units |  |  |
|  | 0 |  |
|  | 30 |  |
|  | 60 |  |
|  | 90 |  |
|  | 120 |  |

8

6. A submarine is rising from a depth of −125 feet at a speed of 0.6 foot per second. Write an equation that represents the depth of the submarine as it rises to the surface.

| | Independent Quantity | Dependent Quantity |
|---|---|---|
| Label | | |
| Units | | |
| | 0 | |
| | 30 | |
| | 60 | |
| | 90 | |
| | 120 | |

Determine the unit rate of change for each table of values.

7.

| | Independent Quantity | Dependent Quantity |
|---|---|---|
| Label | Time | Height |
| Units | seconds | meters |
| | 0 | 0 |
| | 1 | 15 |
| | 2 | 30 |
| | 3 | 45 |
| | 4 | 60 |

The unit rate of change is 15 meters per second.

8.

| | Independent Quantity | Dependent Quantity |
|---|---|---|
| Label | Time | Height |
| Units | seconds | meters |
| | 0 | 108 |
| | 1 | 96 |
| | 2 | 84 |
| | 3 | 72 |
| | 4 | 60 |

NAME_____ DATE_____

**9.**

| | Independent Quantity | Dependent Quantity |
|---|---|---|
| Label | **Time** | **Depth** |
| Units | **minute** | **meters** |
| | 0 | 0 |
| | 1 | −14 |
| | 2 | −28 |
| | 3 | −42 |
| | 4 | −56 |

**10.**

| | Independent Quantity | Dependent Quantity |
|---|---|---|
| Label | **Time** | **Depth** |
| Units | **minute** | **feet** |
| | 0 | −520 |
| | 1 | −455 |
| | 2 | −390 |
| | 3 | −325 |
| | 4 | −260 |

**11.**

| | Independent Quantity | Dependent Quantity |
|---|---|---|
| Label | **Time** | **Depth** |
| Units | **minutes** | **meters** |
| | 0 | 0 |
| | 1 | −18.5 |
| | 2 | −37 |
| | 3 | −55.5 |
| | 4 | −74 |

**12.**

| | Independent Quantity | Dependent Quantity |
|---|---|---|
| Label | **Time** | **Height** |
| Units | **seconds** | **feet** |
| | 0 | 0 |
| | 1 | 13.2 |
| | 2 | 26.4 |
| | 3 | 39.6 |
| | 4 | 52.8 |

© Carnegie Learning

**8**

Use the given information to answer each question.

**13.** A hot air balloon is rising at a rate of 9.5 meters per second. Write an equation that represents the height of the balloon as it takes off from the ground. How high will the balloon be after 1 minute?

Independent variable: $t$ = time in seconds

Dependent variable: $h$ = height in meters

$h = 9.5t$

1 minute = 60 seconds

$h = 9.5t$

$h = 9.5(60)$

$h = 570$

The hot air balloon will be 570 meters high.

NAME_____ DATE _____

14. A helium balloon is rising at a rate of 5 feet per second. Write an equation that represents the height of the balloon as it floats up from the ground. How high will the balloon be after 5 minutes?

15. A diver is diving at a rate of 0.5 meter per second. Write an equation that represents the depth of the diver as she dives below the surface. How deep will the diver be after 30 seconds?

8

**16.** A submarine is diving at a rate of 0.65 foot per second. Write an equation that represents the depth of the submarine as it dives below the surface. How long will it take for the submarine to reach its goal depth of −195 feet?

**17.** A diver is rising from a depth of −27 feet at a speed of 0.3 foot per second. Write an equation that represents the depth of the diver as he rises to the surface. How long will it take for the diver to reach the surface of the water?

NAME_____ DATE _____

8

18. A helicopter is rising at a rate of 12.5 meters per second. Write an equation that represents the height of the helicopter as it takes off from the ground. How long will it take the helicopter to reach 1875 meters?

19. A submarine is diving at a rate of 0.45 foot per second. Its goal depth is −94.5 feet. Write an inequality that represents the time the submarine is below the surface until it reaches its goal depth. How long will the submarine be below sea level before it reaches its goal depth of −94.5 feet?

8

**20.** A diver is rising from a depth of –24 feet at a speed of 0.2 foot per second. Write an inequality that represents the time the diver is below sea level as he rises to the surface. How long will the diver be below sea level before reaching the surface of the water?

NAME_____ DATE _____

# Emptying a Tank
## Using Multiple Representations to Solve Problems

## Problem Set

Use the given information to answer each question.

1. Fernando is using a garden hose to fill his backyard pool at a rate of 10 gallons per minute. The pool already contains 9000 gallons of water. The capacity of the pool is 12,000 gallons. Define the independent and dependent variables and the unit rate of change. Write an equation that represents the amount of water in the pool as it is being filled. How many gallons of water will be in the pool after 2.5 hours?

Independent variable: $t$ = time in minutes

Dependent variable: $w$ = amount of water in gallons

Unit rate of change = 10 gallons per minute

$w = 9000 + 10t$

2.5 hours = 150 minutes

$w = 9000 + 10(150)$

$w = 9000 + 1500$

$w = 10,500$

There will be 10,500 gallons of water in the pool.

8

**2.** Jada is draining her fish tank at a rate of 1.2 gallons per minute. The tank contains 114 gallons of water. Define the independent and dependent variables and the unit rate of change. Write an equation that represents the amount of water in the tank as it is being drained. How many minutes will it take Jada to drain the entire tank?

NAME_____ DATE _____

3. Roberto opened a savings account and has been saving money for college. Each month, he deposits $75 into the savings account, which now contains $1800. Define the independent and dependent variables and the unit rate of change. Write an equation that represents the amount of money in the savings account. When did Roberto's savings account contain $1000?

**8**

**4.** Rodell is downloading music to his MP3 player. The MP3 player can store 16 GB of music. One song uses about 4 MB of storage. (1 GB = 1024 MB) Rodell currently has 6 GB of space left on his MP3 player. Define the independent and dependent variables and the unit rate of change. Write an equation that represents the storage space left on Rodell's MP3 player. How many additional songs can Rodell store on his MP3 player?

NAME_____ DATE _____

5. Serena is running a 26-mile marathon. The table shows how far she ran at different times during the race. Define the independent and dependent variables and the unit rate of change. (Assume Serena runs at a constant rate.) Write an equation that represents the data shown in the table. Complete the table.

| Time | Distance |
|------|----------|
| hours | miles |
| 0.1 | 1 |
| 0.2 | 2 |
| 0.3 | 3 |
|  | 10 |
|  | 20 |
|  | 26 |

8

6. Jada is refilling her fish tank after cleaning it. The table shows the amount of water in the tank while she is filling it. Define the independent and dependent variables and the unit rate of change. (Assume the tank is filled at a constant rate.) Write an equation that represents the data shown in the table. Complete the table.

| Time | Water |
|---|---|
| minutes | gallons |
| 1 | 8 |
| 2 | 16 |
| 3 | 24 |
| 4 | |
| 5 | |
| 6 | |

7. Ling is saving money for a new car. The table shows the amount of money in her savings account over a 5-month period. Define the independent and dependent variables and the unit rate of change. (Assume Ling saves the same amount of money each month.) Write an equation that represents the data shown in the table. Complete the table.

| Time | Savings |
|---|---|
| months | dollars |
| 0 | 1350 |
| 1 | 1500 |
| 2 | 1650 |
| 3 | |
| 4 | |
| 5 | |

© Carnegie Learning

NAME_____ DATE_____

8. The graph shows the relationship between two quantities. Complete the table. Define the independent and dependent variables and the unit rate of change. Write an equation that represents the data shown.

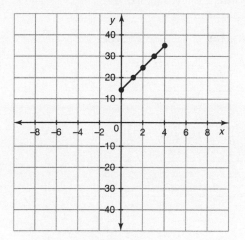

| x | y |
|---|---|
|   |   |
|   |   |
|   |   |
|   |   |
|   |   |

**8**

9. The graph shows the relationship between two quantities. Complete the table. Define the independent and dependent variables and the unit rate of change. Write an equation that represents the data shown.

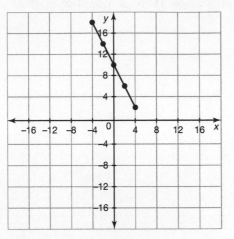

| x | y |
|---|---|
|   |   |
|   |   |
|   |   |
|   |   |
|   |   |

NAME_____ DATE _____

**10.** The graph shows the relationship between two quantities. Complete the table. Define the independent and dependent variables and the unit rate of change. Write an equation that represents the data shown.

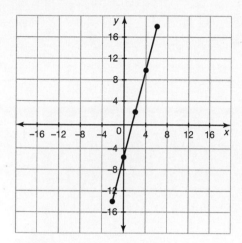

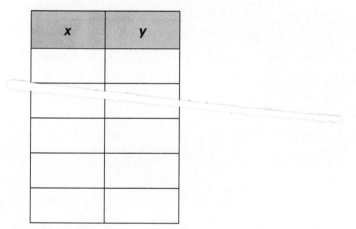

| x | y |
|---|---|
|   |   |
|   |   |
|   |   |
|   |   |

8

# Lesson 9.1 Skills Practice

NAME_____ DATE _____

## Earth Measure
### Introduction to Geometry and Geometric Constructions

## Vocabulary

Write the term that best completes the statement.

1. _____ means to have the same size, shape, and measure.

2. In geometry, a construction can also be called a(n) _____.

3. A(n) _____ is a ruler with no numbers.

4. _____ is the study of shapes and measurement.

5. When you _____ a geometric figure, the figure is created with the use of tools such as a ruler, straightedge, compass, or protractor.

6. _____ are line segments that have the same length.

7. A(n) _____ is described as a straight continuous arrangement of an infinite number of points.

8. A(n) _____ is part of a circle, or the curve between two points on a circle.

9. A(n) _____ is a tool used to create arcs and circles.

10. When you _____ a geometric figure, the figure is created without the use of tools.

11. The point at which two or more lines or arcs intersect or cross is called a(n) _____.

12. A(n) _____ is described as a location in space, and it has no size or shape.

13. _____ are two or more lines that are located in the same plane.

14. A(n) _____ can be used to approximate the measure of an angle.

15. A(n) _____ is a portion of a line that includes two points and the points between those two points.

16. The points where a line segment begins and ends are called the _____.

17. When you _____ a geometric figure, the figure is created using only a compass and a straightedge.

18. A(n) _____ is described as a flat surface with an infinite length and width but no depth.

19. Lines that are not located in the same plane are called _____.

## Problem Set

Make a sketch and a drawing of each given figure.

1.

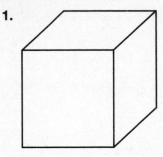
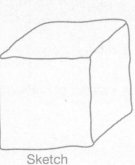
Sketch
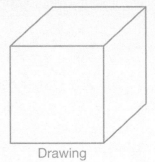
Drawing

Answers may vary.

2.

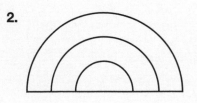

NAME_____ DATE _____

3.

4.

5.

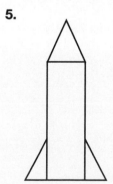

**6.**

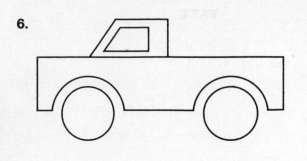

Construct each circle with the given radius and center.

**7.** Construct a circle using $\overline{AB}$ as the radius and $A$ as the center.

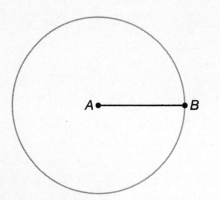

NAME_____ DATE _____

**8.** Construct a circle using $\overline{CD}$ as the radius and $D$ as the center.

D

C

**9.** Construct a circle using $\overline{EF}$ as the radius and $F$ as the center.

E•————•F

**10.** Construct a circle using $\overline{GH}$ as the radius and $H$ as the center.

•H

G•

© Carnegie Learning

**11.** Construct a circle using $\overline{JK}$ as the radius and $K$ as the center.

J

K

**12.** Construct a circle using $\overline{LM}$ as the radius and $L$ as the center.

L

M

Construct each arc using the given information.

**13.** Construct an arc using $\overline{AB}$ as the radius and $A$ as the center. Make the arc approximately one inch long and make sure it does not pass through $B$.

Answers will vary.

A•————————•B

NAME_____ DATE _____

**14.** Construct an arc using $\overline{CD}$ as the radius and $D$ as the center. Make the arc approximately one inch long and make sure it does not pass through $C$.

C•————————•D

**15.** Construct an arc using $\overline{EF}$ as the radius and $E$ as the center. Make the arc approximately one inch long and make sure it does not pass through $F$.

E•
|
F•

**16.** Construct an arc using $\overline{GH}$ as the radius and $H$ as the center. Make the arc approximately one inch long and make sure it passes through $G$.

•H
G•

© Carnegie Learning

**17.** Construct an arc using $\overline{JK}$ as the radius and $K$ as the center. Make the arc approximately one inch long and make sure it passes through $J$.

J
•
|
|
|
|
•
K

**18.** Construct an arc using $\overline{LM}$ as the radius and $L$ as the center. Make the arc approximately one inch long and make sure it passes through $M$.

L
•
\
•
M

Construct each line segment using the given information.

**19.** Duplicate $\overline{AB}$.

A •————————————• B

NAME_____ DATE _____

**20.** Duplicate $\overline{CD}$.

C •————————• D

**21.** Duplicate $\overline{EF}$.

E •——————————————————————• F

**22.** Construct a line segment that is twice the length of $\overline{JK}$.

J •——————• K

**23.** Construct a line segment that is twice the length of $\overline{PQ}$.

P•————————————————•Q

**9**

**24.** Construct a line segment that is three times the length of $\overline{WX}$.

W •————————• X

**NAME**_____  **DATE** _____

## Angles and More Angles
### Measuring and Constructing Angles

## Vocabulary

Match each definition to its corresponding term.

1. an angle whose measure is greater than 0°, but less than 90°

   **a.** ray

2. to divide into two equal parts

   **b.** angle

3. a portion of a line that begins at a point and extends infinitely in one direction

   **c.** vertex

4. a ray that is drawn through the vertex of an angle and divides the angle into two congruent angles

   **d.** sides of an angle

5. an angle whose measure is equal to 180°

   **e.** degrees

6. two rays that share a common endpoint to form an angle

   **f.** acute angle

7. a unit of measure for angles

   **g.** right angle

8. formed by two rays that share a common endpoint

   **h.** obtuse angle

9. an angle whose measure is greater than 90°, but less than 180°

   **i.** straight angle

10. the common endpoint of the two rays that form an angle

    **j.** congruent angles

11. two or more angles that have equal measures

    **k.** bisect

12. an angle whose measure is equal to 90°

    **l.** angle bisector

## Problem Set

Use a protractor to draw each angle with the given measure.

**1.** 40° angle

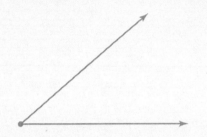

**2.** 150° angle

**3.** 75° angle

**4.** 110° angle

**5.** 160° angle

**6.** 25° angle

NAME_____DATE_____

**7.** 55° angle                       **8.** 15° angle

Construct each angle using a compass and straightedge.

**9.** Construct an angle that is congruent to ∠A.

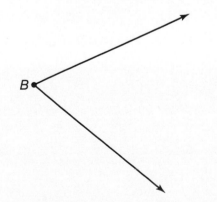

**10.** Construct an angle that is congruent to ∠B.

**11.** Construct an angle that is congruent to ∠C.

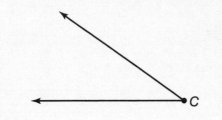

**12.** Construct an angle that is congruent to ∠D.

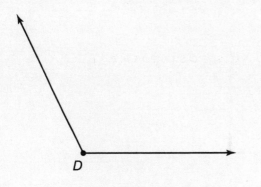

**13.** Construct an angle that is twice the measure of ∠E.

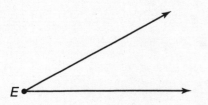

NAME_____DATE_____

**14.** Construct an angle that is twice the measure of ∠F.

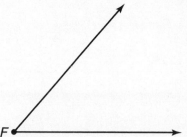

Construct the angle bisector of each given angle using a compass and straightedge.

**15.** Construct the bisector of ∠G.

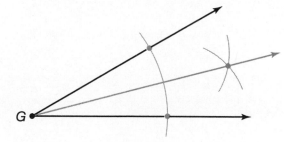

**16.** Construct the bisector of ∠H.

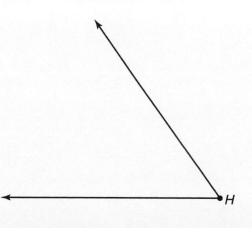

**17.** Construct the bisector of ∠J.

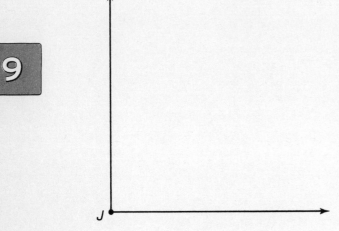

**18.** Construct the bisector of ∠K.

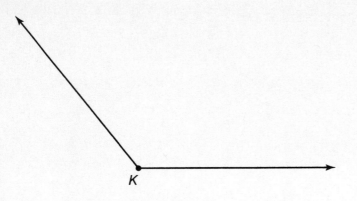

NAME_____DATE_____

**19.** Construct an angle that is one-fourth the measure of ∠M.

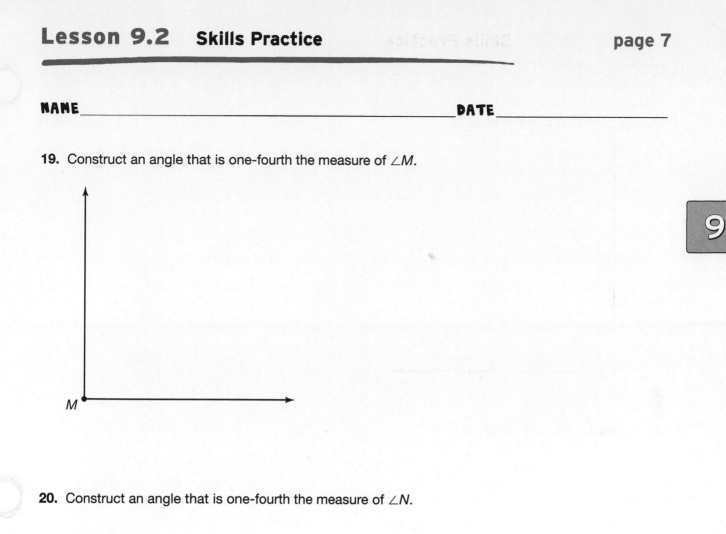

**20.** Construct an angle that is one-fourth the measure of ∠N.

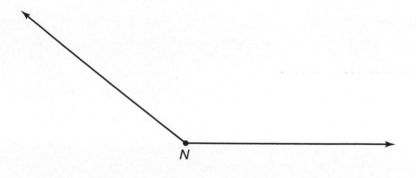

9

NAME_____DATE_____

## Special Angles
### Complements, Supplements, Midpoints, Perpendiculars, and Perpendicular Bisectors

9

## Vocabulary

Draw an example of each term. Provide an explanation when necessary.

1. supplementary angles

2. complementary angles

3. perpendicular

4. midpoint of a segment

5. segment bisector

6. perpendicular bisector

**7.** adjacent angles

**8.** linear pair

**9.** vertical angles

## Problem Set

Calculate the measure of an angle that is complementary to each given angle.

**1.** 30° angle

60°

**2.** 70° angle

**3.** 45° angle

**4.** 5° angle

**5.** 22° angle

**6.** 57° angle

**7.** 11° angle

**8.** 84° angle

NAME_____DATE_____

Calculate the measure of an angle that is supplementary to the given angle.

**9.** 60° angle

120°

**10.** 100° angle

**11.** 35° angle

**12.** 134° angle

**13.** 78° angle

**14.** 129° angle

**15.** 13° angle

**16.** 162° angle

Perform each given construction.

**17.** Construct a line perpendicular to the given line through point *A*.

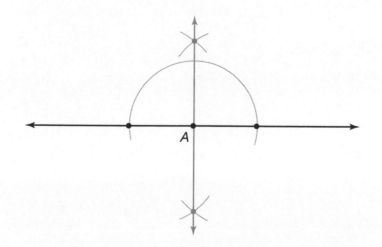

**9**

**18.** Construct a line perpendicular to the given line through point *B*.

**19.** Construct a line perpendicular to the given line through point *C*.

NAME_____DATE_____

**20.** Construct a line perpendicular to the given line through point $D$.

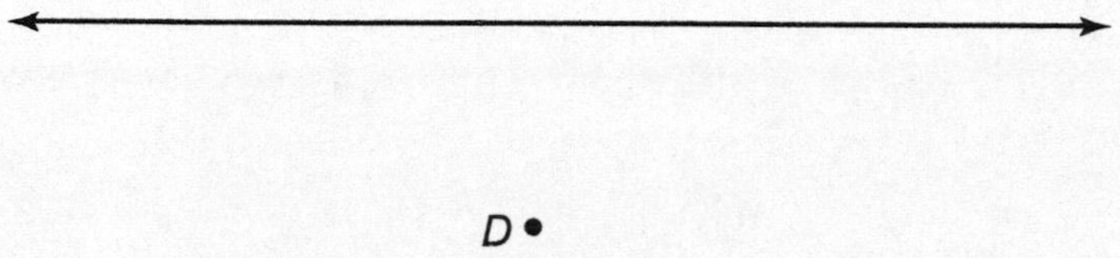

$D \bullet$

**21.** Construct the perpendicular bisector of $\overline{EF}$.

$E$            $F$

**22.** Construct the perpendicular bisector of $\overline{GH}$.

G ————————————— H

**23.** Construct the midpoint of $\overline{JK}$.

J ————————————— K

NAME_____ DATE_____

**24.** Construct the midpoint of $\overline{LM}$.

L •————————————————————• M

Identify the angle pairs in each given diagram.

**25.** Name all pairs of adjacent angles in the diagram shown.

∠1 and ∠2, ∠2 and ∠3, ∠3 and ∠4, ∠4 and ∠1.

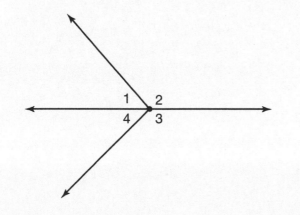

**26.** Name all pairs of adjacent angles in the diagram shown.

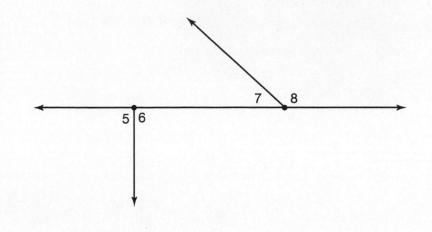

**27.** Name all pairs of adjacent angles in the diagram shown.

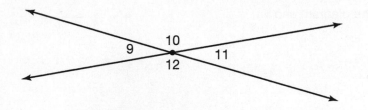

NAME_____ DATE _____

**28.** Name all pairs of adjacent angles in the diagram shown.

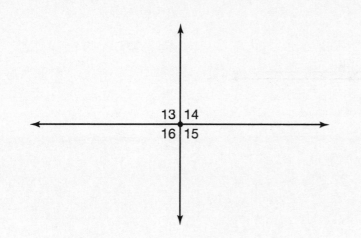

**29.** Name all linear pairs in the diagram shown.

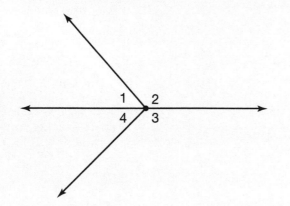

**30.** Name all linear pairs in the diagram shown.

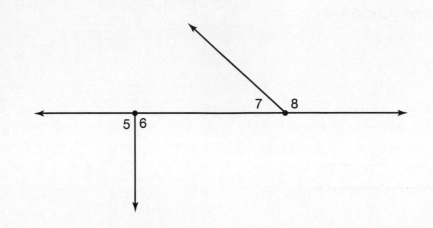

**31.** Name all linear pairs in the diagram shown.

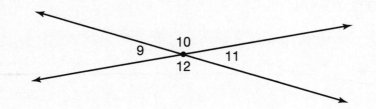

NAME_____ DATE_____

**32.** Name all linear pairs in the diagram shown.

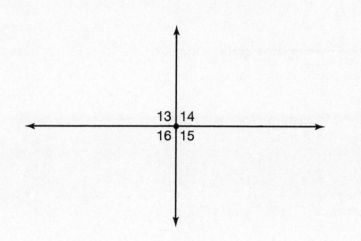

**33.** Name all vertical angle pairs in the diagram shown.

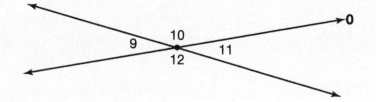

**34.** Name all vertical angle pairs in the diagram shown.

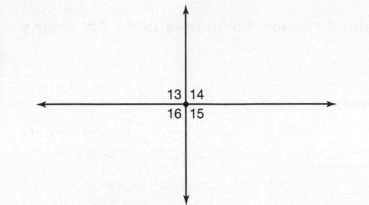

NAME_____DATE_____

## Pulling a One-Eighty!
### Triangle Sum, Exterior Angle, and Exterior Angle Inequality Theorems

## Vocabulary

Write the term that best completes each statement.

1. The _____ states that the measure of an exterior angle of a triangle is greater than the measure of either of the remote interior angles of the triangle.

2. The _____ states that the sum of the measures of the interior angles of a triangle is 180°.

3. The _____ states that the measure of an exterior angle of a triangle is equal to the sum of the measures of the remote interior angles of the triangle.

4. The _____ are the two angles that are non-adjacent to the specified exterior angle.

## Problem Set

Determine the measure of the unknown angle in each triangle.

1.
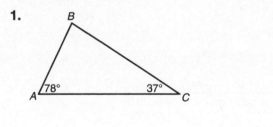

2.
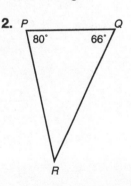

$m\angle B = 180° - (78° + 37°) = 65°$

© Carnegie Learning

**3.**

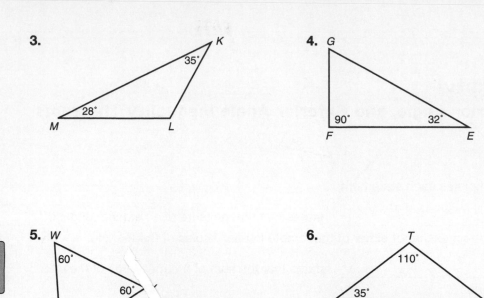

**4.**

**5.** W

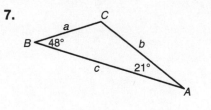

**6.**

List the side lengths from shortest to longest for each diagram.

**7.**

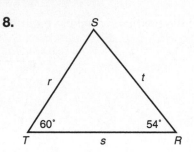

**8.**

$m\angle C = 180° - (48° + 21°) = 111°$

The shortest side of a triangle
is opposite the smallest angle.
So, the side lengths from shortest
to longest are $a$, $b$, $c$.

NAME_____ DATE_____

**9.**

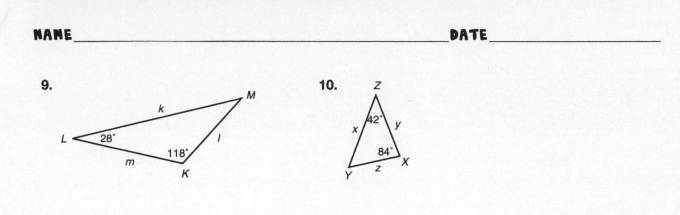

**10.**

**11.**

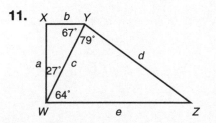

**12.**

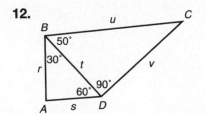

Identify the interior angles, the exterior angle, and the remote interior angles of each triangle.

**13.**

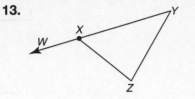

**14.**

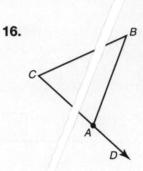

Interior angles: ∠XYZ, ∠YZX, ∠ZXY

Exterior angle: ∠WXZ

Remote interior angles: ∠XYZ, ∠YZX

**15.**

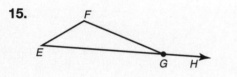

**16.**

**17.**

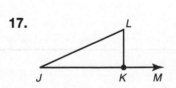

**18.**

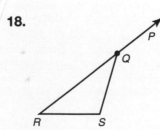

NAME_____ DATE_____

Solve for x in each diagram.

**19.**

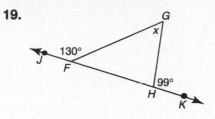

$m\angle GFH = 180° - 130° = 50°$

$m\angle GHK = m\angle GFH + m\angle FGH$

$\qquad 99° = 50° + x$

$\qquad 49° = x$

**20.**

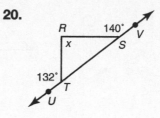

**21.**

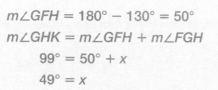

**22.**

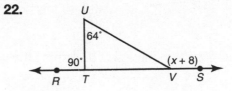

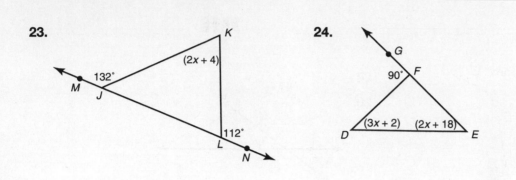

**23.**

**24.**

Compare the angles in each triangle and determine the unknown information.

**25.**

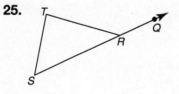

**26.**

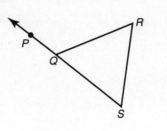

$m\angle$ _QRT_ $> m\angle RST$

$m\angle RTS$ _<_ $m\angle QRT$

$m\angle PQR$ _____ $m\angle QRS$

$m\angle QSR$ _<_ $m\angle$ _____

NAME_____DATE_____

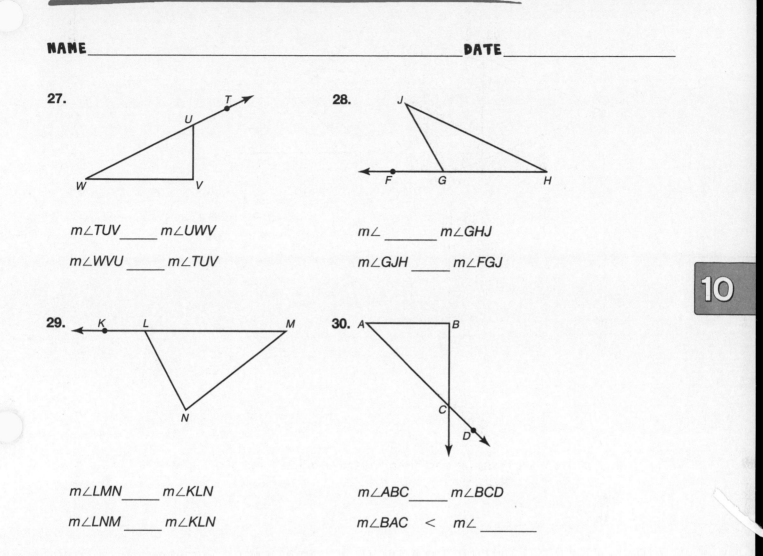

27.

m∠TUV_____m∠UWV

m∠WVU_____m∠TUV

28.

m∠_____m∠GHJ

m∠GJH_____m∠FGJ

29.

m∠LMN_____m∠KLN

m∠LNM_____m∠KLN

30.

m∠ABC_____m∠BCD

m∠BAC  <  m∠_____

# Lesson 10.2 Skills Practice

NAME_____ DATE_____

## Triangle Construction I
### Constructing Triangles

## Problem Set

Determine whether each combination of given sides and/or angles determines a unique triangle.

**1.** You are given three angles.

No.

**2.** You are given three sides.

**3.** You are given two sides and the included angle.

**4.** You are given two angles and a side not specified.

**5.** You are given two angles.

**6.** You are given two sides.

Construct each triangle using the given sides and/or angles.

**7.** Construct △PQR using the three line segments shown.

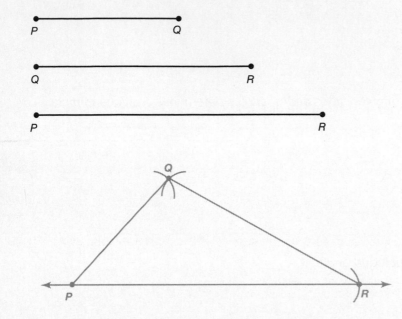

**10**

**8.** Construct △UVW using the three line segments shown.

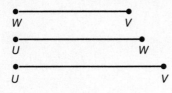

**NAME**_____ **DATE**_____

9. Construct △*DEF* using the three line segments shown.

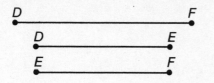

10. Construct △*MNP* using the three line segments shown.

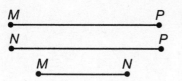

**11.** Construct △HJK using the three line segments shown.

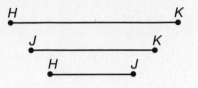

10

**12.** Construct △ABC using the two line segments and included angle shown.

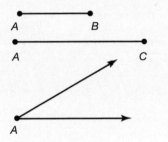

**NAME**_____ **DATE**_____

**13.** Construct △PQR using the two line segments and included angle shown.

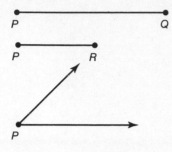

**14.** Construct △DEF using the two line segments and included angle shown.

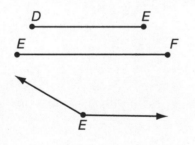

10

**15.** Construct △*KMN* using the two line segments and included angle shown.

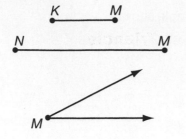

**16.** Construct △*WXZ* using the two line segments and included angle shown.

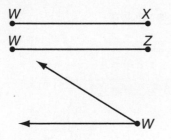

NAME_____DATE_____

## Triangle Construction II
### Congruent Figures and Constructing Congruent Triangles

## Vocabulary

Define each term in your own words.

**1.** geometric figures

**2.** congruent geometric figures

**3.** corresponding sides

**4.** corresponding angles

**5.** included angle

**6.** included side

## Problem Set

Use measuring tools to determine whether the given figures are congruent. If the figures are congruent, then identify and list the corresponding sides and angles. If the figures are not congruent, explain why they are not.

**1.**

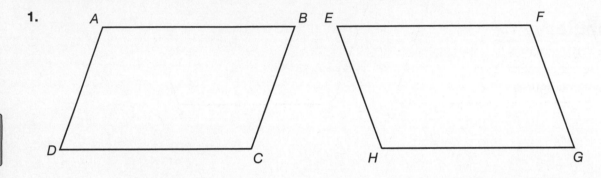

The figures are congruent.

$\overline{AB} \cong \overline{FE}$, $\overline{BC} \cong \overline{EH}$, $\overline{CD} \cong \overline{HG}$, $\overline{AD} \cong \overline{FG}$, $\angle A \cong \angle F$, $\angle B \cong \angle E$, $\angle C \cong \angle H$, and $\angle D \cong \angle G$

**2.**

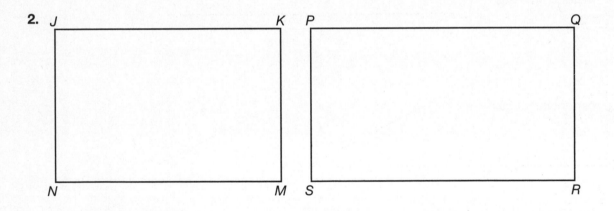

NAME_____   DATE_____

3.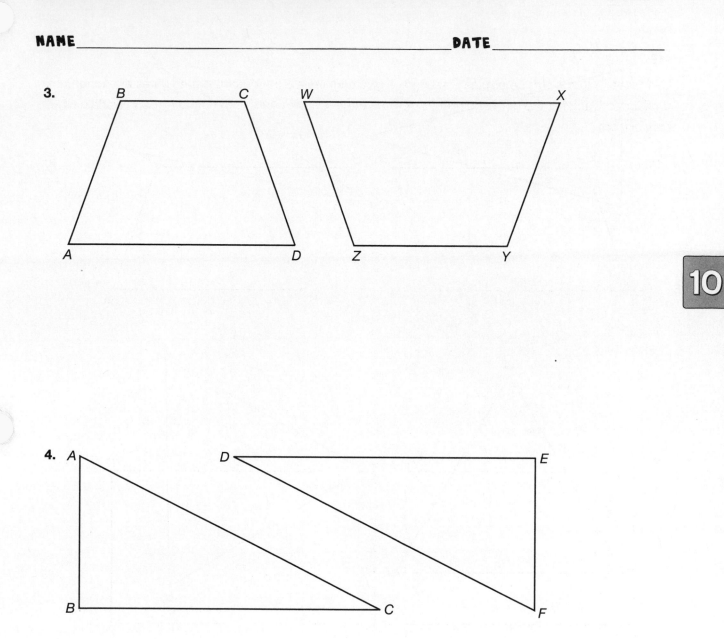

4.

**5.**

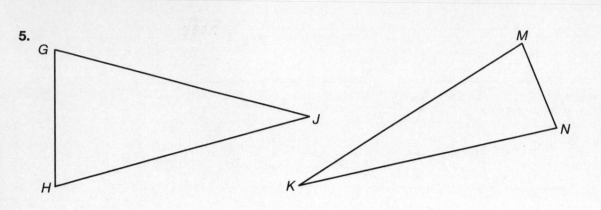

**6.**

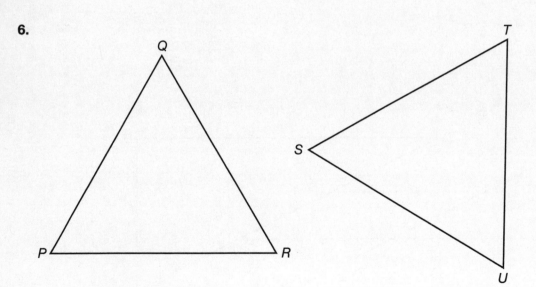

NAME_____ DATE_____

Construct each triangle using the given sides and/or angles.

**7.** Three sides are given.

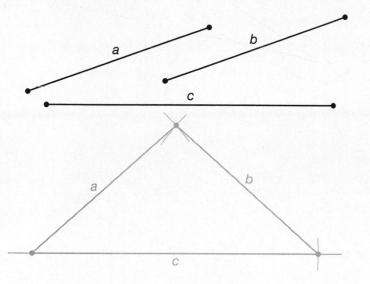

**8.** Three sides are given.

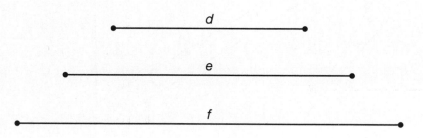

**9.** Three sides are given.

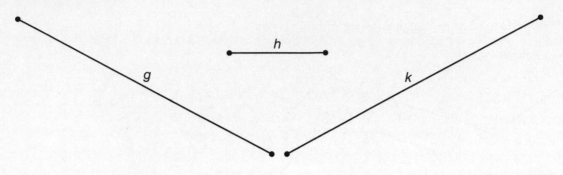

**10.** Two sides and the included angle are given.

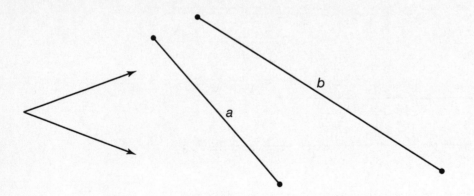

NAME_____ DATE_____

**11.** Two sides and the included angle are given.

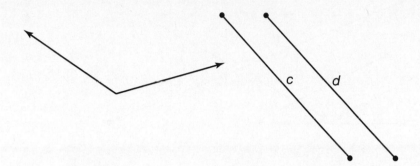

**12.** Two sides and the included angle are given.

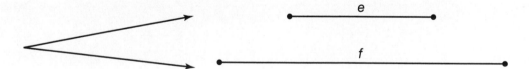

**13.** Two angles and the included side are given.

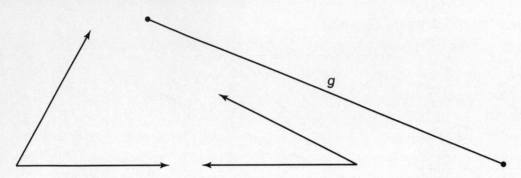

NAME_____DATE_____

**14.** Two angles and the included side are given.

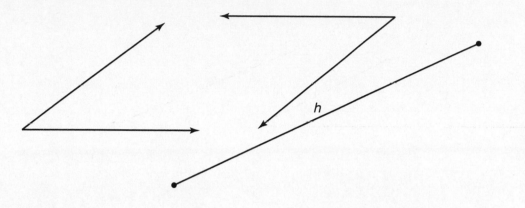

Use the congruence symbol to show the corresponding sides and angles that are congruent based on each congruence statement.

**15.** △MAT ≅ △JEF

$\overline{MA} \cong \overline{JE}, \overline{AT} \cong \overline{EF}, \overline{MT} \cong \overline{JF}, \angle M \cong \angle J,$
$\angle A \cong \angle E, \angle T \cong \angle F$

**16.** △LMN ≅ △GHJ

**17.** △CAT ≅ △DOG

**18.** △ABC ≅ △KTV

**19.** △PQR ≅ △XYZ

**20.** △DEF ≅ △RST

NAME_____   DATE_____

## Pasta Anyone?
### Triangle Inequality Theorem

## Vocabulary

Use the given figure to complete the statement.

**1.** According to the Triangle Inequality Theorem, _____ + _____ > *AC*.

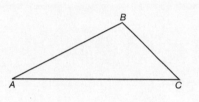

## Problem Set

Without measuring the angles, list the angles of each triangle in order from least to greatest measure.

**1.**

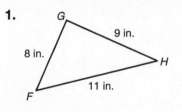

8 in.
9 in.
11 in.
G
H
F

The smallest angle of a triangle is
opposite the shortest side. So, the
angles from least to greatest
are ∠*H*, ∠*F*, ∠*G*.

**2.**

Y
4.7 cm
3.6 cm
X   2.1 cm   W

© Carnegie Learning

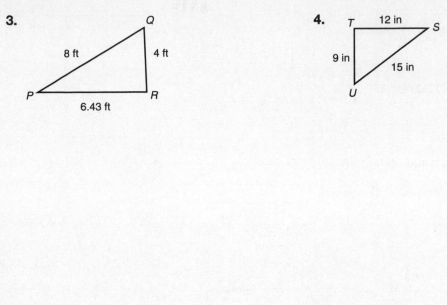

3.

8 ft, 4 ft, 6.43 ft (triangle P, Q, R)

4.

12 in, 9 in, 15 in (triangle T, S, U)

5.

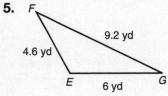

9.2 yd, 4.6 yd, 6 yd (triangle F, E, G)

6.

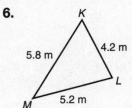

5.8 m, 4.2 m, 5.2 m (triangle K, L, M)

Determine whether it is possible to form a triangle using segments with the given measurements. Explain your reasoning.

**7.** 3 in., 2.9 in., 5 in.

Yes. Because $3 + 2.9 = 5.9$, and 5.9 is greater than 5.

**8.** 8 ft, 9 ft, 11 ft

NAME_____ DATE_____

**9.** 4 m, 5.1 m, 12.5 m

**10.** 7.4 cm, 8.1 cm, 9.8 cm

**11.** 10 yd, 5 yd, 21 yd

**12.** 13.8 km, 6.3 km, 7.5 km

**13.** 112 mm, 300 mm, 190 mm

**14.** 20.2 in., 11 in., 8.2 in.

**15.** 30 cm, 12 cm, 17 cm

**16.** 8 ft, 8 ft, 8 ft

Write an inequality that expresses the possible lengths of the unknown side of the given triangle.

**17.** What could be the length of $\overline{AB}$?

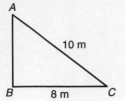

$AB < AC + BC$

$AB < 10\text{ m} + 8\text{ m}$

$AB < 18\text{ m}$

$AC < AB + BC$

$AC - BC < AB$

$10\text{ m} - 8\text{ m} < AB$

$2\text{ m} < AB$

$2\text{ m} < AB < 18\text{ m}$

**18.** What could be the length of $\overline{DE}$?

© Carnegie Learning

NAME_____DATE_____

**19.** What could be the length of $\overline{HI}$?

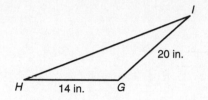

**20.** What could be the length of $\overline{JL}$?

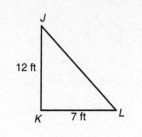

**21.** What could be the length of $\overline{MN}$?

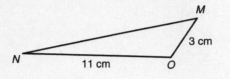

**22.** What could be the length of $\overline{QR}$?

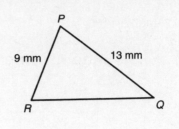

# Lesson 11.1  Skills Practice

NAME_____  DATE_____

## Bigger and Smaller
### Scale Drawings, Scale Models, and Scale Factors

## Vocabulary

Define the term in your own words.

**1.** scale factor

## Problem Set

Use the given grid to enlarge or shrink each drawing.

**1.** Enlarge the drawing.

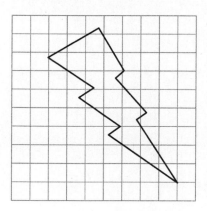 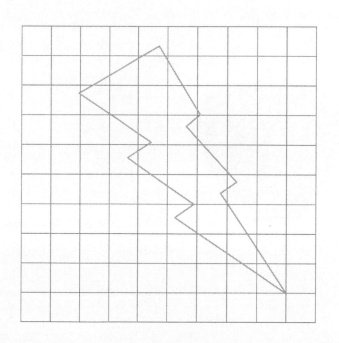

2. Shrink the drawing.

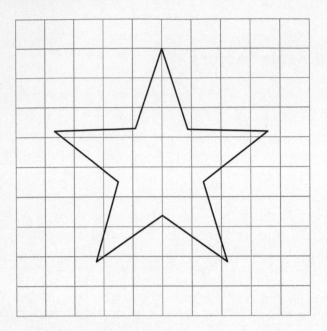

3. Enlarge the drawing.

NAME_____ DATE_____

4. Shrink the drawing.

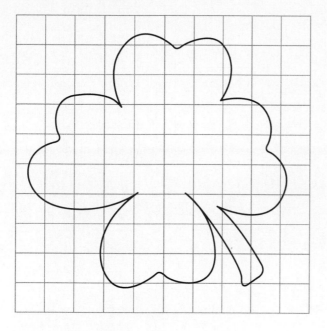
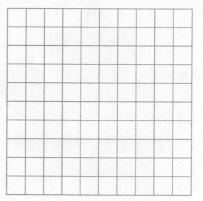

5. Enlarge the drawing.

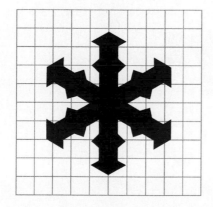

6. Shrink the drawing.

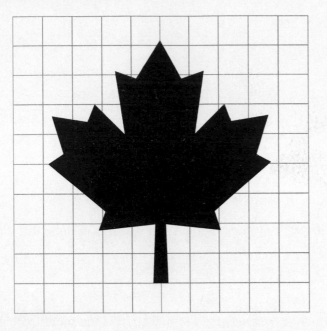

Use the given scale model to answer each question.

7. The model of a 1955 Ford Thunderbird has a scale factor of $\frac{1}{24}$.

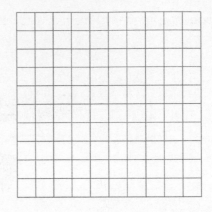

a. If the model car is 7 inches long, how long is the actual car in feet?

The actual car is $7 \cdot 24 = 168$ inches, or $168 \div 12 = 14$ feet long.

b. If the door on a 1955 Ford Thunderbird is actually 3 feet 6 inches wide, how wide is a door on the model in inches?

The actual door is 3 feet 6 inches, or $3 \cdot 12 + 6 = 36 + 6 = 42$ inches wide. The door on the model is $42 \cdot \frac{1}{24} = 1.75$ inches wide.

NAME_____ DATE _____

8. The model of a space shuttle has a scale factor of $\frac{1}{39}$.

    **a.** If the space shuttle model is 3.13 feet in length, how long is the actual space shuttle to the nearest foot?

    **b.** If the actual space shuttle has a wingspan of 78 feet, what is the wingspan of the model to the nearest foot?

11

**9.** The Tyrannosaurus rex model has a scale factor of $\frac{1}{40}$.

a. If the Tyrannosaurus rex model is 0.15 meter tall, how tall would an actual Tyrannosaurus rex have been?

b. If an actual Tyrannosaurus rex was 12 meters long, how long is the model?

NAME_____ DATE _____

**10.** The skyscraper model has a scale factor of $\frac{1}{60}$.

    **a.** If the skyscraper model is 5 feet tall, how tall is the actual skyscraper?

    **b.** If a window in the actual skyscraper is 9 feet tall, how tall is the window in the model?

**11.** The model of the historic Gokstad Viking ship has a scale factor of $\frac{1}{64}$.

**a.** If the ship model is 15 inches long, how long is the actual ship in feet?

**b.** If the mast on the actual ship is 32 feet tall, how tall is the mast on the model in inches?

NAME_____ DATE _____

12. The model of an M1A1 Abrams tank has a scale factor of $\frac{1}{24}$.

    **a.** If the tank model is 6 inches wide, how wide is the actual tank in feet?

    **b.** If the cannon on the actual tank is 17.3 feet long, how long is the cannon on the model tank in feet?

11

11

NAME_____ DATE_____

## Say Cheese!
**Applications of Ratio**

## Vocabulary

Give an example of the term.

**1.** aspect ratio

## Problem Set

Calculate each unknown dimension so that rectangle B is the same shape as rectangle A. The dimensions are listed as "width $\times$ height."

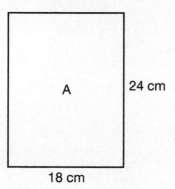

A    24 cm

18 cm

**1.** Rectangle B = 6 cm $\times$ _____

$$\frac{18}{6} = \frac{24}{x}$$

$(18)(x) = (6)(24)$

$18x = 144$

$x = 8$

Rectangle B = 6 cm $\times$ 8 cm

**2.** Rectangle B = _____ $\times$ 3 cm

**3.** Rectangle B = _____ × 32 cm

**4.** Rectangle B = 12 cm × _____

**5.** Rectangle B = 3 cm × _____

**6.** Rectangle B = _____ × 12 cm

NAME_____ DATE_____

Calculate each unknown dimension given the aspect ratio. The dimensions are listed as "width $\times$ height." The aspect ratio is listed as "width : height."

**7.** Rectangle B = 15 in. $\times$ ____, aspect ratio = 3 : 1

$$\frac{15}{x} = \frac{3}{1}$$

$$(15)(1) = (x)(3)$$

$$15 = 3x$$

$$5 = x$$

Rectangle B = 15 in. $\times$ 5 in.

**8.** Rectangle B = 6 in. $\times$ ____, aspect ratio = 1 : 1.75

**9.** Rectangle B = ____ $\times$ 8 in., aspect ratio = 2.5 : 1

**10.** Rectangle B = _____ × 21 in., aspect ratio = 2:3

**11.** Rectangle B = 27 in. × _____, aspect ratio = 1.5:1

11

**12.** Rectangle B = _____ × 30 in., aspect ratio = 5:3

NAME_____ DATE_____

Calculate the aspect ratio for each rectangular shape. Write each aspect ratio using whole numbers. The dimensions are listed as "width × height."

**13.** football field = 160 ft × 360 ft

aspect ratio $= \dfrac{160}{360}$

$= \dfrac{4}{9}$

aspect ratio = 4:9

**14.** driveway = 12 ft × 20 ft

**15.** soccer field = 60 yd × 100 yd

**16.** doorway = 32 in. × 80 in.

**17.** lacrosse goal = 6 ft × 6 ft

**18.** garden = 5 ft × 20 ft

© Carnegie Learning

Use the given information to answer each question.

19. If you built a model of a redwood tree at a 1 : 80 scale, the model would be 4.5 feet tall.
    How tall is the redwood tree?

    $$\frac{4.5}{x} = \frac{1}{80}$$

    $(4.5)(80) = (x)(1)$

    $360 = x$

    The redwood tree is 360 feet tall.

**11**

20. If you built a model of a mountain at a 1 : 4000 scale, the model would be 5 feet tall.
    How tall is the mountain?

NAME_____ DATE_____

21. If you built a model of a single die at a 24:1 scale, the model would be 12 inches tall. How tall is a single die?

22. If you built a model of a daisy flower at a 5:1 scale, the model would be 20 inches wide. How wide is a daisy flower?

11

**23.** If you built a model of a ranch style house at a 1 : 10 scale, the model would be 2 feet tall.
How tall is the house?

**11**

**24.** If you built a model of a football at a 4 : 1 scale, the model would be 44 inches wide.
How wide is a football?

NAME_____ DATE_____

# No GPS? Better Get the Map Out!
## Exploring Scale Drawings

## Vocabulary

Write the term that best completes the sentence.

1. The purpose of a(n) _____ is to create an accurate drawing of either a very large or very small object.

## Problem Set

Write a scale as a ratio to represent each sentence.

1. A scale drawing is four times as large as the original object.

   4:1

2. An object is one eighth of the size of its scale model.

3. An object is twice the size of its scale drawing.

4. A scale drawing is one tenth the size of the original object.

5. A scale model is the same size as the original object.

6. A scale drawing is fifty times as large as the original object.

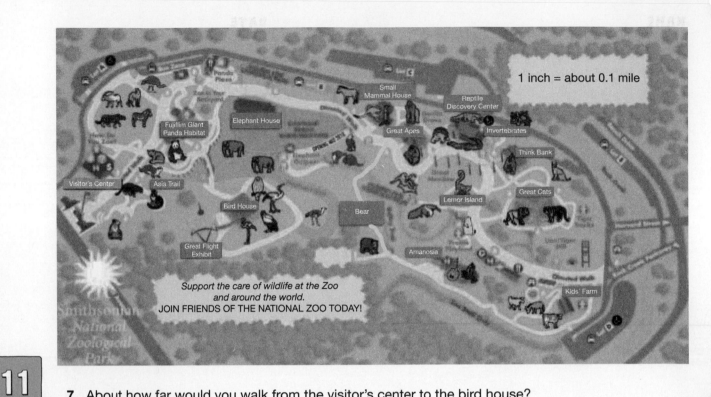

1 inch = about 0.1 mile

Support the care of wildlife at the Zoo
and around the world.
JOIN FRIENDS OF THE NATIONAL ZOO TODAY!

**7.** About how far would you walk from the visitor's center to the bird house?

about 0.3 mile

**8.** About how far would you walk from the pandas to see the great cats?

**9.** About how far would you walk from the kids' farm back to the visitor's center?

**10.** About how far would you walk from the bears to the great apes?

**11.** About how far would you walk from the elephants to the reptiles?

NAME_____ DATE _____

12. About how much farther would you walk from the visitor's center to see the great cats than to see the great apes?

Choose the scale that would produce each scale drawing described.

13. Determine which scale would produce the largest scale drawing of an object.

1:2

1 in.:2 ft

2 ft:1 ft

Each scale written with the same units for both terms is 1:2, 1:24, 2:1.
The scale that would produce the largest scale drawing is 2:1.

14. Determine which scale would produce the largest scale drawing of an object.

1:10

1 cm:1 m

1 mm:1 m

15. Determine which scale would produce the smallest scale drawing of an object.

1:25

1 in.:25 ft

25 in.:1 ft

**16.** Determine which scale would produce the smallest scale drawing of an object.

5:1

2 m:1 cm

2 m:1 mm

**17.** Determine which scale would produce the largest scale drawing of an object.

1:200

2 m:1 cm

1 cm:2 m

**18.** Determine which scale would produce the smallest scale drawing of an object.

1:50

1 in.:5 ft

1 ft:5 ft

# Lesson 11.3  Skills Practice

NAME_____ DATE _____

Determine whether a scale model with the given scale is larger or smaller than the original object.

**19.** 1 in.:6 in.

Scale = scale size:actual size
The scale model is smaller than the
original object.

**20.** 5 cm:1 cm

**21.** 6 cm:1 m

**22.** 1 cm:1 mm

**23.** 2 ft:1 in.

**24.** 1 in.:4 ft

Use the given information to answer each question.

**25.** A scale model of a skyscraper was built at a scale of 1:250 and is 1.4 meters tall. What is the height of the original skyscraper?

$$\frac{1}{250} = \frac{1.4}{x}$$

$(1)(x) = (250)(1.4)$

$x = 350$

The height of the original skyscraper is 350 meters.

**26.** Serena created a scale model of a bank check to present to a charity. The model was created at a scale of 8:1 and is 4 feet long. What is the length of the original check?

**27.** The height of the U.S. Capitol Building is 287 feet. The height of a scale model of the building is 2.87 feet. What is the scale of the model?

NAME_____ DATE _____

28. The length of a pencil is 7 inches. Shawna created a scale model of the pencil for art class. The model is 35 inches long. What is the scale of the model?

29. A scale model of the Washington Monument was built at a scale of 1 : 300 and is 1.85 feet tall. What is the height of the Washington Monument?

30. The height of a sycamore tree is 65 feet. The height of a scale model of the tree is 1.625 feet. What is the scale of the model?

NAME_____ DATE _____

## Houses for Our Feathered Friends!
### Creating Blueprints

## Problem Set

Determine reasonable measurements for the pieces used to make each object. The construction pieces for each item to be built with the appropriate measurements.

**1.** bookends

Answers will vary.

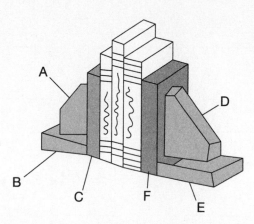

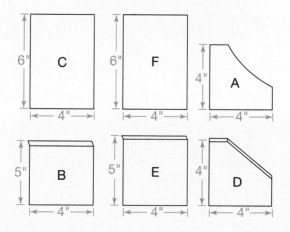

© Carnegie Learning

**2.** birdfeeder

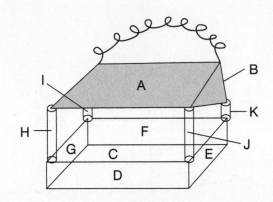

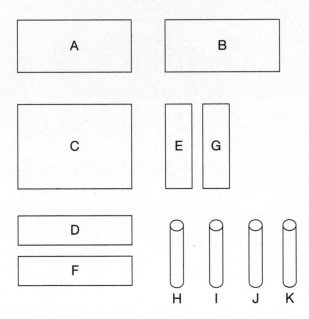

NAME_____ DATE_____

**3.** dollhouse

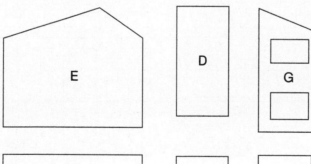
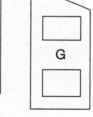

**4.** crib

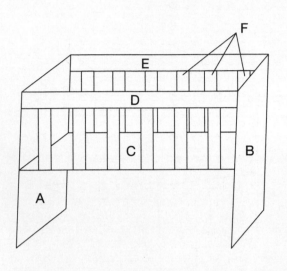

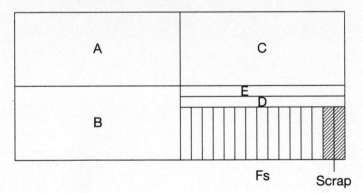

**NAME**_____ **DATE** _____

Draw and label a simple blueprint for each item to be built.

**5.** bookshelf

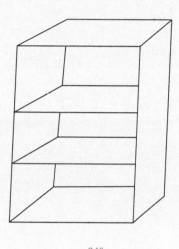

© Carnegie Learning

11

**6.** ramp

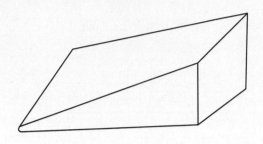

**11**

**7.** gate

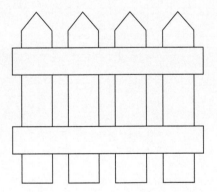

NAME_____ DATE_____

**8.** tray

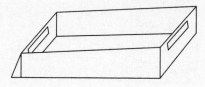

11

# Lesson 12.1  Skills Practice

NAME_____  DATE _____

## Introduction to Circles
### Circle, Radius, and Diameter

## Vocabulary

Define each term in your own words.

**1.** circle

**2.** center of a circle

**3.** radius of a circle

**4.** diameter of a circle

## Problem Set

Use the circle shown to answer each question.

**1.** Name the circle.

The circle shown is Circle *B*.

**2.** Identify a radius of the circle.

**3.** Identify a diameter of the circle.

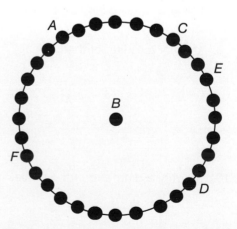

**4.** Name the circle.

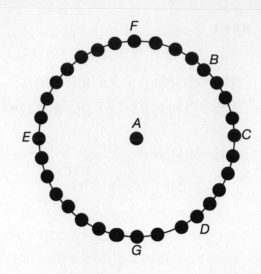

**5.** Identify a radius of the circle.

**6.** Identify a diameter of the circle.

**7.** Identify a different diameter of the circle.

**12**

**8.** Name the circle.

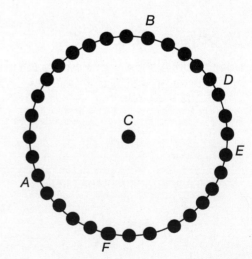

**9.** Identify a radius of the circle.

**10.** Identify a diameter of the circle.

© Carnegie Learning

NAME_____ DATE _____

Determine if the circles are congruent.

**11.**

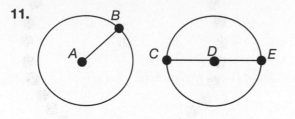

Line segment *AB* is a radius of Circle *A* and is 2 centimeters.

Line segment *CE* is a diameter of Circle *D* and is 4 centimeters.

The diameter of Circle *A* equals 4 centimeters.

The diameter of Circle *A* equals the diameter of Circle *D*.

Circle *A* and Circle *D* are congruent.

**12.**

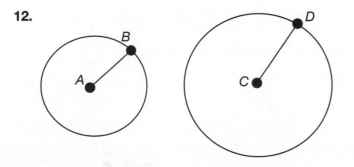

Line segment *AB* is a radius of Circle *A* and is 7 inches.

Line segment *CD* is a radius of Circle *C* and is 12 inches.

13. The radius of Circle A is 5 centimeters. The radius of Circle B is 5 centimeters.

14. The diameter of Circle A is 7 millimeters. The radius of Circle B is 7 millimeters.

15. The radius of Circle A is 3 inches. The diameter of Circle B is 6 inches.

16. The radius of Circle A is 5 centimeters. The radius of Circle B is 8 centimeters.

**12**

17. The radius of Circle A is 4 inches. The diameter of Circle B is 7 inches.

18. The diameter of Circle A is 12 centimeters. The radius of Circle B is 6 centimeters.

NAME_____ DATE _____

Construct each figure using congruent circles.

**19.** Construct an equilateral triangle using congruent circles.

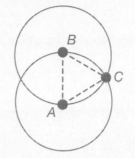

**20.** Construct an equilateral quadrilateral using congruent circles.

**21.** Construct an equilateral hexagon using congruent circles.

12

12

# Lesson 12.2 Skills Practice

NAME_____ DATE _____

## But Most of All, I Like Pi!
### Circumference of a Circle

## Vocabulary

Define the term in your own words.

**1.** pi

## Problem Set

Use a string and a centimeter ruler to measure the radius and circumference of each circle. Calculate the ratio of the circumference of the circle to its diameter.

**1.**

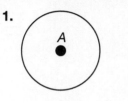

Answers will vary. The ratio should be ≈ 3.14.

**2.**

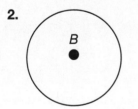

**3.**

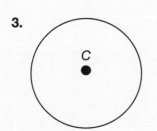

© Carnegie Learning

4.

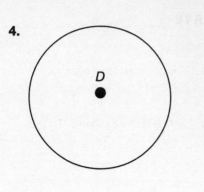

5.

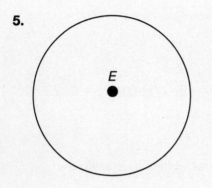

6.

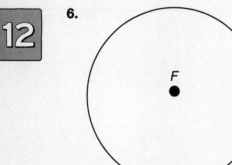

NAME_____ DATE _____

Calculate each value using the formula for the circumference of a circle. Round your answer to the nearest hundredth, if necessary.

**7.** The diameter of a circle is 6 centimeters. Calculate the circumference of the circle using the circumference formula. Let $\pi = 3.14$.

$C = \pi d$

$C = (3.14)(6)$

$C = 18.84$

The circumference of the circle is 18.84 centimeters.

**8.** The radius of a circle is 8.2 centimeters. Calculate the circumference of the circle using the circumference formula. Let $\pi = 3.14$.

**9.** The diameter of a circle is 7.5 inches. Calculate the circumference of the circle using the circumference formula. Let $\pi = 3.14$.

**10.** The radius of a circle is 16.3 millimeters. Calculate the circumference of the circle using the circumference formula. Let $\pi = 3.14$.

**11.** The diameter of a circle is 14 centimeters. Calculate the circumference of the circle using the circumference formula. Let $\pi = 3.14$.

**12.** The radius of a circle is 2.1 inches. Calculate the circumference of the circle using the circumference formula. Let $\pi = 3.14$.

NAME_____ DATE _____

Calculate each value using the formula for the circumference of a circle. Round your answer to the nearest hundredth, if necessary.

13. The circumference of a circle is 56 centimeters. Calculate the diameter of the circle using the circumference formula. Let $\pi = 3.14$.

$$C = \pi d$$

$$56 = (3.14)d$$

$$\frac{56}{3.14} = \frac{3.14d}{3.14}$$

$$17.83 \approx d$$

The diameter of the circle is approximately 17.83 centimeters.

14. The circumference of a circle is 25.12 centimeters. Calculate the radius of the circle using the circumference formula. Let $\pi = 3.14$.

12

**15.** The circumference of a circle is 112.8 millimeters. Calculate the diameter of the circle using the circumference formula. Let $\pi = 3.14$.

**16.** The circumference of a circle is 49.6 inches. Calculate the radius of the circle using the circumference formula. Let $\pi = 3.14$.

**12**

NAME_____ DATE_____

17. The circumference of a circle is 47.73 millimeters. Calculate the diameter of the circle using the circumference formula. Let $\pi = 3.14$.

18. The circumference of a circle is 56.52 centimeters. Calculate the radius of the circle using the circumference formula. Let $\pi = 3.14$.

12

# Lesson 12.3 Skills Practice

NAME_____ DATE_____

## One *Million* Sides
### Area of a Circle

## Vocabulary

Define the term in your own words.

1. inscribed circle

## Problem Set

Use the figure to answer each question. Let $\pi$ = 3.14. Round your answer to the nearest hundredth, if necessary.

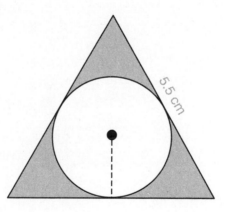

1. Use a centimeter ruler to measure the sides of the equilateral triangle. Then calculate the perimeter of the equilateral triangle.

   $P = 3s$

   $P = 3(5.5)$

   $P = 16.5$

   The perimeter of the triangle is 16.5 centimeters.

**2.** Use a centimeter ruler to measure the radius of the inscribed circle. Then calculate the circumference of the inscribed circle.

**3.** Calculate the area of the equilateral triangle in terms of the perimeter.

12

**4.** Calculate the area of the inscribed circle.

NAME_____ DATE _____

Use the figure to answer each question. Let $\pi = 3.14$. Round your answer to the nearest hundredth, if necessary.

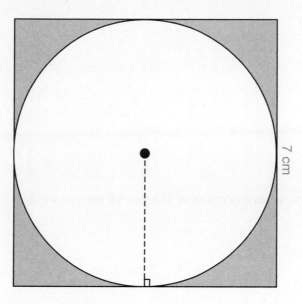

7 cm

5. Use a centimeter ruler to measure the sides of the square. Then calculate the perimeter of the square.

   $P = 4s$

   $P = 4(7)$

   $P = 28$

   The perimeter of the square is 28 centimeters.

6. Use a centimeter ruler to measure the radius of the inscribed circle. Then calculate the circumference of the inscribed circle.

7. Calculate the area of the square in terms of the perimeter.

12

8. Calculate the area of the inscribed circle.

NAME_____ DATE _____

Use the figure to answer each question. Let $\pi = 3.14$. Round your answer to the nearest hundredth, if necessary.

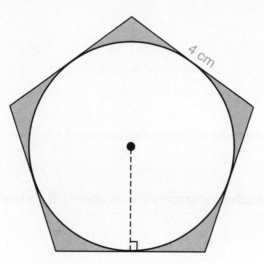

4 cm

9. Use a centimeter ruler to measure the sides of the equilateral pentagon. Then calculate the perimeter of the equilateral pentagon.

$P = 5s$

$P = 5(4)$

$P = 20$

The perimeter of the pentagon is 20 centimeters.

10. Use a centimeter ruler to measure the radius of the inscribed circle. Then calculate the circumference of the inscribed circle.

11. Calculate the area of the equilateral pentagon in terms of the perimeter.

**12**

12. Calculate the area of the inscribed circle.

NAME_____ DATE _____

Use the figure to answer question. Let $\pi = 3.14$. Round your answer to the nearest hundredth, if necessary.

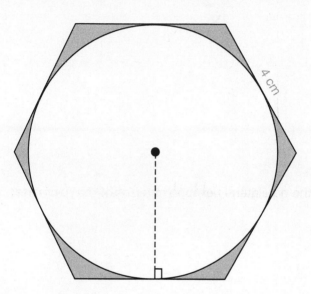

4 cm

13. Use a centimeter ruler to measure the sides of the equilateral hexagon. Then calculate the perimeter of the equilateral hexagon.

$P = 6s$

$P = 6(4)$

$P = 24$

The perimeter of the hexagon is 24 centimeters.

**14.** Use a centimeter ruler to measure the radius of the inscribed circle. Then calculate the circumference of the inscribed circle.

**15.** Calculate the area of the equilateral hexagon in terms of the perimeter.

12

**16.** Calculate the area of the inscribed circle.

NAME_____ DATE _____

## It's About Circles!
### Unknown Measurements

## Problem Set

Use the area and circumference formulas to answer each question. Let $\pi = 3.14$. Round your answer to the nearest hundredth, if necessary.

1. Jaleesa is buying a round backyard pool. The distance around the edge of the pool is 38 feet. Find the area that the pool will cover.

$$C = 2\pi r$$

$$38 = 2(3.14)r$$

$$38 = 6.28r$$

$$6.05 \approx r$$

$$A = \pi r^2$$

$$A = (3.14)(6.05)^2$$

$$A \approx 114.93$$

The pool will cover about 114.93 square feet.

2. Belinda is digging a round flower garden in her backyard. She has 19 feet of rubber edging to place around the garden. What is the area of the new garden?

3. Carlos is spreading mulch in a circle on top of an area where he has planted some seeds. He has enough mulch to cover an area that is 12.5 square feet. How much rubber edging does Carlos need to encircle the mulch that will cover the seeds?

NAME_____ DATE _____

4.  Jose is adding mulch to an existing round flower bed. The length of the rubber edging around the flower bed is 25.12 feet. What is the area that Jose needs to cover with mulch?

5.  Eva is decorating for a birthday party. She would like to add a paper streamer around the edge of a round table. The table covers an area of 19.5 square feet. What is the minimum length of the paper streamer Eva needs?

12

6. Nami is adding a mosaic pattern to the top of a small round table. The distance around the edge of the table top is 4.7 feet. What is the area that Nami needs to cover with the mosaic pattern?

NAME_____ DATE _____

Find the area of each shaded region. Let $\pi = 3.14$. Round your answer to the nearest hundredth, if necessary.

**7.**

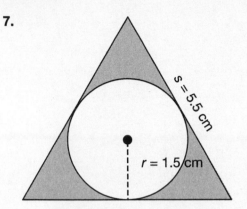

Area of the triangle:

$A = \frac{1}{2}Pr$

$A = \frac{1}{2}(3 \times 5.5)(1.5)$

$A \approx 12.38$

Area of the circle:

$A = \pi r^2$

$A = (3.14)(1.5)^2$

$A \approx 7.07$

Area of the shaded region = Area of the triangle − Area of the circle

$\approx 12.38 - 7.07$

$\approx 5.31$

The area of the shaded region is approximately 5.31 square centimeters.

**8.**

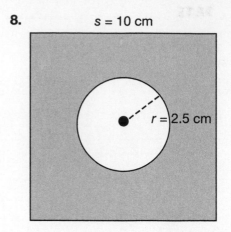

$s = 10$ cm

$r = 2.5$ cm

NAME_____ DATE _____

9.

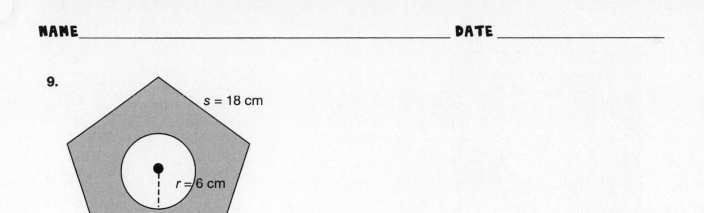

**10.**

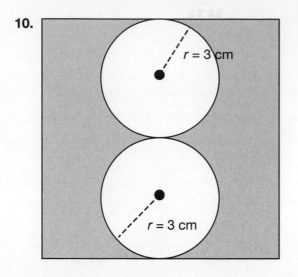

NAME_____ DATE _____

11.

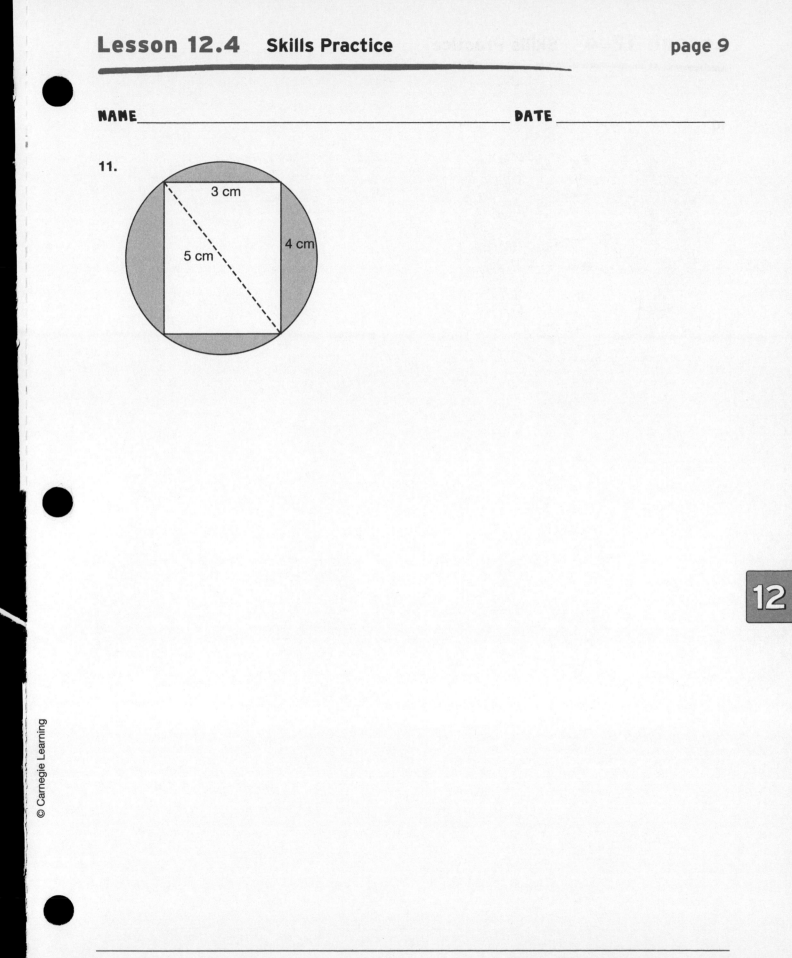

**12.**

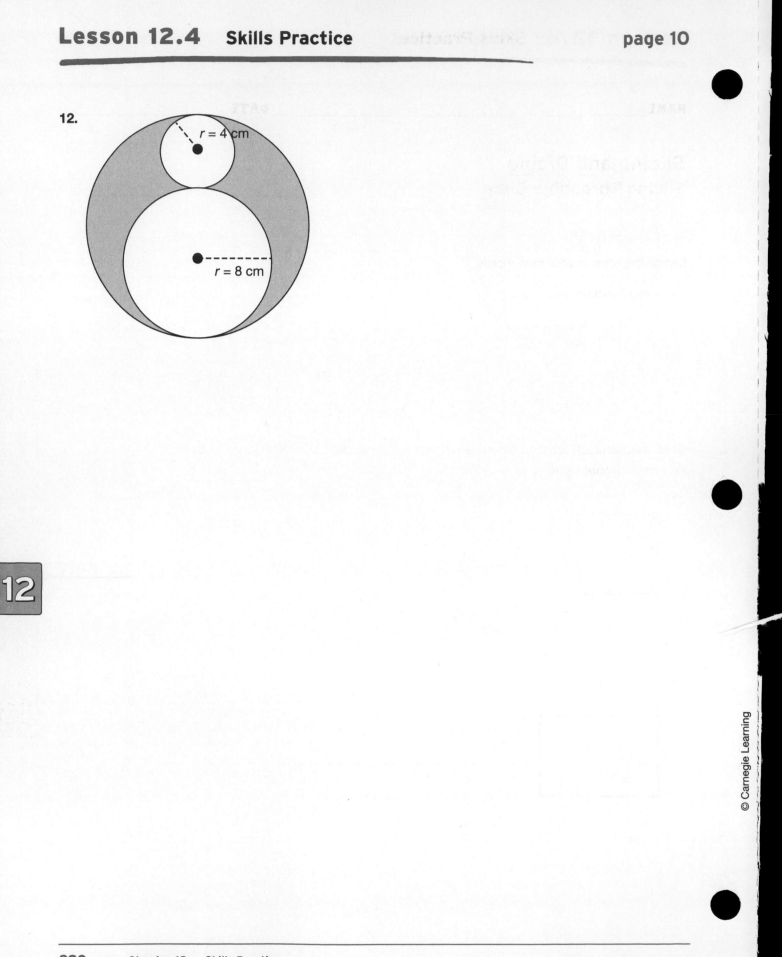

# Lesson 13.1 Skills Practice

NAME_____ DATE _____

## Slicing and Dicing
### Slicing Through a Cube

## Vocabulary

Define the term in your own words.

1. cross-section

## Problem Set

Sketch a plane intersecting a cube such that the cross-section looks like each given two-dimensional figure.

1.

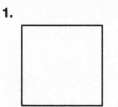

Answers may vary.

2.

© Carnegie Learning

3.

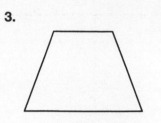

4.

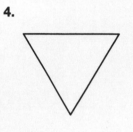

5.

**13**

6.

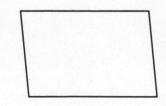

NAME_____ DATE _____

**7.**

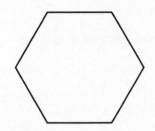

**8.**

Describe the cross-section that results from the intersection of a plane and a cube as described in each problem.

**9.** A plane intersects a cube perpendicular to its base. The plane bisects the base into two congruent triangles.

The cross-section is a rectangle.

**10.** A plane intersects exactly three vertices of a cube.

13

11. A plane intersects a cube parallel to its base.

12. A plane intersects exactly three faces of a cube.

13. A plane intersects five faces of a cube, but does not intersect the sixth face.

14. A plane intersects a cube and is perpendicular to its base. The plane intersects two opposite lateral faces of the cube, but is not perpendicular to any lateral faces.

15. A plane intersects every face of a cube.

16. A plane intersects two opposite vertices of the base, but is not perpendicular to the base. The plane intersects two edges of the other base.

NAME_____ DATE_____

## The Right Stuff
### Slicing Through Right Rectangular Prisms

## Problem Set

Sketch a plane intersecting a right rectangular prism that is not a cube such that the cross-section looks like each given two-dimensional figure.

**1.**

 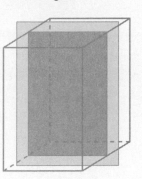

Answers may vary.

**2.**

3.

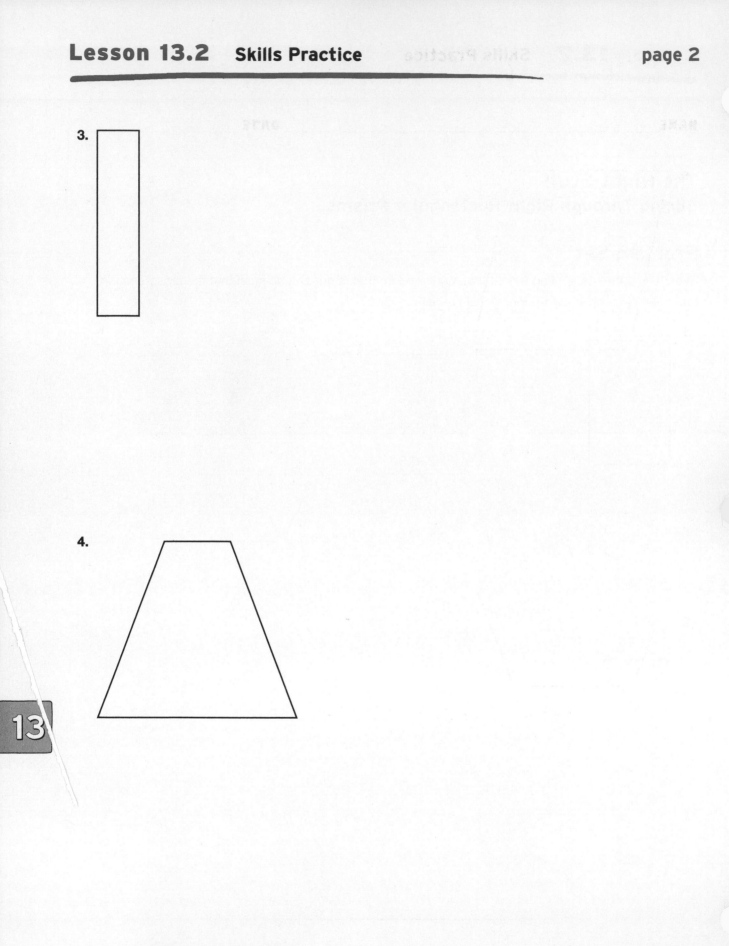

4.

NAME_____ DATE_____

5.

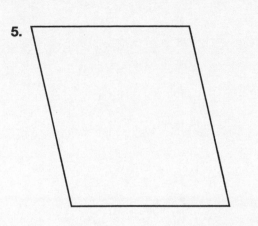

6.

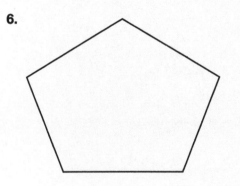

**7.**

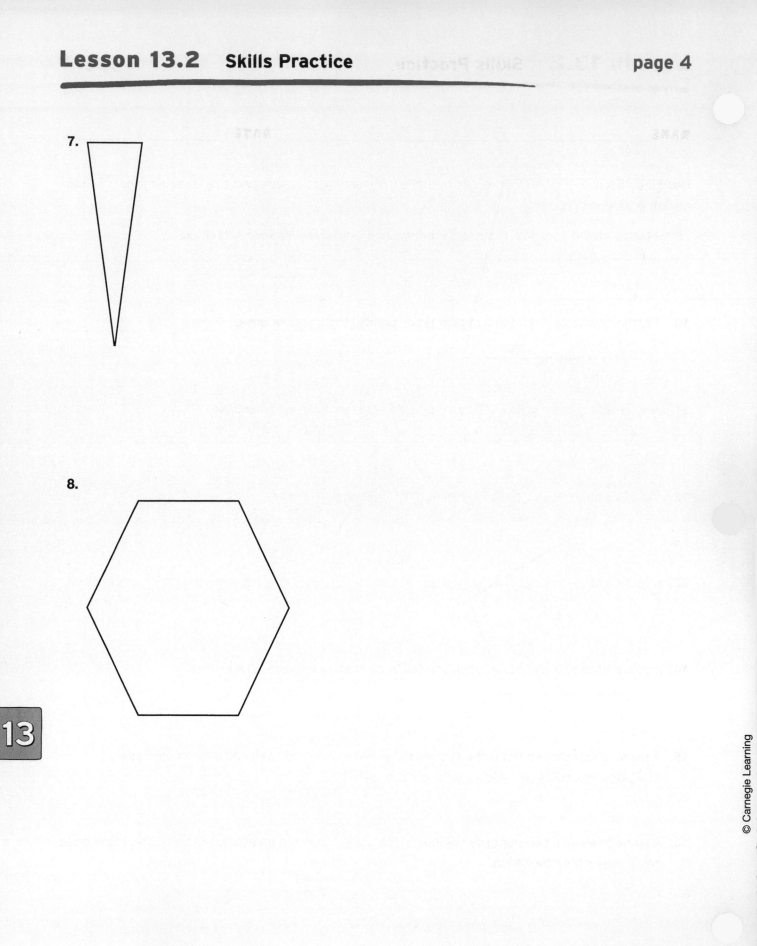

**8.**

NAME_____ DATE _____

Describe the cross-section that results from the intersection of a plane and a right rectangular prism as described in each problem.

**9.** A plane intersects a right rectangular prism such that it only intersects three faces.

The cross-section is a triangle.

**10.** A plane intersects a right rectangular prism parallel to its square base.

**11.** A plane intersects a right rectangular prism parallel to its rectangular base.

**12.** A plane intersects exactly five faces of a right rectangular prism.

**13.** A plane intersects a right rectangular prism such that exactly one edge of the prism is in the plane.

**14.** A plane intersects a right rectangular prism such that it intersects all six faces.

**15.** A plane intersects two opposite vertices of the base, but is not perpendicular to the base.

The plane intersects two edges of the other base.

**16.** A plane intersects two opposite vertices of the base, but is not parallel to the base. The plane does not intersect the other base.

13

13

NAME _____  DATE _____

# And Now On To Pyramids
## Slicing Through Right Rectangular Pyramids

## Vocabulary

Fill in each blank with the appropriate key term from the given word bank.

| pyramid | base | lateral face | lateral edge |
|---------|------|--------------|--------------|
| vertex | height | regular pyramid | slant height |

1. A _____ is a polyhedron formed by connecting one polygonal face to several triangular faces.

2. A _____ is a pyramid in which the base is a regular polygon.

3.

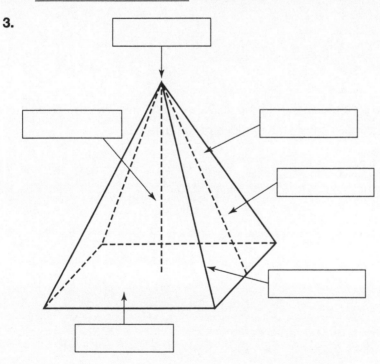

## Problem Set

Sketch a plane intersecting a right rectangular pyramid to achieve each stated goal.

1. Sketch a plane intersecting a square pyramid such that the cross-section looks like the given square.

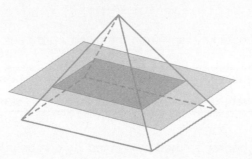

Answers may vary.

2. Sketch a plane intersecting a square pyramid such that the cross-section looks like the given triangle. The plane should not pass through any of the vertices of the pyramid.

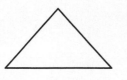

© Carnegie Learning

**NAME**_____ **DATE** _____

3. Sketch a plane intersecting a square pyramid such that the cross-section looks like the given trapezoid. The plane should not pass through any of the vertices of the pyramid.

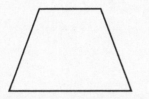

4. Sketch a plane intersecting a right rectangular pyramid that is not a square pyramid such that the cross-section looks like the given rectangle.

**5.** Sketch a plane intersecting a square pyramid such that the cross-section looks like the given triangle.

**6.** Sketch a plane intersecting a right rectangular pyramid that is not a square pyramid such that the plane passes through the vertex and two opposite vertices of the base.

NAME_____ DATE _____

7. Sketch a plane intersecting a right rectangular pyramid that is not a square pyramid such that the plane passes through two opposite vertices of the base and does not pass through the vertex.

8. Sketch a plane intersecting a square pyramid such that the plane passes through two consecutive vertices of the base and does not pass through any other vertices of the pyramid.

13

Describe the cross-section that results from the intersection of a plane and a right rectangular pyramid as described in each problem.

**9.** A plane intersects a square pyramid perpendicular to its base and passing through the vertex.

The cross-section is a triangle.

**10.** A plane intersects a square pyramid parallel to its base.

**11.** A plane intersects a right rectangular pyramid that is not a square pyramid parallel to its base.

**12.** A plane intersects a square pyramid perpendicular to its base, but does not pass through the vertex. The plane is also parallel to two edges of the base.

**13.** A plane intersects a rectangular pyramid perpendicular to its base such that it intersects only two lateral faces.

**14.** A plane intersects a right rectangular pyramid such that it passes through two consecutive vertices of the base and does not pass through any other vertices in the pyramid.

**15.** A plane intersects a square pyramid such that it passes through the vertex and two opposite vertices of the base.

**16.** A plane intersects a square pyramid such that it passes through all four lateral faces, is not parallel to the base, and is parallel to two edges of the base.

NAME_____ DATE _____

## Backyard Barbeque
### Introduction to Volume and Surface Area

## Vocabulary

Answer each problem.

1. Suppose you measured the amount of rice that would fit into a cube.

   Using math terms, describe what the amount of rice in the cube represents. Explain your answer.

2. Use a real life example to describe surface area.

## Problem Set

Calculate the volume of the rectangular prism.

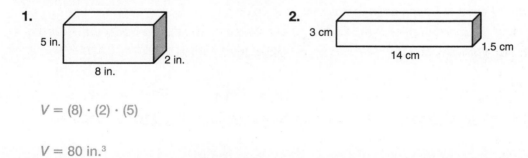

1.

5 in.

2 in.

8 in.

$V = (8) \cdot (2) \cdot (5)$

$V = 80$ in.$^3$

2.

3 cm

14 cm

1.5 cm

13

© Carnegie Learning

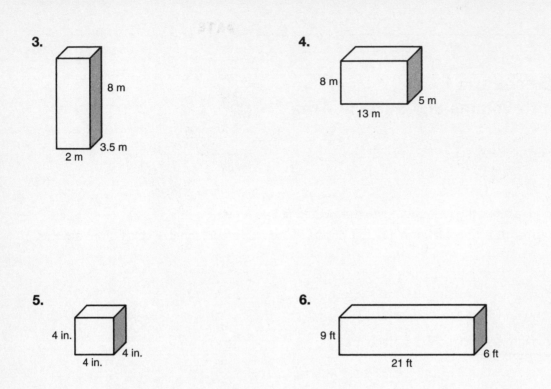

**3.**

8 m

3.5 m

2 m

**4.**

8 m

13 m

5 m

**5.**

4 in.

4 in.

4 in.

**6.**

9 ft

21 ft

6 ft

Describe how you would separate each solid to calculate the volume.

**7.**

Separate the solid into two rectangular
prisms – one prism is the bottom of the "L",
and the other prism is the top of the "L".

**8.**

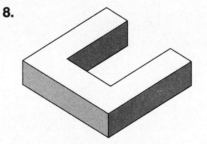

13

NAME_____   DATE_____

9.

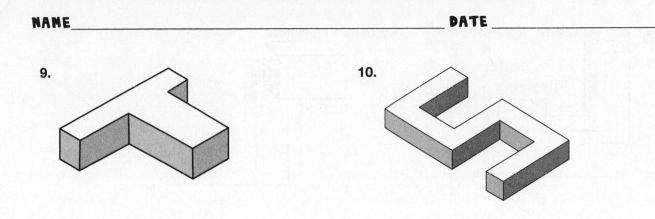

10.

11.

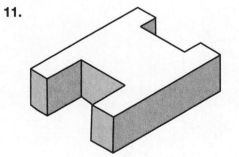

12.

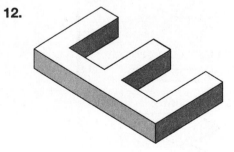

13

Calculate the volume of the solid formed by rectangular prisms.

**13.**

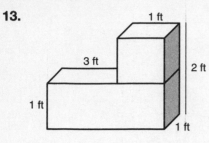

$V = \text{top prism} + \text{bottom prism}$

$V = (1)(1)(1) + (4)(1)(1)$

$V = 1 + 4$

$V = 5 \text{ ft}^3$

**14.**

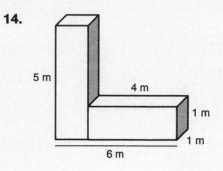

**15.**

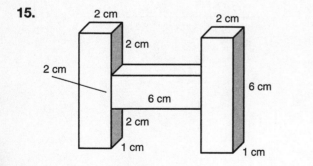

**16.**

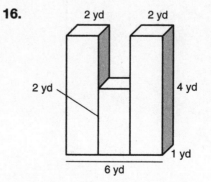

NAME_____ DATE _____

**17.**

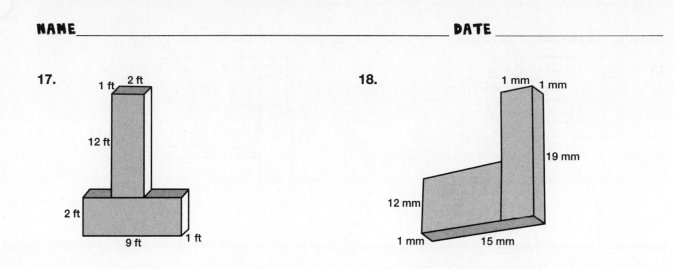

**18.**

Calculate the surface area of the rectangular prism.

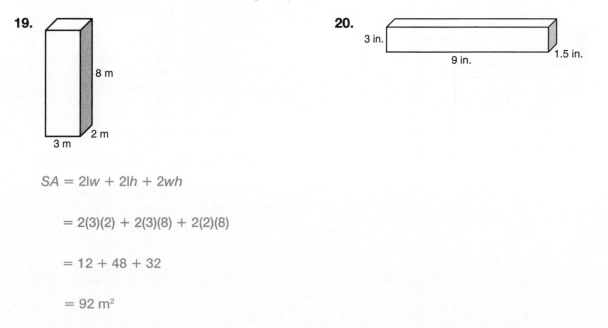

**19.**

$SA = 2lw + 2lh + 2wh$

$= 2(3)(2) + 2(3)(8) + 2(2)(8)$

$= 12 + 48 + 32$

$= 92 \text{ m}^2$

**20.**

© Carnegie Learning

13

**21.**

6 cm
11 cm
4 cm

**22.**

12 m
23 m
5 m

**23.**

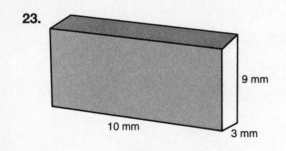

9 mm
10 mm
3 mm

**24.**

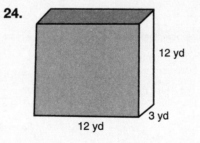

12 yd
12 yd
3 yd

**NAME**_____ **DATE** _____

Determine the number of polygonal surfaces each given solid has. Then describe the surfaces.

**25.**

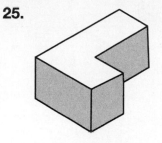

There are 8 polygonal surfaces. Six surfaces
are lateral faces in the shapes of rectangles.
Two polygonal surfaces are bases that have
an "L" shape.

**26.**

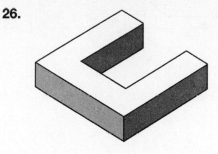

**27.**

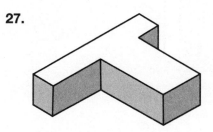

**28.**

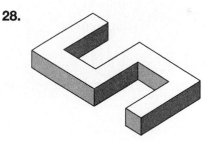

13

**29.**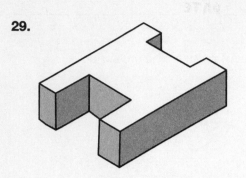

**30.**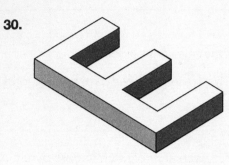

NAME_____  DATE _____

## Famous Pyramids
### Applying Volume and Surface Area Formulas

## Problem Set

Calculate the surface area of each square pyramid.

**1.**

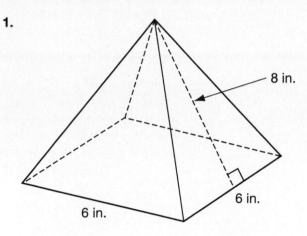

8 in.

6 in.

6 in.

$SA = 2bs + b^2$

$SA = 2(6)(8) + (6)^2$

$SA = 132$ in$^2$

13

2.

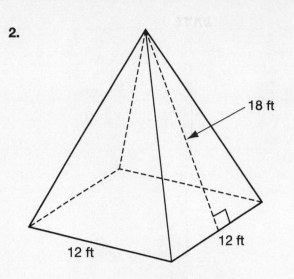

18 ft

12 ft          12 ft

3.

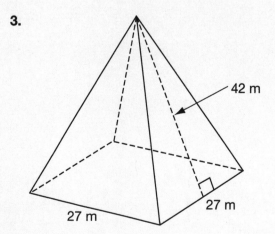

42 m

27 m        27 m

NAME_____     DATE _____

**4.**

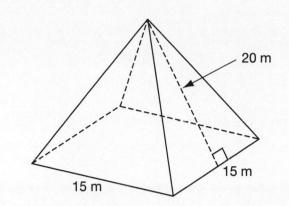

20 m

15 m

15 m

**5.**

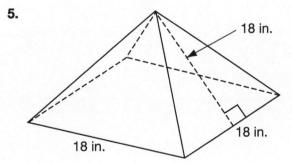

18 in.

18 in.

18 in.

13

**6.**

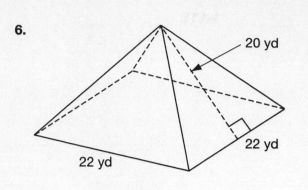

20 yd

22 yd

22 yd

**7.**

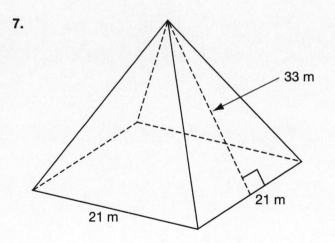

33 m

21 m

21 m

13

NAME_____ DATE _____

8.

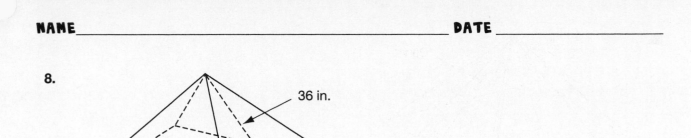

36 in.

40 in.

40 in.

9.

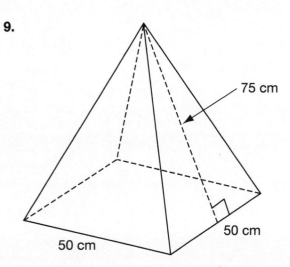

75 cm

50 cm

50 cm

13

**10.**

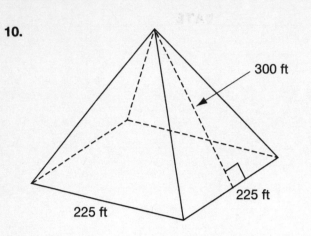

300 ft

225 ft

225 ft

Calculate the volume of the square pyramid.

**11.**

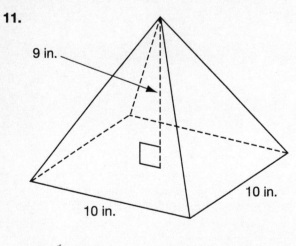

9 in.

10 in.

10 in.

$V = \frac{1}{3}b^2h$

$V = \frac{1}{3}(10)^2(9)$

$V = 300 \text{ in}^3$

© Carnegie Learning

NAME_____ DATE _____

**12.**

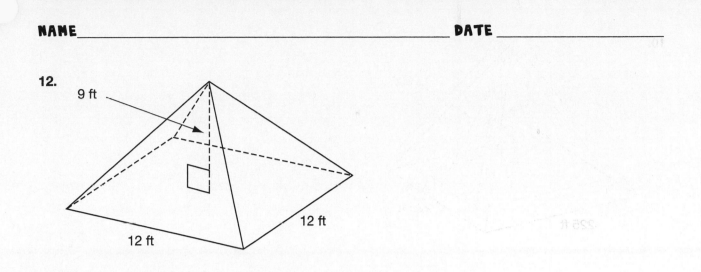

9 ft

12 ft

12 ft

**13.**

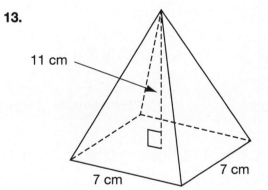

11 cm

7 cm

7 cm

13

**14.**

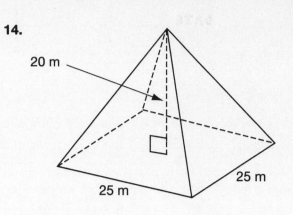

20 m

25 m

25 m

**15.**

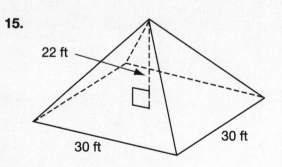

22 ft

30 ft

30 ft

13

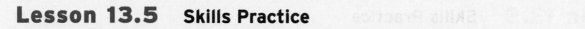

NAME_____ DATE _____

**16.**

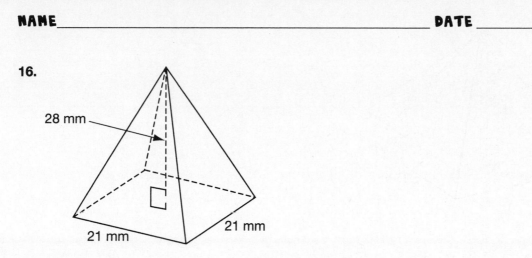

28 mm

21 mm          21 mm

**17.**

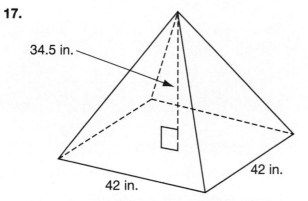

34.5 in.

42 in.          42 in.

**18.**

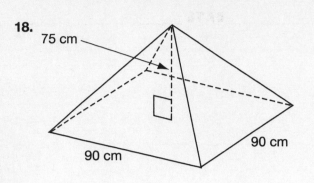

75 cm

90 cm        90 cm

**19.**

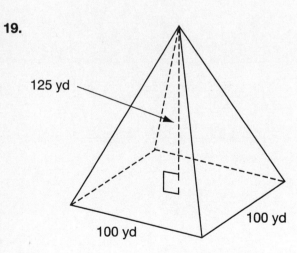

125 yd

100 yd        100 yd

NAME_____ DATE _____

**20.**

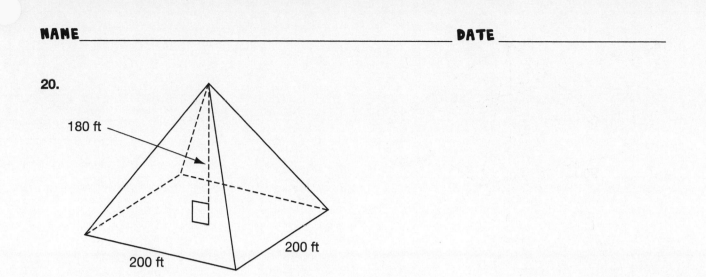

180 ft

200 ft

200 ft

13

NAME_____ DATE _____

## We Want to Hear from You!
**Formulating Questions and Collecting Data**

## Vocabulary

Match each definition to the corresponding term.

1. the facts or numbers gathered by a survey            **a.** census

2. the characteristic used to describe a sample        **b.** data

3. the collection of data from every member of       **c.** parameter
   a population

4. a method of collecting information about a certain    **d.** population
   group of people by asking a question or set of
   questions

5. the characteristic used to describe a population    **e.** sample

6. the entire set of items from which data can be     **f.** statistic
   selected

7. the data collected from part of a population        **g.** survey

14

## Problem Set

Determine whether the data collected in each survey represent a census or a sample.

1. Ms. Carey concludes that 85% of the students in the school have at least one pet after she conducts a survey of the students in her class.

   The data represent a sample.

2. Paul reports that one out of every five boys on the boys' varsity basketball team can dunk a basketball after he conducts a survey of the boys on the team.

3. After examining eight cartons of eggs at a local supermarket, Sheila concludes that one out of every 12 eggs packaged in the U.S. is cracked.

4. Jorge surveys each of the teachers in his school. He concludes that 64% of the teachers in his school enjoy reading as a hobby.

5. After surveying each of the members of the Horse Club, Susana reports that four out of every five members own two or more horses.

6. Chris surveys each of the students in his seventh grade class. He concludes that 50% of all seventh graders have at least one sibling.

7. Alex surveys each of the employees of the Burger Barn. He reports that 35% of all fast-food employees are satisfied with their hourly pay rate.

8. There are 14 twelve-year-old students and 10 thirteen-year-old students in Kiana's seventh grade math class. She surveys each of the thirteen-year-old students and concludes that 20% of all thirteen-year-old students in the school still sleep with a teddy bear.

© Carnegie Learning

14

NAME_____ DATE _____

9. Jacob surveys each of the actors in the school play. He concludes that 22% of the actors in the school play have previous acting experience.

10. Lynn surveys 50 customers at a local supermarket. She concludes that 54% of all supermarket customers prefer generic brands over name brands.

Determine whether each survey result is a parameter or a statistic.

11. According to an online poll, 35% of all U.S. citizens live in an apartment.

    The result is a statistic.

12. According to Ms. Carey's survey of the students in her class, 50% of her students have at least one dog.

13. A local newspaper conducted a survey last week. Of the 2300 subscribers, 1276 responded. Based on the survey, the editor concludes that 95% of the newspaper's subscribers will renew their subscription next year.

14. According to a random telephone survey of 1000 residents of Jackson County, 43% of the residents of Jackson County eat out at a restaurant more than once per week.

15. Mr. Rembrandt gives a survey to each of the students in the Art Club. He concludes that 90% of the Art Club members would like to visit the High Museum of Art in Atlanta.

14

16. The state police set up a roadblock on Highway 31 to determine how many drivers wear their seatbelts. They conclude that eight out of every ten drivers in Georgia wear their seatbelts.

17. Each senior at Jackson County High School completes a survey. The principal concludes that 68% of the students in the senior class have an after-school job.

18. Each senior at Jackson County High School completes a survey. The principal concludes that 83% of the students at Jackson County High School plan to attend a college or university after graduating from high school.

19. According to a random telephone survey, 74% of all working adults in the U.S. are satisfied with their current job.

20. After surveying each of his lunch customers, Mario concludes that 100% of his customers prefer his pizza to the pizza at the Pizza Barn.

Use the Sample Class Data at the end of Chapter 14, Lesson 1 to answer each question. Write your answer as a complete sentence.

21. How many students in the class are male?

In the class, 9 out of 20 students are male.

22. How many students in the class are female?

© Carnegie Learning

NAME_____ DATE _____

**23.** How many students in the class have blond hair?

**24.** What percent of the students in the class have brown hair?

**25.** What percent of the students do not carry a cell phone?

**26.** What percent of the students spend at least 2 hours doing homework every week?

**27.** How many students are male and spend at least 2 hours doing homework every week?

**28.** How many students are female and spend at least 2 hours doing homework every week?

**29.** What percent of the students are female and chose Reality as their favorite type of TV show?

**30.** What percent of the students are male and chose Sports as their favorite type of TV show?

14

NAME_____ DATE _____

## Dealing with Data: Selecting a Sample
### Collecting Data through Random Sampling

## Vocabulary

Write the term that best completes each statement.

1. Charlie uses the _____ on his computer to choose 5 random two-digit numbers.

2. Ms. Brown gives a survey to a(n) _____ of students in her English class.

3. Jill selects 15 random one-digit numbers from the fifth line of a(n) _____.

## Problem Set

Determine if each given sample is random or not random. Explain.

1. Rashid chooses each player on the soccer team whose last name starts with a vowel to participate in a survey about team sports.

   The sample is not random because team members whose last names start with consonants have no chance of being selected.

2. Mr. Tamez chooses the first seven students to raise their hands in his math class to participate in a survey.

3. Ms. Patel, the chess team captain, writes the names of each of the twelve team members on separate slips of paper. She places the slips in a box, shakes it, and selects five slips with her eyes closed. The five members whose names are chosen will complete a survey about the chess team.

14

4. Ms. Searcy has 36 students in her English class. The students are seated in 6 rows. The students in each row are assigned a different number 1 through 6. Ms. Searcy rolls a 6-sided number cube to select a row. She rolls it again to select one of the students in that row. The selected student is given a survey about Ms. Searcy's English class.

5. A local restaurant is conducting a survey to determine the eating habits of the county's residents. They hand a survey to the first 50 customers of the day.

6. Customers at Bull's Eye Grocery can win a $25 gift card for throwing a bull's eye on the dart board after they check out. Winners are also given a survey about their shopping experience at Bull's Eye Grocery.

7. The first 50 nurses at a nursing convention write their names on slips of paper and place them in a drawing box. After the box is shaken, 20 names are pulled from the box and each person chosen completes a survey about their transportation to the convention.

8. Prior to a Boy Scout meeting, Jerry cuts 75 slips of paper and places an "X" on 10 slips. He places each of the slips in a box and shakes it up. As the 63 members arrive, they each draw a slip of paper. Jerry gives a survey to each of the 9 Boy Scouts who drew a slip with an "X" on it.

**14**

NAME_____ DATE _____

9. Every student at Weston Middle School attends a pep rally in the gymnasium. Students are allowed to sit anywhere on the bleachers. During the pep rally, the principal hands each student on the lowest row a survey about the pep rally.

10. Professor Jensen leaves a stack of surveys on a table and invites each student to fill one out as they leave class. The survey asks about their satisfaction with the class. Only 22 of the 28 students complete the survey.

Use the Random Number Table at the end of Chapter 14 in your textbook to answer each question.

11. Beginning on line 10, write the first seven random digits.

The first seven random digits are 2, 9, 4, 7, 8, 5, and 9.

12. Beginning on line 15, write the first five random two-digit numbers.

13. Beginning on line 9, write the first four random three-digit numbers.

14. Beginning on line 17, write the first three random four-digit numbers.

15. Mr. Horowitz needs four random numbers 01 through 50. Use line 1 to determine the first four random numbers that meet his requirements.

14

© Carnegie Learning

**16.** Use line 2 to determine the first five random numbers 50 through 99.

Use Ms. Saunders' Class List and the Random Number Table at the end of Chapter 14 in your textbook to answer each question.

| Ms. Saunders' Class List | | | |
|---|---|---|---|
| **Student Name** | **Student Number** | **Student Name** | **Student Number** |
| Amos (M) | 11 | Jerome (M) | 21 |
| Emilio (M) | 12 | Cristina (F) | 22 |
| Julia (F) | 13 | Pedro (M) | 23 |
| Olivia (F) | 14 | Jada (F) | 24 |
| Mattie (F) | 15 | Wei (F) | 25 |
| Aki (M) | 16 | Lakyta (F) | 26 |
| Sherwin (M) | 17 | Nelson (M) | 27 |
| Noah (M) | 18 | Tonya (F) | 28 |
| Belinda (F) | 19 | Luisa (F) | 29 |
| Mario (M) | 20 | Lavon (M) | 30 |

**17.** The students in Ms. Saunders' class are each given a student number (11 through 30) as shown in the class list. Use line 14 of the Random Number Table to determine the first four random student numbers.

The first four random student numbers are 14, 24, 22, and 19.

**18.** Ms. Saunders randomly selects 3 students in her class according to their student number. She uses line 18 of the Random Number Table. What are the students' names?

NAME_____ DATE _____

19. Ms. Saunders randomly selects 3 boys in her class using line 8 of the Random Number Table. What are the students' names?

20. Ms. Saunders randomly selects 3 girls in her class using line 10 of the Random Number Table. What are the students' names?

21. Ms. Saunders randomly selects 2 girls in her class using line 20 of the Random Number Table. What are the students' names?

22. Ms. Saunders randomly selects 2 boys in her class using line 15 of the Random Number Table. What are the students' names?

Generate a set of random numbers using the *randInt* function on your graphing calculator. Write the command you use to generate the random numbers. If you do not have a graphing calculator, use the Random Number Table to generate the random numbers and write the line you use for selecting the numbers.

23. Generate five different random numbers 1 through 20.

    Answers will vary.

    I used the command randInt (1, 20) to generate the numbers 8, 2, 5, 19, and 11.

24. Generate five different random numbers 1 through 100.

**25.** Generate five different random numbers 1 through 1000.

**26.** Generate five different random numbers 50 through 100.

**27.** Generate five different random numbers 100 through 200.

**28.** Generate five different random numbers 1000 through 9999.

NAME_____ DATE _____

## Floor Plans and Tiles
### Random Sampling

## Vocabulary

Define the term in your own words.

**1.** dot plot

## Problem Set

Sample Class Data from Mr. Puckett's Math class is shown. Use the data and the Random Number Table at the end of Chapter 14 when necessary to answer each question.

| Mr. Puckett's Math Class | | | | |
|---|---|---|---|---|
| **Student Number** | **Student Name** | **Gender** | **Number of Siblings** | **Number of Pets** |
| 11 | Anna | F | 1 | 3 |
| 12 | Jerome | M | 0 | 0 |
| 13 | Andrew | M | 1 | 1 |
| 14 | Mei | F | 0 | 4 |
| 15 | Gene | M | 0 | 0 |
| 16 | Laura | F | 5 | 4 |
| 17 | Horace | M | 0 | 1 |
| 18 | Augustine | F | 2 | 3 |
| 19 | Beatrice | F | 1 | 2 |

14

| Mr. Puckett's Math Class | | | | |
|---|---|---|---|---|
| Student Number | Student Name | Gender | Number of Siblings | Number of Pets |
| 20 | Fernando | M | 0 | 1 |
| 21 | Quentin | M | 1 | 3 |
| 22 | Rika | F | 1 | 6 |
| 23 | Violet | F | 3 | 3 |
| 24 | Terrence | M | 1 | 6 |
| 25 | Nathan | M | 2 | 3 |
| 26 | Jasmine | F | 0 | 1 |
| 27 | Ramona | F | 0 | 2 |
| 28 | Phillip | M | 1 | 0 |
| 29 | Alicia | F | 3 | 4 |
| 30 | Douglas | M | 2 | 7 |

1. Mr. Puckett wants to know the mean number of siblings his students have. He chooses the students with student numbers 11 through 15 as his sample. Determine the mean number of siblings for the students in this sample.

   The mean number of siblings is $\frac{2}{5}$ or 0.4 based on the sample.

2. Select a random sample of 5 students using a Random Number Table or random number generator. Determine the mean number of siblings for the students in your sample.

**14**

NAME_____ DATE _____

3. Determine the actual mean number of siblings for the 20 students in Mr. Puckett's class.

4. Mr. Puckett wants to know the mean number of pets his students have. He chooses the first 5 students to voluntarily raise their hands as his sample. The students selected are Laura, Augustine, Rika, Terrence, and Nathan. Determine the mean number of pets for the students in this sample.

5. Select a random sample of 5 students using a Random Number Table or random number generator. Determine the mean number of pets for the students in your sample.

6. Determine the actual mean number of pets for the 20 students in Mr. Puckett's class.

The Employee Roster of Fish & Chips Seafood Buffet is shown. Use the table and the Random Number Table at the end of Chapter 14 when necessary to answer each question.

| Employee Roster of Fish & Chips Seafood Buffet | | | | |
|---|---|---|---|---|
| Employee Number | Employee Name | Position | Years of Experience | Miles Driven to Work Daily |
| 51 | Ralph | Cook | 1 | 12 |
| 52 | Betty | Cashier | 2 | 5 |
| 53 | Liang | Manager | 10 | 8 |
| 54 | Steve | Cook | 1 | 15 |
| 55 | Cheryl | Cashier | 2 | 25 |
| 56 | Bart | Cashier | 3 | 20 |
| 57 | Ulysses | Cook | 2 | 14 |
| 58 | Wilma | Cook | 4 | 11 |
| 59 | Jerry | Manager | 8 | 8 |
| 60 | Sabrina | Cook | 1 | 12 |
| 61 | Althea | Manager | 7 | 13 |
| 62 | Tiffany | Cook | 2 | 15 |
| 63 | Meredith | Cashier | 1 | 4 |
| 64 | Gregory | Cook | 4 | 9 |
| 65 | Patricia | Cashier | 3 | 16 |
| 66 | Bob | Manager | 12 | 30 |
| 67 | Ignatius | Cook | 5 | 22 |
| 68 | Xavier | Cashier | 3 | 19 |
| 69 | Linda | Manager | 9 | 7 |
| 70 | Howard | Cook | 2 | 6 |

NAME_____ DATE _____

7. Ms. Gibson, the owner of Fish & Chips Seafood Buffet, wants to determine the mean number of miles driven to work by her employees. She surveys the first 5 employees to arrive at work today. The employees selected are Cheryl, Bart, Tiffany, Patricia, and Bob. Determine the mean number of miles driven to work daily by the employees in the sample.

The mean number of miles driven to work is $\frac{106}{5}$ or 21.2 miles based on the sample.

8. Select a random sample of 5 employees using a Random Number Table or random number generator. Determine the mean number of miles driven to work daily based on your sample.

9. Determine the actual mean number of miles driven to work daily for the 20 employees.

10. Ms. Gibson wants to determine the mean years of experience of her employees. At the managers' meeting, she surveys each of the managers. Determine the mean years of experience of the employees based on Ms. Gibson's sample.

14

11. Select a random sample of 5 employees using a Random Number Table or random number generator. Determine the mean years of experience for the employees in your sample.

12. Determine the actual mean years of experience for the 20 employees.

14

# Lesson 14.4   Skills Practice

NAME_____ DATE _____

## What Does the Data Mean?
### Using Samples, Centers, and Spreads to Describe Data

## Vocabulary

Write the term(s) or phrase from the box that best completes each statement.

| | | |
|---|---|---|
| variability | spread | range |
| mean absolute deviation | | deviation from the mean |

1. The _____ of data describes how "spread out" the data is. This can also be described as the _____ of data.

2. The _____ is the average of the absolute values of the deviations of each data value from the mean.

3. The _____ is calculated by subtracting the mean from each data value in a sample.

4. The _____ of data refers to the minimum and maximum values in a data set.

© Carnegie Learning

14

## Problem Set

Complete the table. First calculate the mean of the data. Then for each data value, calculate the deviation from the mean and the absolute value of each deviation. Finally, calculate the mean absolute deviation.

1.

| Data | Mean | Deviation From the Mean | Absolute Value of the Deviation From the Mean |
|------|------|-------------------------|-----------------------------------------------|
| 35 |  | $35 - 41 = -6$ | 6 |
| 18 |  | $18 - 41 = -23$ | 23 |
| 58 | 41 | $58 - 41 = 17$ | 17 |
| 65 |  | $65 - 41 = 24$ | 24 |
| 29 |  | $29 - 41 = -12$ | 12 |
| Mean Absolute Deviation | | | 16.4 |

$$\text{Mean} = \frac{35 + 18 + 58 + 65 + 29}{5}$$

$$= \frac{205}{5}$$

$$= 41$$

$$\text{Mean Absolute Deviation} = \frac{6 + 23 + 17 + 24 + 12}{5}$$

$$= \frac{82}{5}$$

$$= 16.4$$

14

NAME_____ DATE _____

2.

| Data | Mean | Deviation From the Mean | Absolute Value of the Deviation From the Mean |
|------|------|-------------------------|-----------------------------------------------|
| 19 | | | |
| 26 | | | |
| 45 | | | |
| 73 | | | |
| 27 | | | |
| Mean Absolute Deviation | | | |

3.

| Data | Mean | Deviation From the Mean | Absolute Value of the Deviation From the Mean |
|------|------|-------------------------|-----------------------------------------------|
| 61 | | | |
| 55 | | | |
| 57 | | | |
| 64 | | | |
| 86 | | | |
| Mean Absolute Deviation | | | |

14

4.

| Data | Mean | Deviation From the Mean | Absolute Value of the Deviation From the Mean |
|------|------|-------------------------|-----------------------------------------------|
| 62   |      |                         |                                               |
| 49   |      |                         |                                               |
| 9    |      |                         |                                               |
| 92   |      |                         |                                               |
| 15   |      |                         |                                               |
| Mean Absolute Deviation | | |                                          |

5.

| Data | Mean | Deviation From the Mean | Absolute Value of the Deviation From the Mean |
|------|------|-------------------------|-----------------------------------------------|
| 24   |      |                         |                                               |
| 21   |      |                         |                                               |
| 66   |      |                         |                                               |
| 34   |      |                         |                                               |
| 44   |      |                         |                                               |
| Mean Absolute Deviation | | |                                          |

14

NAME_____ DATE _____

6.

| Data | Mean | Deviation From the Mean | Absolute Value of the Deviation From the Mean |
|------|------|-------------------------|-----------------------------------------------|
| 59 | | | |
| 13 | | | |
| 83 | | | |
| 95 | | | |
| 42 | | | |
| Mean Absolute Deviation | | | |

Calculate the five number summary and the Interquartile Range for the data set.

**7.** Data Set: 16, 97, 59, 54, 28

  Data in ascending order: 16, 28, 54, 59, 97

  Minimum = 16                          First quartile: 16, 28

  Maximum = 97                          $Q1 = \dfrac{16 + 28}{2}$

  Median = 54                                $= 22$

                                        Third quartile: 59, 97

                                        $Q3 = \dfrac{59 + 97}{2}$

                                              $= 78$

                                        IQR $= 78 - 22$

                                              $= 56$

**8.** Data Set: 29, 47, 85, 96, 52

**14**

NAME_____ DATE _____

9. Data Set: 29, 62, 16, 65, 83, 62, 96, 61

10. Data Set: 78, 13, 79, 87, 68, 4, 68, 98

**11.** Data Set: 96, 15, 59, 50, 9, 27, 42, 97, 29

**12.** Data Set: 12, 63, 97, 52, 91, 71, 2

NAME DATE

Construct a box-and-whisker plot for the five number summary.

**13.** Minimum = 16, Q1 = 22, Median = 54, Q3 = 78, Maximum = 97

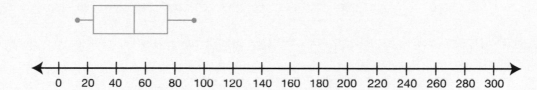

**14.** Minimum = 129, Q1 = 138, Median = 152, Q3 = 190.5, Maximum = 196

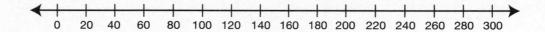

**15.** Minimum = 16, Q1 = 45, Median = 62, Q3 = 174, Maximum = 196

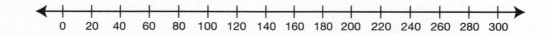

**16.** Minimum = 4, Q1 = 140.5, Median = 173, Q3 = 183, Maximum = 198

14

**17.** Minimum = 9, Q1 = 21, Median = 42, Q3 = 77.5, Maximum = 97

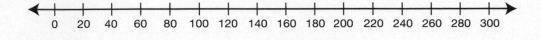

**18.** Minimum = 2, Q1 = 112, Median = 163, Q3 = 191, Maximum = 197

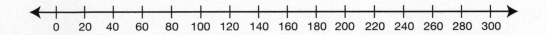

# Lesson 14.5   Skills Practice

NAME_____ DATE _____

## Taking a Survey
### Using Sample Size

## Vocabulary

Write a definition for the following term in your own words.

1. sample size

## Problem Set

Mr. Helton gives a survey to the 20 students in his U.S. History class. Use the results of the survey and the Random Number Table at the end of Chapter 14 to answer each question.

| Student Number | Student Name | Hours Spent Online per Week | Hours Spent Watching TV per Week |
|---|---|---|---|
| 20 | Hyacinth | 14 | 10 |
| 21 | Daniel | 10 | 12 |
| 22 | Gloria | 7 | 15 |
| 23 | June | 0 | 14 |
| 24 | Hector | 8 | 5 |
| 25 | Jill | 14 | 3 |
| 26 | Hannah | 0 | 9 |
| 27 | Scott | 20 | 10 |
| 28 | Emily | 5 | 20 |
| 29 | Iris | 10 | 0 |
| 30 | Juan | 10 | 10 |
| 31 | Brian | 25 | 4 |
| 32 | Tabitha | 0 | 5 |
| 33 | Jamal | 14 | 14 |
| 34 | Laura | 11 | 10 |
| 35 | Grant | 5 | 5 |
| 36 | Joelle | 15 | 5 |
| 37 | Brad | 7 | 14 |
| 38 | Tony | 5 | 20 |
| 39 | Naomi | 20 | 10 |

NAME_____ DATE _____

1. Select 2 students from Mr. Helton's class using the Random Number Table at the end of Chapter 14. Determine the mean number of hours spent online weekly for the 2 students in your random sample.

   Answers will vary.

   I used Line 1 of the Random Number Table to select Emily (5 hours) and Juan (10 hours). The mean number of hours spent online weekly is $\frac{15}{2}$ or 7.5 hours for this sample.

2. Select 5 students from Mr. Helton's class using a different line in the Random Number Table. Determine the mean number of hours spent online weekly for the 5 students in your random sample.

3. Select 8 students from Mr. Helton's class using a different line in the Random Number Table. When using the Random Number Table, it may be necessary to use more than one line to select 8 students. Determine the mean number of hours spent online weekly for the 8 students in your random sample.

4. Determine the actual mean number of hours spent online weekly for the 20 students in the class. Discuss how the means changed as the random sample size increased.

14

5. Select 2 students from Mr. Helton's class using the Random Number Table. Determine the mean number of hours spent watching television weekly for the 2 students in your random sample.

6. Select 5 students from Mr. Helton's class using a different line in the Random Number Table. Determine the mean number of hours spent watching television weekly for the 5 students in your random sample.

7. Select 8 students from Mr. Helton's class using a different line in the Random Number Table. Determine the mean number of hours spent watching television weekly for the 8 students in your random sample.

8. Determine the actual mean number of hours spent watching television weekly for the 20 students in the class. Discuss how the means changed as the random sample size increased.

NAME_____ DATE _____

Julie is writing a paper for her college statistics course. She gives surveys to 20 adults at a Board of Education meeting. Use the information listed in the table to answer the question.

| ID Number | Name | Number of Automobiles Owned in Your Life | Number of Homes Owned in Your Life |
|:---:|:---:|:---:|:---:|
| 40 | Charlie | 5 | 3 |
| 41 | Lonnie | 2 | 1 |
| 42 | Belinda | 4 | 0 |
| 43 | Rafael | 3 | 2 |
| 44 | Thomas | 8 | 1 |
| 45 | Marla | 2 | 2 |
| 46 | Carlota | 4 | 4 |
| 47 | Ernest | 7 | 0 |
| 48 | Mike | 2 | 3 |
| 49 | Beverly | 3 | 4 |
| 50 | Quincy | 6 | 2 |
| 51 | Marcus | 7 | 0 |
| 52 | Maeko | 7 | 2 |
| 53 | Allison | 2 | 0 |
| 54 | Rosa | 3 | 1 |
| 55 | Adrian | 5 | 4 |
| 56 | Kayla | 2 | 2 |
| 57 | Robert | 6 | 3 |
| 58 | Diane | 3 | 5 |
| 59 | Jack | 5 | 2 |

14

**9.** Select 2 people from Julie's study using the Random Number Table. Determine the mean number of automobiles owned for the 2 people in your random sample.

Answers will vary.

I used Line 10 of the table to select Ernest (7 automobiles) and Maeko (7 automobiles). The mean number of automobiles owned is $\frac{14}{2}$ or 7 automobiles for this sample.

**10.** Select 5 people from Julie's study using a different line in the Random Number Table. Determine the mean number of automobiles owned for the 5 people in your random sample.

**11.** Select 8 people from Julie's study using a different line in the Random Number Table. Determine the mean number of automobiles owned for the 8 people in your random sample.

**12.** Determine the actual mean number of automobiles owned for the 20 people in the study. Discuss how the means changed as the random sample size increased.

NAME_____ DATE _____

**13.** Select 2 people from Julie's study using the Random Number Table. Determine the mean number of homes owned for the 2 people in your random sample.

**14.** Select 5 people from Julie's study using a different line in the Random Number Table. Determine the mean number of homes owned for the 5 people in your random sample.

**15.** Select 8 people from Julie's study using a different line in the Random Number Table. Determine the mean number of homes owned for the 8 people in your random sample.

**16.** Determine the actual mean number of homes owned for the 20 people in the study. Discuss how the means changed as the random sample size increased.

14

14

NAME_____   DATE _____

**15**

# Checking the Papers and the Blogs
## Comparing Measures of Center of Two Populations

## Problem Set

Describe the distribution of both data sets for each plot shown.

1. The line plot shows the number of hours of video games per week played by boys and girls.

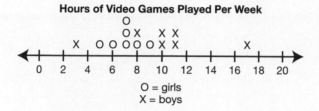

**Hours of Video Games Played Per Week**

O = girls
X = boys

The distribution of the girls' data is symmetric. The distribution of the boys' data is roughly symmetric, too.

2. The stem-and-leaf plot shows the total points earned per game by two different teams.

**Points Scored Per Game**

| Sharks | | Tigers |
|---:|:---:|:---|
| 9 | 5 | 3589 |
| 83 | 6 | 489 |
| 743 | 7 | 02 |
| 8710 | 8 | 2 |

5|3 = 53

3. The line plot shows the number of texts sent per week by teachers and students.

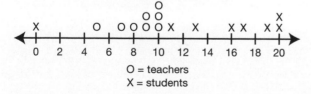

**Number of Tests Sent Per Week**

O = teachers
X = students

15

4. The stem-and-leaf plot shows the number of books sold per day by two different book sellers.

**Books Sold Per Day**

| Big Book Buy | | Online Books |
|---:|:---:|:---|
| 98750 | 25 | |
| 420 | 26 | |
| 53 | 27 | |
| 0 | 28 | 0 |
| | 29 | 58 |
| | 30 | |
| | 31 | 889 |
| | 32 | 47899 |

25|5 = 255

5. The line plot shows the number of reps performed per exercise by Jan and Gavin.

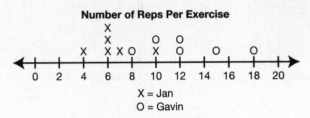

**Number of Reps Per Exercise**

X = Jan
O = Gavin

6. The stem-and-leaf plot shows the number of tweets sent per day by two celebrities.

**Number of Tweets Per Day**

| KJamz | | Pepper |
|---:|:---:|:---|
| | 0 | 23667 |
| 55 | 1 | 0015 |
| 643 | 2 | 0 |
| 4300 | 3 | |
| | 4 | |
| 0 | 5 | |

2|4 = 24

NAME_____ DATE _____

Estimate the means of both data sets from each of the plots shown. Then determine the actual means.

**7.**

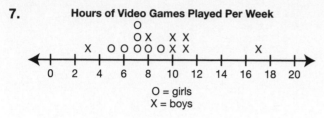

**Hours of Video Games Played Per Week**

O = girls
X = boys

Estimate: girls = 7; boys = 10

Actual: girls = 49 ÷ 7 = 7

boys = 70 ÷ 7 = 10

**8.**     **Points Scored Per Game**

| Sharks | | Tigers |
|---:|:---:|:---|
| 9 | 5 | 3589 |
| 83 | 6 | 489 |
| 743 | 7 | 02 |
| 8710 | 8 | 2 |

5|3 = 53

**9.**     **Number of Tests Sent Per Week**

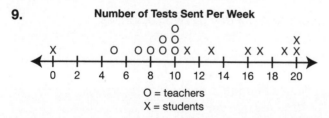

O = teachers
X = students

**15**

**10.** **Books Sold Per Day**

| Big Book Buy | | Online Books |
|---:|:---:|:---|
| 98750 | 25 | |
| 420 | 26 | |
| 53 | 27 | |
| 0 | 28 | 0 |
| | 29 | 58 |
| | 30 | |
| | 31 | 889 |
| | 32 | 47899 |

25|5 = 255

**11.** **Number of Reps Per Exercise**

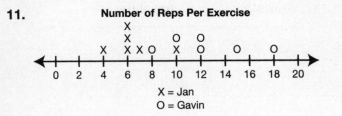

X = Jan
O = Gavin

**12.** **Number of Tweets Per Day**

| KJamz | | Pepper |
|---:|:---:|:---|
| | 0 | 23667 |
| 55 | 1 | 0015 |
| 643 | 2 | 0 |
| 4300 | 3 | |
| | 4 | |
| 0 | 5 | |

2|4 = 24

**896** • **Chapter 15**  Skills Practice

NAME_____ DATE _____

Determine the mean absolute deviation for both data sets in each plot.

**13.**

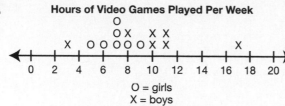

**Hours of Video Games Played Per Week**

O = girls
X = boys

Girls' Mean Absolute Deviation:

$$\frac{2 + 1 + 0 + 0 + 0 + 1 + 2}{7} = \frac{6}{7} \approx 0.86$$

Boys' Mean Absolute Deviation:

$$\frac{7 + 2 + 0 + 0 + 1 + 1 + 7}{7} = \frac{18}{7} \approx 2.57$$

| Girls | | Boys | |
|---|---|---|---|
| **Deviation** | **Absolute** | **Deviation** | **Absolute** |
| $5 - 7 = -2$ | $|-2| = 2$ | $3 - 10 = -7$ | $|-7| = 7$ |
| $6 - 7 = -1$ | $|-1| = 1$ | $8 - 10 = -2$ | $|-2| = 2$ |
| $7 - 7 = 0$ | $0$ | $10 - 10 = 0$ | $0$ |
| $7 - 7 = 0$ | $0$ | $10 - 10 = 0$ | $0$ |
| $7 - 7 = 0$ | $0$ | $11 - 10 = 1$ | $|1| = 1$ |
| $8 - 7 = 1$ | $|1| = 1$ | $11 - 10 = 1$ | $|1| = 1$ |
| $9 - 7 = 2$ | $|2| = 2$ | $17 - 10 = 7$ | $|7| = 7$ |

**15**

**14.** **Points Scored Per Game**

| Sharks | | Tigers |
|---|---|---|
| 9 | 5 | 3589 |
| 83 | 6 | 489 |
| 743 | 7 | 02 |
| 8710 | 8 | 2 |

5|3 = 53

| | Sharks | | Tigers | |
|---|---|---|---|---|
| **Deviation** | **Absolute** | **Deviation** | **Absolute** |
| | | | |
| | | | |
| | | | |
| | | | |
| | | | |
| | | | |
| | | | |
| | | | |
| | | | |
| | | | |

NAME_____ DATE_____

**15.**

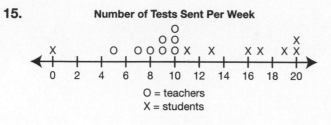

**Number of Tests Sent Per Week**

O = teachers
X = students

| Teachers | | Students | |
|---|---|---|---|
| **Deviation** | **Absolute** | **Deviation** | **Absolute** |
| | | | |
| | | | |
| | | | |
| | | | |
| | | | |
| | | | |
| | | | |
| | | | |

15

**16.** **Books Sold Per Day**

Big Book Buy | Online Books
| | |
| 98750 | 25 | |
| 420 | 26 | |
| 53 | 27 | |
| 0 | 28 | 0 |
| | 29 | 58 |
| | 30 | |
| | 31 | 889 |
| | 32 | 47899 |

25|5 = 255

| Big Book Buy | | Online Books | |
|---|---|---|---|
| **Deviation** | **Absolute** | **Deviation** | **Absolute** |
| | | | |
| | | | |
| | | | |
| | | | |
| | | | |
| | | | |
| | | | |
| | | | |
| | | | |
| | | | |
| | | | |

NAME_____ DATE_____

**15**

17.

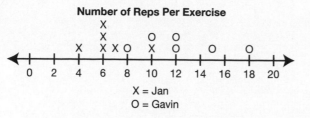

Number of Reps Per Exercise

X = Jan
O = Gavin

| Jan | | Gavin | |
|---|---|---|---|
| Deviation | Absolute | Deviation | Absolute |
| | | | |
| | | | |
| | | | |
| | | | |
| | | | |
| | | | |

15

## 18. Number of Tweets Per Day

| KJamz | | Pepper |
|---:|:---:|:---|
| | 0 | 23667 |
| 55 | 1 | 0015 |
| 643 | 2 | 0 |
| 4300 | 3 | |
| | 4 | |
| 0 | 5 | |

2|4 = 24

| KJamz | | Pepper | |
|---|---|---|---|
| **Deviation** | **Absolute** | **Deviation** | **Absolute** |
| | | | |
| | | | |
| | | | |
| | | | |
| | | | |
| | | | |
| | | | |
| | | | |
| | | | |
| | | | |

**NAME**_____ **DATE** _____

Determine the five number summary and IQR for both data sets in each plot.

**19.**

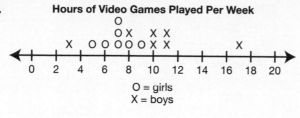

**Hours of Video Games Played Per Week**

O = girls
X = boys

|  | Girls | Boys |
|---|---|---|
| Minimum | 5 | 3 |
| Q1 | 6 | 8 |
| Median | 7 | 10 |
| Q3 | 8 | 11 |
| Maximum | 9 | 17 |
| IQR | 8 − 6 = 2 | 11 − 8 = 3 |

**20.**

**Points Scored Per Game**

| Sharks | | Tigers |
|---|---|---|
| 9 | 5 | 3589 |
| 83 | 6 | 489 |
| 743 | 7 | 02 |
| 8710 | 8 | 2 |

5|3 = 53

|  | Sharks | Tigers |
|---|---|---|
| Minimum |  |  |
| Q1 |  |  |
| Median |  |  |
| Q3 |  |  |
| Maximum |  |  |
| IQR |  |  |

© Carnegie Learning

**15**

**21.**

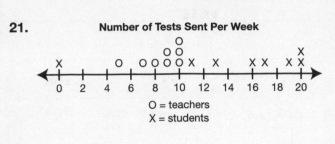

**Number of Tests Sent Per Week**

O = teachers
X = students

|  | Teachers | Students |
|---|---|---|
| Minimum |  |  |
| Q1 |  |  |
| Median |  |  |
| Q3 |  |  |
| Maximum |  |  |
| IQR |  |  |

**22.**  **Books Sold Per Day**

| Big Book Buy |  | Online Books |
|---|---|---|
| 98750 | 25 |  |
| 420 | 26 |  |
| 53 | 27 |  |
| 0 | 28 | 0 |
|  | 29 | 58 |
|  | 30 |  |
|  | 31 | 889 |
|  | 32 | 47899 |

25|5 = 255

|  | Big Book Buy | Online Books |
|---|---|---|
| Minimum |  |  |
| Q1 |  |  |
| Median |  |  |
| Q3 |  |  |
| Maximum |  |  |
| IQR |  |  |

© Carnegie Learning

NAME_____ DATE _____

**23.**

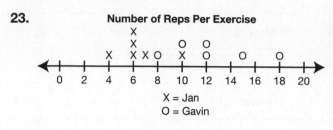

Number of Reps Per Exercise

X = Jan
O = Gavin

|  | Jan | Gavin |
|---|---|---|
| Minimum |  |  |
| Q1 |  |  |
| Median |  |  |
| Q3 |  |  |
| Maximum |  |  |
| IQR |  |  |

**24.  Number of Tweets Per Day**

| KJamz |  | Pepper |
|---|---|---|
|  | 0 | 23667 |
| 55 | 1 | 0015 |
| 643 | 2 | 0 |
| 4300 | 3 |  |
|  | 4 |  |
| 0 | 5 |  |

2|4 = 24

|  | KJamz | Pepper |
|---|---|---|
| Minimum |  |  |
| Q1 |  |  |
| Median |  |  |
| Q3 |  |  |
| Maximum |  |  |
| IQR |  |  |

15

NAME_____ DATE _____

## Can Podcasts Affect Ratings?
**Comparing Measures of Center of Two Populations**

## Problem Set

Use lines 10–13 of the random number table to select random samples from a data set of 50 middle school students.

*Line 10* 29478 59652 50414 31966 87912 87154 12944 49862 96566 48825

*Line 11* 96155 95009 27429 72918 08457 78134 48407 26061 58754 05326

*Line 12* 29621 66583 62966 12468 20245 14015 04014 35713 03980 03024

*Line 13* 12639 75291 71020 17265 41598 64074 64629 63293 53307 48766

1. Choose a random sample of 6 students from Line 10. Assign students 2-digit numbers 50–99.

    85, 96, 52, 50, 66, 87

2. Choose a random sample of 7 students from Line 12. Assign students 2-digit numbers 20–79.

3. Choose a random sample of 6 students from Line 13. Assign students 2-digit numbers 45–94.

4. Choose a random sample of 5 students from Lines 10–11. Assign students 3-digit numbers 250–299.

5. Choose a random sample of 5 students from Lines 12–13. Assign students 3-digit numbers 250–349.

6. Choose a random sample of 6 students from Lines 10–13. Assign students 4-digit numbers 9000–9999

Display the data from each table in either a back-to-back stem-and-leaf plot or two line plots using the same scale. Describe the distribution of the data.

7. Create a back-to-back stem-and-leaf plot from the data in the table showing students' sales of two different fund-raising items.

| Raffle Tickets Sold | Candy Bars Sold |
|---|---|
| 23 | 9 |
| 15 | 8 |
| 35 | 0 |
| 28 | 12 |
| 30 | 15 |
| 11 | 5 |
| 30 | 3 |
| 32 | 30 |
| 8 | 20 |
| 27 | 12 |

**Fund-raising Items Sold**

| Raffle Tickets Sold | | Candy Bars Sold |
|---:|:---:|:---|
| 8 | 0 | 03589 |
| 51 | 1 | 225 |
| 873 | 2 | 0 |
| 5200 | 3 | 0 |

1|2 = 12

The data for raffle tickets is skewed left and the data for candy bars is skewed right.

NAME_____ DATE _____

8. Create two line plots using the same scale from the data in the table showing two friends' weekly volunteer hours.

| Luke | Kylie |
|------|-------|
| 5 | 5 |
| 9 | 6 |
| 8 | 3 |
| 9 | 4 |
| 7 | 6 |
| 8 | 5 |
| 9 | 8 |
| 9 | 9 |
| 6 | 6 |
| 8 | 7 |

**9.** Create a back-to-back stem-and-leaf plot from the data in the table showing students' math test scores from two different classrooms.

| Ms. Kinzer | Mr. Hannon |
|:---:|:---:|
| 85 | 88 |
| 78 | 90 |
| 77 | 93 |
| 90 | 84 |
| 91 | 85 |
| 93 | 92 |
| 76 | 95 |
| 91 | 90 |
| 79 | 79 |
| 86 | 89 |

NAME_____ DATE _____

10. Create two line plots using the same scale from the data in the table showing the amount of money each sibling spent per week.

| Julio | Linda |
|-------|-------|
| 10 | 18 |
| 6 | 15 |
| 15 | 16 |
| 9 | 17 |
| 12 | 10 |
| 5 | 13 |
| 10 | 17 |
| 11 | 18 |
| 10 | 17 |
| 7 | 9 |

15

**11.** Create two line plots using the same scale from the data in the table showing cars sold per month by two different salespeople.

| Salesperson A | Salesperson B |
|:---:|:---:|
| 18 | 5 |
| 10 | 6 |
| 9 | 4 |
| 12 | 10 |
| 17 | 9 |
| 18 | 7 |
| 20 | 6 |
| 14 | 6 |
| 18 | 2 |
| 17 | 5 |

**NAME**_____ **DATE** _____

12. Create a back-to-back stem-and-leaf plot from the data in the table showing daily temperature in degrees Fahrenheit for two cities.

| Sunnyville | Cooltown |
|:---:|:---:|
| 68 | 72 |
| 70 | 69 |
| 75 | 63 |
| 80 | 58 |
| 76 | 70 |
| 75 | 50 |
| 77 | 63 |
| 69 | 52 |
| 75 | 54 |
| 81 | 53 |

**15**

Tell whether the mean or median is the best measure of center for the data shown in each. Explain why.

**13.** median (skewed left)

**14.**

| 0 | 5 |
|---|---|
| 1 | 23 |
| 2 | 0125 |
| 3 | 05 |
| 4 | 1 |

2|0 = 20

**15.**

| 5 | 0012 |
|---|------|
| 6 | 355 |
| 7 | 3 |
| 8 | 1 |

**16.**

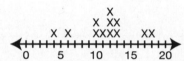

**17.**

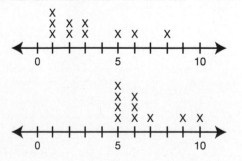

**18.**

| 10 | 2 | 24 |
|----|---|-----|
|    | 3 | 0 |
| 5420 | 4 | 113 |
| 99311 | 5 | 01228 |

© Carnegie Learning

# Lesson 15.3 Skills Practice

NAME_____ DATE _____

## Finding Your Spot to Live
### Drawing Conclusions about Two Populations

## Problem Set

Describe the distribution and variation of each graphical display of data.

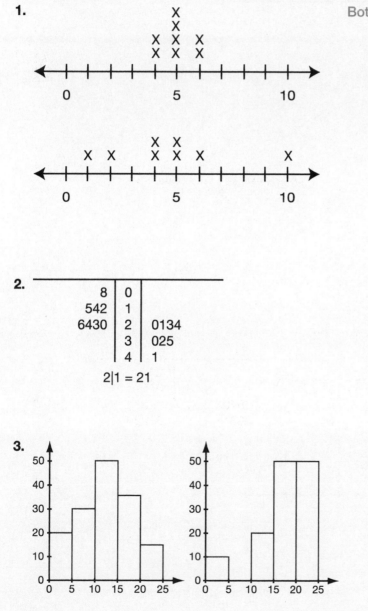

1.

Both sets of data are symmetric.

2.

```
      8  │ 0 │
    542  │ 1 │
   6430  │ 2 │ 0134
         │ 3 │ 025
         │ 4 │ 1
        2│1 = 21
```

3.

15

**4.**

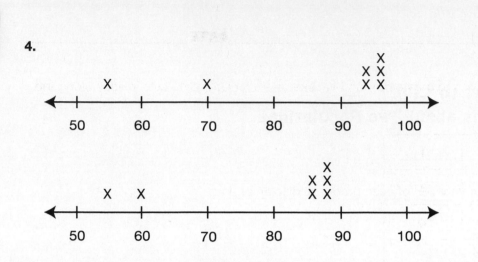

**5.**

| 0 | 7 | 8 |
|---|---|---|
| 965 | 8 | 38 |
| 751 | 9 | 00 |
| 0 | 10 | 000 |

9|0 = 90

**6.**

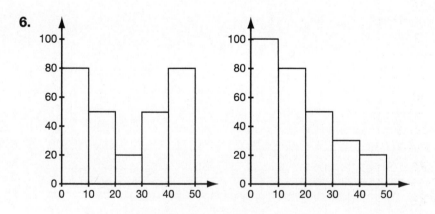

NAME_____ DATE _____

Use the five number summaries to create box-and-whisker plots for both data sets in each along the same number line.

**7.**

| | | |
|---|---|---|
| Minimum | 4 | 1 |
| Q1 | 6 | 3 |
| Median | 8 | 4 |
| Q3 | 10 | 7 |
| Maximum | 12 | 15 |
| IQR | 4 | 4 |

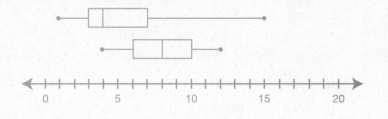

**8.**

| | | |
|---|---|---|
| Minimum | 0 | 3 |
| Q1 | 10 | 8 |
| Median | 15 | 10 |
| Q3 | 17 | 11 |
| Maximum | 20 | 17 |
| IQR | 7 | 3 |

**9.**

| | | |
|---|---|---|
| Minimum | 25 | 10 |
| Q1 | 35 | 20 |
| Median | 40 | 25 |
| Q3 | 45 | 45 |
| Maximum | 50 | 50 |
| IQR | 10 | 25 |

**15**

**10.**

| | | |
|---|---|---|
| Minimum | 1 | 5 |
| Q1 | 2 | 7 |
| Median | 3 | 10 |
| Q3 | 4 | 13 |
| Maximum | 11 | 18 |
| IQR | 2 | 6 |

**11.**

| | | |
|---|---|---|
| Minimum | 0 | 0 |
| Q1 | 15 | 5 |
| Median | 35 | 10 |
| Q3 | 37 | 12 |
| Maximum | 40 | 25 |
| IQR | 22 | 7 |

**12.**

| | | |
|---|---|---|
| Minimum | 40 | 10 |
| Q1 | 60 | 40 |
| Median | 70 | 70 |
| Q3 | 80 | 80 |
| Maximum | 100 | 100 |
| IQR | 20 | 40 |

NAME_____ DATE_____

Compare the box-and-whisker plots in each and describe the variation.

**13.**

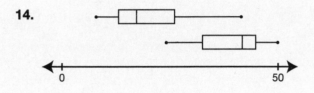

The data on the bottom is symmetric and the data on top is skewed right.

**14.**

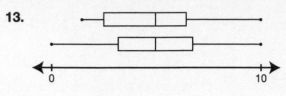

**15.**

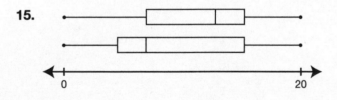

**16.**

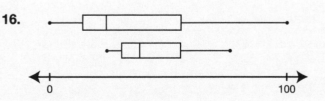

**17.**

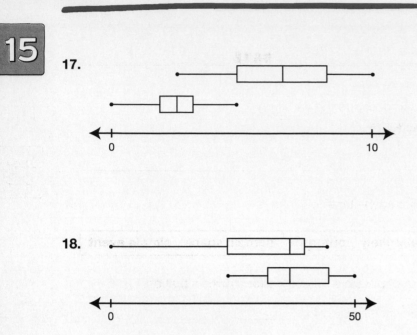

**18.**

NAME _____ DATE _____

## Rolling, Rolling, Rolling ...
### Defining and Representing Probability

## Vocabulary

Write the term from the box that best completes each statement.

| experiment   probability   event   equally likely   outcome   sample space   simple event |

1. A(n) _____ is one or a group of possible outcomes for a given situation.

2. A list of all possible outcomes of an experiment is called a(n) _____ .

3. A(n) _____ is a situation involving chance that leads to results.

4. The measure of the likelihood that an event will occur is its _____.

5. The result of an experiment is a(n) _____.

6. An event consisting of one outcome is a(n) _____.

7. When the probabilities of all the outcomes of an experiment are equal, then the probabilities are called _____.

## Problem Set

List the sample space for each experiment.

1. Peter writes each day of the week on a slip of paper and puts all of the slips of paper in a bag. Peter chooses one slip of paper from the bag.

   The sample space is {Sunday, Monday, Tuesday, Wednesday, Thursday, Friday, Saturday}.

**2.** Tina spins the spinner shown one time.

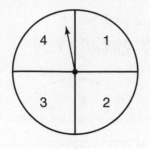

**3.** A drawer contains 4 black socks, 2 brown socks, and 2 blue socks. Samuel picks one sock from the drawer.

**4.** Stefan picks one of the colors in the American flag.

**5.** Jonetta tosses a coin two times.

**6.** Roni spins the spinner shown one time.

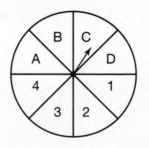

© Carnegie Learning

NAME_____ DATE _____

List the possible outcome or outcomes for each event.

**7.** The spinner shown stops on an even number.

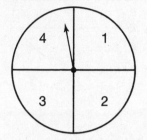

The outcomes for the event are 2 and 4.

**8.** The spinner shown stops on a letter.

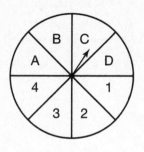

**9.** choosing a weekend when choosing a day of the week

**10.** getting a number greater than 3 when rolling a number cube

**11.** getting a number less than 7 when rolling a number cube

**12.** getting the same result when tossing a coin two times

Calculate each probability.

**13.** Eva spins the following spinner one time. Calculate P(even number).

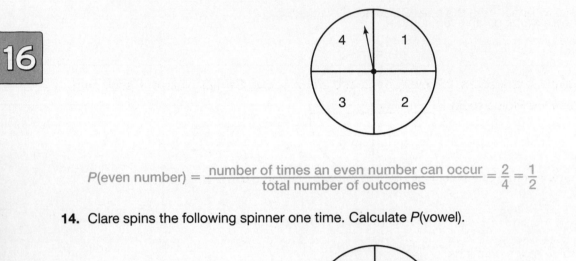

$$P(\text{even number}) = \frac{\text{number of times an even number can occur}}{\text{total number of outcomes}} = \frac{2}{4} = \frac{1}{2}$$

**14.** Clare spins the following spinner one time. Calculate P(vowel).

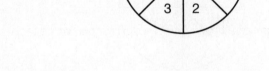

**15.** Emmett spins the following spinner one time. Calculate P(letter).

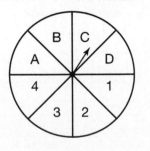

NAME_____ DATE _____

16

16. Peter writes the days of the week on slips of paper and puts the slips of paper in a bag. Peter chooses one slip of paper from the bag. Calculate $P$(weekend).

17. A drawer contains 4 black socks, 2 brown socks, and 2 blue socks. Samuel picks one sock from the drawer. Calculate $P$(blue sock).

18. Javier rolls a number cube one time. Calculate $P$(number greater than 3).

19. Alice rolls a number cube one time. Calculate $P$(number less than 7).

20. Jeanine spins the following spinner one time. Calculate $P$(shape with exactly 4 sides).

Predict $P(A)$ for each spinner. Write your answer as a fraction.

**21.**

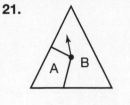

The probability is about $\frac{1}{3}$.

**22.**

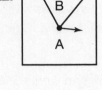

**23.**

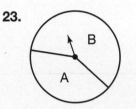

**24.**

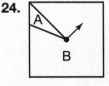

**25.**

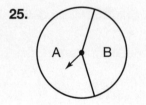

**26.**

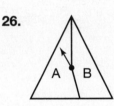

Estimate the probability of each event occurring. Write your answer as a fraction, a decimal, and a percent.

**27.** It is sunny on July 4 in Houston, Texas.

The probability is about $\frac{9}{10} = 0.9 = 90\%$.

**28.** A car makes a left turn at an intersection in which you must turn either left or right.

**29.** A car makes a left turn at an intersection in which you can turn left, turn right, or go straight.

NAME_____ DATE _____

16

**30.** You see a 5-year old child at the movies after 10 PM.

**31.** A customer pays for a pack of gum with a $100 dollar bill.

**32.** You are sleeping at 2 AM.

Calculate each probability.

**33.** A bag contains 6 red marbles, 4 blue marbles, and 10 green marbles. You choose one marble from the bag without looking. Calculate $P$(blue).

$$P(\text{blue}) = \frac{\text{number of times you can choose a blue marble}}{\text{total number of marbles}}$$

$$= \frac{4}{20}$$

$$= \frac{1}{5}$$

**34.** A shopping bag contains 18 red potatoes and 12 white potatoes. You choose one potato from the bag without looking. Calculate $P$(white potato).

16

**35.** A cooler contains 5 bottles of lemonade, 7 bottles of water, and 6 bottles of iced tea. You choose one bottle from the cooler without looking. Calculate P(iced tea).

**36.** A jar contains 14 quarters, 26 dimes, 11 nickels, and 7 pennies. You choose one coin from the jar without looking. Calculate P(dime).

**37.** There are 4 cherry-flavored yogurts and 12 strawberry-flavored yogurts on a store shelf. Margaret chooses a yogurt without looking. Calculate P(cherry).

NAME_____ DATE _____

**38.** Ronald ordered 12 DVDs. Four are historical, two are science fiction, and the rest are comedies. When they arrive, he determines which DVD to watch first by choosing one from the order without looking. What is the probability that the first DVD he watches is a comedy?

**39.** There are 15 female kittens and 21 male kittens at a pet shelter. An advertising director randomly chooses one kitten to be in a commercial. What is the probability that he chooses a male kitten?

**40.** A website selling backpacks offers 3 blue backpacks, 8 black backpacks, 2 red backpacks, and 2 green backpacks. Judy likes them all and tells her brother to randomly pick one for her. What is the probability that he picks a black backpack?

# Lesson 16.2 Skills Practice

NAME_____ DATE _____

## Toss the Cup
### Determining Experimental Probability

## Vocabulary

Define the term in your own words.

1. experimental probability

## Problem Set

Determine each experimental probability.

1. Suppose you toss a coin 20 times and record the results shown in the table. Complete the table and calculate the experimental probability of tossing tails.

| Result | Tally | Total |
|--------|-------|-------|
| Heads | ⊔⊓ ||| | 8 |
| Tails | ⊔⊓ ⊔⊓ || | 12 |
| | | 20 |

$P(\text{tails}) = \dfrac{12}{20} = 60\%$

**2.** Suppose you roll a number cube 40 times and record the results shown in the table. Complete the table and calculate the experimental probability of rolling an even number.

| Result | Tally | Total |
|--------|-------|-------|
| 1 | LH1 | |
| 2 | LHI II | |
| 3 | IIII | |
| 4 | LHI I | |
| 5 | LHI LHI | |
| 6 | LHI III | |
| | | |

**3.** Suppose you put two socks of one color and one sock of another color into a bag, and you choose one sock without looking. You repeat this 15 times, and you record the results shown in the table. Note that you always put the sock you chose back into the bag before choosing the next sock. Complete the table and calculate the experimental probability of choosing the sock that was a different color than the other two.

| Result | Tally | Total |
|--------|-------|-------|
| White | LHI LHI II | |
| Brown | III | |
| | | |

16

4. Suppose that you write the letters *A*, *B*, *C*, and *D* on four equal-size slips of paper. Then, you put them in a bag and choose one slip from the bag without looking. You repeat this 40 times and record the results shown in the table. Note that you always put the slip you chose back into the bag before choosing the next slip. Complete the table and calculate the experimental probability of choosing *D*.

| Result | Tally | Total |
|--------|-------|-------|
| A | LHT II | |
| B | LHT LHT II | |
| C | LHT LHT II | |
| D | LHT IIII | |
| | | |

5. Suppose that you put 2 dimes, 2 nickels, and 1 penny into a bag. Then, you choose one coin from the bag without looking, and record the results shown. You repeat this experiment 25 times. Note that you always put the coin you chose back into the bag before choosing the next coin. Complete the table and calculate the experimental probability of choosing a nickel.

| Result | Tally | Total |
|--------|-------|-------|
| Dime | LHT LHT II | |
| Nickel | LHT IIII | |
| Penny | IIII | |
| | | |

**16**

6. Use a paper clip as the arrow part of the spinner. Place a pencil point through the paper clip and then on the center of the circle. Spin the spinner 30 times. Record the data in the table. Then, calculate the experimental probability of spinning a number greater than 1.

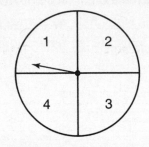

| Result | Tally | Total |
|--------|-------|-------|
| 1 | 卌 I | |
| 2 | 卌 IIII | |
| 3 | 卌 II | |
| 4 | 卌 III | |
| | | |

Calculate each experimental probability using the given data.

7. The table shows the results of Randy tossing a coin several times. Calculate the experimental probability of tossing heads.

| Result | Total |
|--------|-------|
| Heads | 66 |
| Tails | 84 |

$$P(\text{heads}) = \frac{66}{150} = \frac{11}{25} = 44\%$$

© Carnegie Learning

NAME_____ DATE _____

8. Misty stood at an intersection for one hour and recorded whether cars turned left or right. The table shows the data. Calculate the experimental probability of turning right.

| Result | Total |
|--------|-------|
| Left | 24 |
| Right | 9 |

9. Angelina recorded the results of spinning a game spinner several times. She recorded the data in the table. Calculate the experimental probability of spinning orange.

| Result | Total |
|--------|-------|
| Red | 5 |
| Yellow | 7 |
| Green | 2 |
| Orange | 8 |
| Blue | 3 |

10. Bettina recorded the results of spinning a spinner several times. She recorded the data in the table. Calculate the experimental probability of spinning purple.

| Result | Total |
|--------|-------|
| Gray | 5 |
| White | 5 |
| Purple | 0 |

11. The table shows the results of Roger rolling a number cube several times. Calculate the experimental probability of rolling a multiple of 3.

| Result | Total |
|--------|-------|
| 1 | 13 |
| 2 | 10 |
| 3 | 18 |
| 4 | 11 |
| 5 | 12 |
| 6 | 16 |

NAME_____ DATE _____

12. While selling lemonade at his lemonade stand, Steve recorded whether a customer gave him exact change or not. He recorded the data in the table. Calculate the experimental probability that the next customer will give Steve the exact change.

| Result | Total |
|---|---|
| Gave exact change | 14 |
| Did not give exact change | 4 |

Suppose the probabilities for the letters on a spinner are known to be:

$$P(A) = \frac{1}{4} \qquad P(B) = \frac{1}{3} \qquad P(C) = \frac{5}{12}$$

Predict the number of times you would land on each letter if you were to spin the spinner the number of times given.

13. You spin the spinner 12 times.

$P(A)$ :

$$\frac{x}{12} = \frac{1}{4}$$

$$4x = 12$$

$$x = 3 \text{ times}$$

$P(B)$ :

$$\frac{x}{12} = \frac{1}{3}$$

$$3x = 12$$

$$x = 4 \text{ times}$$

$P(C)$ :

$$\frac{x}{12} = \frac{5}{12}$$

$$12x = 60$$

$$x = 5 \text{ times}$$

14. You spin the spinner 36 times.

$P(A)$ :

$P(B)$ :

$P(C)$ :

**16**

15. You spin the spinner 60 times.

    $P(A)$ :                    $P(B)$ :                    $P(C)$ :

16. You spin the spinner 96 times.

    $P(A)$ :                    $P(B)$ :                    $P(C)$ :

17. You spin the spinner 144 times.

    $P(A)$ :                    $P(B)$ :                    $P(C)$ :

18. You spin the spinner 6000 times.

    $P(A)$ :                    $P(B)$ :                    $P(C)$ :

NAME_____   DATE _____

## Double Your Fun
### Determining Theoretical Probability

## Vocabulary

Explain the similarities and differences between the two terms.

**1.** theoretical probability and experimental probability

## Problem Set

Make an array to show the possible outcomes for each experiment and then use the array to determine the theoretical probability.

**1.** Two number cubes are rolled and the product of the two numbers shown is calculated. Calculate $P$(multiple of 6).

|  |  | Number Cube 1 | | | | | |
|---|---|---|---|---|---|---|---|
|  |  | 1 | 2 | 3 | 4 | 5 | 6 |
| Number Cube 2 | 1 | 1 | 2 | 3 | 4 | 5 | 6 |
|  | 2 | 2 | 4 | 6 | 8 | 10 | 12 |
|  | 3 | 3 | 6 | 9 | 12 | 15 | 18 |
|  | 4 | 4 | 8 | 12 | 16 | 20 | 24 |
|  | 5 | 5 | 10 | 15 | 20 | 25 | 30 |
|  | 6 | 6 | 12 | 18 | 24 | 30 | 36 |

The multiples of 6 in the table are 6, 12, 18, 24, 30 and 36.

$P$(multiple of 6) $= \dfrac{15}{36} = \dfrac{5}{12}$

**2.** Harriet spins the spinner two times. She determines the product of the two numbers. Calculate *P*(product is between 20 and 50).

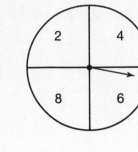

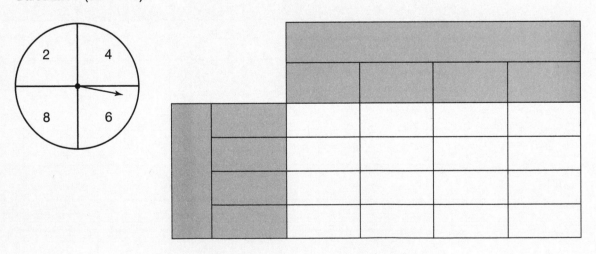

**3.** Harriet spins the spinner two times. She determines the sum of the two numbers. Calculate *P*(sum < 8).

NAME_____  DATE _____

4. Kyle writes the numbers 1 through 3 on papers and puts them in a bag. He chooses one paper, writes the number down, returns it to the bag, and chooses another number. He subtracts the smaller number from the greater number. Calculate $P(1)$.

5. Mike spins each spinner one time. He determines the product of the two numbers. Calculate
   *P*(multiple of 10).

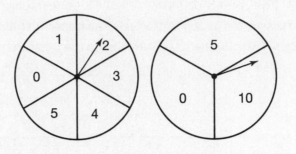

|   |   |   |   |   |   |   |
|---|---|---|---|---|---|---|
|   |   |   |   |   |   |   |
|   |   |   |   |   |   |   |
|   |   |   |   |   |   |   |
|   |   |   |   |   |   |   |

NAME_____ DATE _____

6. Jerry writes the letters *M*, *A*, *T*, and *H* on papers and puts them in bag 1. He writes the letters *Y*, *E*, and *S* on papers and puts them in bag 2. He pulls one paper from bag 1, writes the letter down, pulls one paper out of bag 2, and writes the letter next to the letter from bag 1. Calculate the probability that the two letters spell a word. (The words are MY, ME, HE, and AS.)

16

Predict the number of times you would get each outcome given the theoretical probability of the outcome and the number of times you spin the spinner.

7. $P(\text{red}) = \frac{3}{8}$; you spin 40 times

$$\frac{x}{40} = \frac{3}{8}$$

$$8x = 120$$

$$x = 15 \text{ times}$$

8. $P(\text{multiple of 5}) = \frac{3}{4}$; you spin 200 times

© Carnegie Learning

**9.** $P(4) = \frac{7}{12}$; you spin 60 times

**10.** $P(\text{blue}) = \frac{8}{9}$; you spin 450 times

**11.** $P(\text{odd number}) = \frac{1}{2}$; you spin 100 times

**12.** $P(3) = \frac{9}{40}$; you spin 2000 times

Determine if each probability can be determined experimentally, theoretically, or both. Explain your reasoning.

**13.** the probability that a new medicine will have side effects

Experimental. The only way to determine side effects is to have a small group of people try the medicine.

**14.** the probability that two coins will both land heads up when tossed

NAME_____ DATE _____

15. the probability that a paper will jam in a copy machine

16. the probability that a wooden beam will be strong enough to use in a play set

17. the probability that a raffle ticket sold at a fundraiser will be chosen in a raffle

18. the probability that a customer will win a prize at a carnival booth that involves tossing a ring around a bottle

16

# Lesson 16.4 Skills Practice

## A Toss of a Coin
### Simulating Experiments

## Vocabulary

Write the term that best completes each statement.

**1.** Each time you repeat an experiment, it is called a(n) _____.

**2.** A(n) _____ is an experiment that models a real-life situation.

## Problem Set

Conduct each experiment as described and record your results in the table. Use your results to determine the experimental probability.

**1.** At the first intersection of a corn maze, a person can go left, right, or straight. Use the spinner to model the person choosing the direction they will go. Use a paper clip as the arrow part of the spinner. Place a pencil point through the paper clip and then on the center of the circle. Perform 30 trials of the experiment. Record the results in the table using tally marks.

Sample answers are shown.

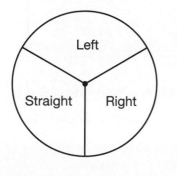

| Result | Tally | Total | Percent (total/30) |
|--------|-------|-------|--------------------|
| Left | ⅢⅢ ⅢⅢ ||| | 13 | ≈ 43% |
| Right | ⅢⅢ |||| | 9 | 30% |
| Straight | ⅢⅢ ||| | 8 | ≈ 27% |

What is your experimental probability that the person turns right?  30%

© Carnegie Learning

16

2. A theater audience is made up of half boys and half girls. One person is chosen at random to volunteer on stage. Toss a coin to model the person being chosen from the audience. Perform 40 trials of the experiment. Record the results in the table using tally marks.

| Result | Tally | Total | Percent (total/40) |
|---|---|---|---|
| Heads (girl) | | | |
| Tails (boy) | | | |

What is your experimental probability that the volunteer is a girl?

3. Two thirds of the fish in a lake are trout. A fisherman catches 1 fish. Roll a number cube to model the fisherman catching the fish. Perform 25 trials of the experiment. Record the results in the table using tally marks.

| Result | Tally | Total | Percent (total/25) |
|---|---|---|---|
| 1, 2, 3, or 4 (trout) | | | |
| 5 or 6 (not trout) | | | |

What is your experimental probability that the fisherman catches a fish that is not a trout?

**NAME**_____ **DATE** _____

4.  A drawer contains 10 white socks and 10 brown socks. The socks are mixed up. Joy chooses 1 sock without looking. Use a number cube to model Joy choosing the sock. Perform 30 trials of the experiment. Record the results in the table using tally marks.

| Result | Tally | Total | Percent (total/30) |
|--------|-------|-------|--------------------|
| Even number (white) | | | |
| Odd number (brown) | | | |

What is your experimental probability that Joy chooses a brown sock?

5.  A multiple-choice quiz has 4 questions. Each question has 3 possible answers. You guess the answer to each question. Use 3 slips of paper, one labeled *correct*, one labeled *incorrect*, and another labeled *incorrect*, to model guessing the answer to one question. Perform 10 trials of the experiment, where each trial consists of pulling a slip of paper from a bag without looking 4 times. Be sure to return the paper you chose back into the bag before choosing again. Record the results in the table.

| Trial Number | Number Correct | Trial Number | Number Correct |
|--------------|----------------|--------------|----------------|
| 1 | | 6 | |
| 2 | | 7 | |
| 3 | | 8 | |
| 4 | | 9 | |
| 5 | | 10 | |

What is your experimental probability that you get at least 2 questions correct?

**16**

6. A basketball player makes a foul shot 75% of the time. He is given the chance to make 2 foul shots. Use the spinner to model the player attempting a foul shot. Perform 20 trials of the experiment, where each trial consists of spinning the spinner 2 times. Record the results in the table.

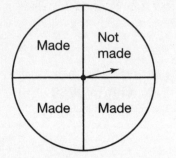

| Trial Number | Number Made | Trial Number | Number Made |
|:---:|:---:|:---:|:---:|
| 1 | | 11 | |
| 2 | | 12 | |
| 3 | | 13 | |
| 4 | | 14 | |
| 5 | | 15 | |
| 6 | | 16 | |
| 7 | | 17 | |
| 8 | | 18 | |
| 9 | | 19 | |
| 10 | | 20 | |

What is your experimental probability that the player makes both foul shots?

NAME_____ DATE _____

Describe a simulation to model each situation and then describe one trial.

7. One in every 4 cereal boxes has a coupon for a free box of cereal. How many boxes of cereal should you expect to buy before you find a coupon?

Sample answer:

Use a spinner with 4 equal sections. Label one section "coupon" and label the other 3 "no coupon." One trial would consist of spinning the spinner 1 time. Count how many trials you perform until it lands on "coupon."

8. A bag contains 5 lemons and 1 lime. You choose a fruit without looking. What is the probability that you choose the lime?

9. From past experience, you know that your probability of getting a ringer in horseshoes is about 20%. You throw 3 horseshoes. What is the probability that all 3 throws are ringers?

10. A stack of cards in a game contains 10 cards that tell the player to move forward a certain number of spaces and 5 cards that tell the player to move back a certain number of spaces. A player selects a card. What is the probability that the player will move back?

11. Joel's batting record shows that his probability of striking out is about 40%. Joel will go to bat 8 times at baseball practice. What is the probability that he strikes out 5 times or more?

12. A test has 20 true/false questions. What is the probability of getting at least 12 questions correct just by guessing?

# Lesson 16.5  Skills Practice

NAME_____ DATE _____

## Roll the Cubes Again
### Using Technology for Simulations

## Vocabulary

Define the term in your own words.

1. spreadsheet

## Problem Set

Describe how to use a spreadsheet for each simulation.

1. Flip a coin 50 times to determine the probability of heads.

   Sample answer:

   Enter =RANDBETWEEN(1, 2) in cell A1. Copy the formula down through cell A50.

   Let 1 represent heads and 2 represent tails.

2. A bag contains 26 slips of paper, each with a different letter of the alphabet. Choose and return a slip of paper from the bag 100 times to determine the probability of getting a vowel (A, E, I, O, U).

**16**

3. The probability that a bus is late is 30%. You want to know the probability that the bus is late 2 days in a row. Perform 40 trials of your experiment.

4. A quiz has 6 true/false questions. You want to know how many questions you would probably answer correctly by guessing. Perform 100 trials of your experiment.

5. You win a game of cards with your friend about 90% of the time. You want to know how many games you would probably win out of 5 games. Perform 25 trials of your experiment.

6. A spinner has 4 equal sections labeled 1 through 4. You spin it twice and calculate the sum of the numbers. Perform 10 trials of your experiment.

NAME_____ DATE _____

Use a spreadsheet to conduct each simulation. Record the results in the table and answer any questions. Describe how you used a spreadsheet for the simulation.

7. The probability that a train is on time is 70%. You will take the train 3 days in a row. Conduct 15 trials.

   Sample answers are shown.

| Trial Number | Days on Time | Trial Number | Days on Time | Trial Number | Days on Time |
|---|---|---|---|---|---|
| 1 | 2 | 6 | 1 | 11 | 1 |
| 2 | 2 | 7 | 3 | 12 | 1 |
| 3 | 3 | 8 | 2 | 13 | 3 |
| 4 | 0 | 9 | 3 | 14 | 2 |
| 5 | 3 | 10 | 2 | 15 | 1 |

What is the experimental probability that the train will be on time all 3 days?

$\frac{5}{15} = \frac{1}{3}$

I entered =RANDBETWEEN(1, 10) in cell A1 and copied it to the right through cell C1. I copied this row down through row 15. I let the numbers 1 through 7 represent the train being on time.

8. A spinner divided into 3 equal sections is labeled *0, 1,* and *2.* You spin the spinner 3 times and calculate the sum of the numbers. Conduct 50 trials.

| Result | Tally | Total | Probability |
|--------|-------|-------|-------------|
| 0 | | | |
| 1 | | | |
| 2 | | | |
| 3 | | | |
| 4 | | | |
| 5 | | | |
| 6 | | | |
| Total | 50 | 50 | 1 |

NAME_____ DATE_____

9. A test consists of 15 multiple choice questions. Each question has 5 possible answers. You guess the answer to each question. Conduct 20 trials.

| Trial Number | Number Correct | Trial Number | Number Correct |
|---|---|---|---|
| 1 | | 11 | |
| 2 | | 12 | |
| 3 | | 13 | |
| 4 | | 14 | |
| 5 | | 15 | |
| 6 | | 16 | |
| 7 | | 17 | |
| 8 | | 18 | |
| 9 | | 19 | |
| 10 | | 20 | |

You need 9 correct answers to pass. What is the experimental probability that you pass by guessing the answers?

**10.** A spinner is divided into two equal sections labeled 1 and 2. A second spinner is divided into three equal sections labeled 1, 2, and 3. You spin each spinner once and then calculate the sum of the numbers. Conduct 50 trials.

| Result | Tally | Total | Probability |
|---|---|---|---|
| 2 | | | |
| 3 | | | |
| 4 | | | |
| 5 | | | |
| Total | 50 | 50 | 1 |

NAME_____ DATE _____

11. Two out of every 5 water bottles have a winning bottle cap. You buy bottles of water until you
    get a winner. Conduct 30 trials.

| Trial Number | Results | Bottles Bought | Trial Number | Results | Bottles Bought |
|---|---|---|---|---|---|
| 1 | | | 16 | | |
| 2 | | | 17 | | |
| 3 | | | 18 | | |
| 4 | | | 19 | | |
| 5 | | | 20 | | |
| 6 | | | 21 | | |
| 7 | | | 22 | | |
| 8 | | | 23 | | |
| 9 | | | 24 | | |
| 10 | | | 25 | | |
| 11 | | | 26 | | |
| 12 | | | 27 | | |
| 13 | | | 28 | | |
| 14 | | | 29 | | |
| 15 | | | 30 | | |

16

Use the results to predict the number of times you will need to buy a water bottle before you get a winner.

12. Shannon plays a game with 2 pennies. Heads is worth 1 point and tails is worth 2 points. She tosses both coins and calculates the sum of the points. Conduct 30 trials.

| Result | Tally | Total | Probability |
|--------|-------|-------|-------------|
| 2 | | | |
| 3 | | | |
| 4 | | | |
| Total | 30 | 30 | 1 |

NAME_____ DATE_____

# Is It Better to Guess?
## Using Models for Probability

## Vocabulary

Choose a term from the box to complete each sentence.

| probability model | uniform probability model | non-uniform probability model |
|---|---|---|

1. A _____ is a list of each possible outcome along with its probability.

2. When all probabilities in a probability model are the same, it is called a
   _____.

3. When all probabilities in a probability model are not the same, it is called a
   _____.

## Problem Set

Construct a probability model for each situation. Determine whether the model is a uniform probability model or a non-uniform probability model.

1. Roll a 10-sided number polyhedron.

| Outcome | 1 | 2 | 3 | 4 | 5 | 6 | 7 | 8 | 9 | 10 |
|---|---|---|---|---|---|---|---|---|---|---|
| Probability | 0.1 | 0.1 | 0.1 | 0.1 | 0.1 | 0.1 | 0.1 | 0.1 | 0.1 | 0.1 |

$P(1) = \frac{1}{10}$, or 0.1

The model is a uniform probability model.

2. Randomly select a painted rock from a bag containing 4 purple rocks, 3 green rocks, 3 orange rocks, and 2 blue rocks.

| Outcome | | | | |
|---|---|---|---|---|
| Probability | | | | |

**17**

3. Spin a spinner with 8 numbered sections of equal size.

| Outcome | | | | | | | | |
|---|---|---|---|---|---|---|---|---|
| Probability | | | | | | | | |

NAME_____ DATE _____

4. Randomly select 1 of 5 members of your hockey team to take the first shot in an overtime shootout.

| Outcome | | | | | |
|---|---|---|---|---|---|
| Probability | | | | | |

5. Spin a spinner with colored sections of equal size. The spinner has 3 blue sections, 3 red sections, and 2 yellow sections.

| Outcome | | | |
|---|---|---|---|
| Probability | | | |

6. Randomly select a female member of the Math Club whose members are Marcus, Isabella, Jasmine, Levi, Joseph, Belinda, Catherine, James, and Julia.

| Outcome | | |
|---|---|---|
| Probability | | |

Use the probability model to answer each question.

| Outcome | 1 | 2 | 3 | 4 | 5 | 6 | 7 | 8 |
|---|---|---|---|---|---|---|---|---|
| Probability | $\frac{2}{25}$ | $\frac{4}{25}$ | $\frac{1}{25}$ | $\frac{5}{25}$ | $\frac{2}{25}$ | $\frac{4}{25}$ | $\frac{3}{25}$ | $\frac{4}{25}$ |

7. What is the probability of an outcome of 4?

$P(4) = \frac{5}{25}$

The probability of an outcome of 4 is $\frac{5}{25}$.

8. What is the probability of an outcome of 7?

17

9. What is the probability of an outcome that is less than 6?

10. What is the probability of an outcome that is greater than 8?

11. What is the probability of an outcome that is an odd number?

12. What is the probability of an outcome that is less than 10?

Use the probability model to answer each question.

| Outcome | A | B | C | D | E | F |
|---|---|---|---|---|---|---|
| Probability | $\frac{2}{20}$ | $\frac{5}{20}$ | $\frac{2}{20}$ | $\frac{7}{20}$ | $\frac{1}{20}$ | $\frac{3}{20}$ |

**13.** What is the probability of an outcome of B?

**14.** What is the probability of an outcome of F?

**15.** What is the probability of an outcome that is not C?

NAME_____ DATE _____

**16.** What is the probability of an outcome that is a consonant?

**17.** What is the probability of an outcome that is not A?

**18.** What is the probability of an outcome that is a vowel?

17

# Lesson 17.2 Skills Practice

NAME_____ DATE _____

## Three Girls and No Boys?
### Creating and Using Probability Models

## Vocabulary

Define each term in your own words.

**1.** tree diagram

**2.** complementary events

## Problem Set

List all of the possible outcomes for each problem situation. Complete the probability model using all the possible outcomes.

**1.** What is the probability that the first 3 students that enter a classroom are boys? List all of the possible outcomes for the first 3 students entering the classroom. Complete the probability model.

Possible outcomes: BBB, BBG, BGB, BGG, GGG, GGB, GBG, GBB

| Outcome | 0 boys | 1 boy | 2 boys | 3 boys |
|---|---|---|---|---|
| Probability | $\frac{1}{8}$ | $\frac{3}{8}$ | $\frac{3}{8}$ | $\frac{1}{8}$ |

The probability that the first 3 students that enter the classroom are boys is $\frac{1}{8}$.

**2.** You toss a coin 2 times. What is the probability that both tosses result in heads? List all of the possible outcomes for the 2 coin tosses. Complete the probability model.

| Outcome | 0 Heads | 1 Heads | 2 Heads |
|---|---|---|---|
| Probability | | | |

**3.** A spinner has 2 equal parts. One part is blue; one part is white. What is the probability that spinning the spinner 3 times will result in only 1 blue result? List all of the possible outcomes for the 3 spins. Complete the probability model.

| Outcome | 0 blue | 1 blue | 2 blue | 3 blue |
|---|---|---|---|---|
| Probability | | | | |

**4.** A spinner has 3 equal parts. One part is red, one part is blue, and one part is yellow. What is the probability that spinning the spinner 2 times will result in 2 yellow results? List all of the possible outcomes of the 2 spins. Complete the probability model.

| Outcome | 0 yellow | 1 yellow | 2 yellow |
|---|---|---|---|
| Probability | | | |

NAME_____ DATE _____

5. A bag contains a purple stone, a yellow stone, and an orange stone. A stone is randomly chosen from the bag, the stone's color is recorded and the stone is replaced in the bag. If you choose a stone from the bag 2 times, what is the probability that only 1 of the chosen stones is purple? List all of the possible outcomes of choosing 2 stones. Complete the probability model.

| Outcome | 0 purple | 1 purple | 2 purple |
|---|---|---|---|
| Probability | | | |

6. A six-sided number cube has two faces with a 1, two faces with a 2, and two faces with a 3. It is tossed 2 times. What is the probability that both tosses result in a 1? List all of the possible outcomes of tossing the number cube 2 times. Complete the probability model.

| Outcome | Zero 1s | One 1 | Two 1s |
|---|---|---|---|
| Probability | | | |

Complete the tree diagram to determine the possible outcomes for each problem situation. Complete the probability model.

**7.** What is the probability that the first 4 students that enter a classroom are girls? Complete the tree diagram to determine all of the possible outcomes for the first 4 students entering the classroom. Complete the probability model.

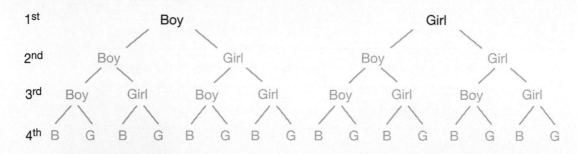

| Outcome | 0 girls | 1 girl | 2 girls | 3 girls | 4 girls |
|---|---|---|---|---|---|
| Probability | $\frac{1}{16}$ | $\frac{4}{16}$ | $\frac{6}{16}$ | $\frac{4}{16}$ | $\frac{1}{16}$ |

The probability that the first 4 students to enter the classroom are girls is $\frac{1}{16}$.

NAME_____ DATE _____

8. You toss a coin 4 times. What is the probability that all 4 tosses result in heads? Complete the tree diagram to determine all of the possible outcomes for the 4 coin tosses. Complete the probability model.

1st                         H                                    T

2nd

3rd

4th

| Outcome | 0 heads | 1 heads | 2 heads | 3 heads | 4 heads |
|---------|---------|---------|---------|---------|---------|
| Probability |     |         |         |         |         |

9. A spinner has 3 equal parts. One part is green, one part is orange, and one part is yellow. What is the probability that spinning the spinner 3 times will result in 0 orange results? Complete the tree diagram to determine all of the possible outcomes of the 3 spins. Complete the probability model.

1$^{st}$          Green                    Orange                    Yellow

2$^{nd}$

3$^{rd}$

| Outcome | 0 orange | 1 orange | 2 orange | 3 orange |
|---|---|---|---|---|
| Probability | | | | |

10. A six-sided number cube has two faces with a 1, two faces with a 2, and two faces with a 3. It is tossed 3 times. What is the probability that all 3 tosses result in a 1? Complete the tree diagram to determine all of the possible outcomes of tossing the number cube 3 times. Complete the probability model.

1$^{st}$          1                        2                        3

2$^{nd}$

3$^{rd}$

| Outcome | Zero 1s | One 1 | Two 1s | Three 1s |
|---|---|---|---|---|
| Probability | | | | |

NAME_____ DATE _____

**11.** A bag contains a red stone, a yellow stone, and a blue stone. A stone is randomly chosen from the bag, the stone's color is recorded and the stone is replaced in the bag. If you choose a stone from the bag 2 times, what is the probability that only 1 of the chosen stones is blue? Complete the tree diagram to determine all of the possible outcomes of choosing 2 stones. Complete the probability model.

1ˢᵗ　　　　Red　　　　　　　Yellow　　　　　　Blue

2ⁿᵈ

| Outcome | 0 blue | 1 blue | 2 blue |
|---|---|---|---|
| Probability | | | |

**12.** A spinner has 4 equal parts. One part is black, one part is white, one part is red, and one part is yellow. What is the probability that spinning the spinner 2 times will result in 2 red results? Complete the tree diagram to determine all of the possible outcomes of the 2 spins. Complete the probability model.

1ˢᵗ　　　　Black　　　　White　　　　Red　　　　Yellow

2ⁿᵈ

| Outcome | 0 red | 1 red | 2 red |
|---|---|---|---|
| Probability | | | |

Identify a complementary event.

**13.** A coin is tossed 1 time. The probability that tossing the coin will result in heads is *P*(heads). What is a complementary event?

*P*(tails)

**14.** A spinner has 2 equal parts. One part is blue, one part is white. The probability that spinning the spinner will result in blue is *P*(blue). What is a complementary event?

**15.** A six-sided number cube is rolled. The probability that the result is less than 3 is *P*(less than 3). What is a complementary event?

**16.** A letter between A and E is chosen. The probability that the result is *A* is *P*(*A*). What is a complementary event?

**17.** A letter between A and E is chosen. The probability that the result is a vowel is *P*(vowel). What is a complementary event?

**18.** A letter between A and E is chosen. The probability that the result is not *D* is *P*(not *D*). What is a complementary event?

# Lesson 17.3 Skills Practice

NAME_____ DATE _____

## Pet Shop Probability
### Determining Compound Probability

## Vocabulary

Define the term in your own words.

**1.** compound event

## Problem Set

Determine each probability using the probability table.

A spinner has 6 parts labeled with the letters *A* through *F*. The probability table shows the probability of spinning each letter on the next spin.

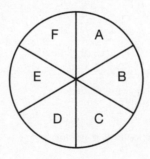

| Outcome | A | B | C | D | E | F |
|---------|---|---|---|---|---|---|
| Probability | $\frac{1}{6}$ | $\frac{1}{6}$ | $\frac{1}{6}$ | $\frac{1}{6}$ | $\frac{1}{6}$ | $\frac{1}{6}$ |

**1.** What is the probability that the next spin is an A or B?

$P(A \text{ or } B) = P(A) + P(B)$

$$= \frac{1}{6} + \frac{1}{6}$$

$$= \frac{2}{6}$$

$$= \frac{1}{3}$$

2.  What is the probability that the next spin is a vowel?

3.  What is the probability that the next spin is not *C*?

4.  What is the probability that the next spin is a consonant?

5. What is the probability that the next spin is a D, E, or F?

6. What is the probability that the next spin is not an A or B?

Marbles were placed in two buckets. The first bucket contains 1 marble of each of the following colors: red, blue, green. The second bucket contains 1 marble of each of the following colors: yellow, green, purple, blue.

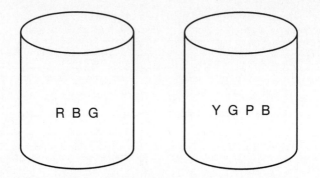

R B G          Y G P B

**17**

**7.** Determine the possible outcomes for choosing 1 marble from each bucket.

RY, RG, RP, RB
BY, BG, BP, BB
GY, GG, GP, GB

**8.** What is the probability of choosing 2 unique colors?

**9.** What is the probability of choosing green from the first bucket and green from the second bucket?

NAME_____ DATE _____

**10.** What is the probability of choosing blue from the first bucket or blue from the second bucket?

17

**11.** What is the probability of choosing red from the first bucket or yellow from the second bucket?

**12.** What is the probability of choosing the same color from each bucket?

A game requires spinning a spinner numbered 1 through 5 and rolling a six-sided number cube.

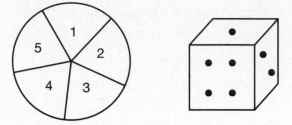

**13.** Determine the possible outcomes for playing the game.

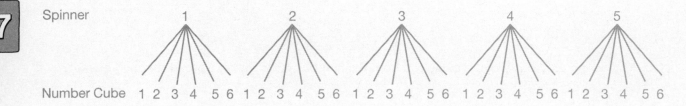

**14.** What is the probability of spinning an even number and rolling an even number?

**15.** What is the probability of spinning an odd number and rolling an odd number?

NAME_____ DATE _____

**16.** What is the probability of spinning a number less than 4 or rolling a number less than 4?

**17.** What is the probability of spinning a number greater than 3 or rolling a number greater than 3?

**18.** What is the probability of spinning a 5 or rolling a 5?

**19.** What is the probability of spinning a 6 or rolling a 6?

# Lesson 17.4 Skills Practice

## What Type of Blood Do You Have?
### Simulating Probability of Compound Events

## Problem Set

Perform a simulation to determine each probability.

1. The preferences of customers at a local movie rental store are given in the table. Perform a simulation to determine the probability that out of the next 5 customers to rent a movie, at least 1 rents a comedy.

| Movie Type | Comedy | Drama | Science | Documentary |
|---|---|---|---|---|
| Percent of Customers | 31% | 42% | 22% | 5% |

Sample answer.

Assign the numbers 00 to 30 to the people who rent a Comedy movie.

Assign the numbers 31 to 72 to the people who rent a Drama movie.

Assign the numbers 73 to 94 to the people who rent a Science Fiction movie.

Assign the numbers 95 to 99 to the people who rent a Documentary.

| Trial Number | Numbers | Number of Customers Who Rent a Comedy |
|:---:|:---:|:---:|
| 1 | 65, 28, 59, 71, 12 | 2 |
| 2 | 13, 85, 30, 10, 94 | 3 |
| 3 | 11, 58, 38, 16, 56 | 2 |
| 4 | 10, 04, 43, 51, 61 | 2 |
| 5 | 20, 17, 26, 45, 27 | 4 |
| 6 | 38, 22, 93, 01, 18 | 3 |
| 7 | 16, 43, 81, 09, 97 | 2 |
| 8 | 66, 56, 92, 98, 56 | 0 |
| 9 | 95, 50, 95, 63, 97 | 0 |
| 10 | 54, 31, 19, 99, 25 | 2 |

Out of the 10 trials, 8 trials had at least 1 customer rent a comedy.

$P$(at least 1 customer rents a comedy) $= \dfrac{8}{10}$

$$= 0.8$$

© Carnegie Learning

NAME_____  DATE _____

2. A survey at a middle school asked students their hair color. The percentage of students with each hair color is shown in the table. Perform a simulation to determine how many students will enter the building before a student with blond hair enters the building.

| Hair Color | Brown | Blond | Red |
|---|---|---|---|
| Percent of Students | 71% | 23% | 6% |

| Trial Number | Numbers | Number of Students to Enter the Building Before A Blond Student |
|---|---|---|
|  |  |  |
|  |  |  |
|  |  |  |
|  |  |  |
|  |  |  |
|  |  |  |
|  |  |  |
|  |  |  |
|  |  |  |
|  |  |  |

NAME _____ DATE _____

3. A survey at a middle school asked students to choose their favorite sport to watch on TV. The percentage of students who prefer each sport is shown in the table. Perform a simulation to determine the probability that out of the next 5 students to enter the building, at least 1 prefers hockey.

| Sport | Football | Baseball | Basketball | Hockey |
|---|---|---|---|---|
| Percent of Students | 32% | 30% | 26% | 12% |

17

**17**

| Trial Number | Numbers | Number of Students Who Prefer Hockey |
|---|---|---|
|  |  |  |
|  |  |  |
|  |  |  |
|  |  |  |
|  |  |  |
|  |  |  |
|  |  |  |
|  |  |  |
|  |  |  |
|  |  |  |

NAME_____ DATE _____

4. The kicker of the high school football team makes 4 out of every 6 field goal attempts. What is the probability that the kicker will successfully make the next 2 field goals? Perform a simulation to determine the probability.

| Trial Number | Numbers | Number of Successful Field Goal Attempts |
|---|---|---|
|  |  |  |
|  |  |  |
|  |  |  |
|  |  |  |
|  |  |  |
|  |  |  |
|  |  |  |
|  |  |  |
|  |  |  |
|  |  |  |

© Carnegie Learning

5. The attendant at a parking garage notices that typically 2 out of every 6 cars that enter the parking garage are white. Perform a simulation to determine how many cars will enter the parking garage before a white car enters the parking garage.

| Trial Number | Numbers | Number of Cars to Enter the Parking Lot Before A White Car |
|---|---|---|
|  |  |  |
|  |  |  |
|  |  |  |
|  |  |  |
|  |  |  |
|  |  |  |
|  |  |  |
|  |  |  |
|  |  |  |
|  |  |  |

NAME_____ DATE _____

6. At a bakery, 3 out of 5 customers who enter the bakery prefer banana nut muffins to the other flavors available. Perform a simulation to determine how many customers will enter the bakery before a customer who prefers banana nut muffins enters the bakery.

| Trial Number | Numbers | Number of Customers to Enter the Bakery Before A Customer Who Prefers Banana Nut Muffins |
|---|---|---|
|  |  |  |
|  |  |  |
|  |  |  |
|  |  |  |
|  |  |  |
|  |  |  |
|  |  |  |
|  |  |  |
|  |  |  |
|  |  |  |

17

17

## Chapter 1

### Lesson 1.1

1. 5 boys : 3 girls, $\frac{5 \text{ boys}}{3 \text{ girls}}$

3. 4 bananas : 1 fruit basket, $\frac{4 \text{ bananas}}{1 \text{ fruit basket}}$

5. 3 blueberry muffins : 6 total muffins, $\frac{3 \text{ blueberry muffins}}{6 \text{ total muffins}}$

7. 4 grape juice boxes : 10 total juice boxes, $\frac{4 \text{ grape juice boxes}}{10 \text{ total juice boxes}}$

9. There are 8 girls at soccer camp.

11. There are 20 tenants who own cats.

13. It costs $11.20 to buy 14 light bulbs.

15. 72 hours

17. 20 oranges

19. $13

21. 16 artichokes

23. 2 oz blue paint

25. 23 students

27. $0.30

29. 2 pencils

31. 25 miles per hour

33. $12 per pound

35. 15 students per teacher

37. 4 bracelets per hour

### Lesson 1.2

1. Because $\frac{15}{35} > \frac{14}{35}$, Deon's recipe has a higher concentration of almonds.

3. Because $\frac{8}{28} > \frac{7}{28}$, Jin's recipe has a higher concentration of macadamia nuts.

5. Because $\frac{24}{88} > \frac{22}{88}$, Leon's recipe has a higher concentration of peanuts.

7. Carmen will need 40 fluid ounces of strawberry juice and 24 fluid ounces of water to make 64 fluid ounces of strawberry drink.

9. Jose will need 18 cups of golden raisins and 12 cups of cashews to make 30 cups of trail mix.

11. Carla will need 32 ounces of green beans and 24 ounces of yellow wax beans to make 56 ounces of bean salad.

### Lesson 1.3

1. $\frac{200 \text{ lb}}{8000 \text{ lb}} = 0.025$

3. $\frac{2 \text{ lb}}{650 \text{ lb}} \approx 0.003$

5. $\frac{110 \text{ lb}}{3000 \text{ lb}} \approx 0.037$

7. 2 miles per 30 minutes, or $\frac{2 \text{ miles}}{30 \text{ minutes}}$

9. 3 miles per 45 minutes, or $\frac{3 \text{ miles}}{45 \text{ minutes}}$

11. 4 lawns per 3 hours, or $\frac{4 \text{ lawns}}{3 \text{ hours}}$

13. The rate 5 feet per 3 seconds is equivalent to 2000 yards per hour.

15. The rate 10 yards per 5 minutes is equivalent to 360 feet per hour.

17. The rate 12 pints per 15 minutes is equivalent to 24 quarts per hour.

19. 48 ounces

21. 2000 pounds

23. 3 yards

25. 1 hour

27. There are 18 pints in 36 cups.

29. There are 8 feet in 96 inches.

31. There are 112 ounces in 7 pounds.

## Lesson 1.4

**1.**

| Boys | 7 | 21 | 42 | 84 |
|---|---|---|---|---|
| Girls | 4 | 12 | 24 | 48 |

**3.**

| Photos | 2 | 10 | 25 | 50 |
|---|---|---|---|---|
| Minutes | 1 | 5 | 12.5 | 25 |

**5.**

| Peaches (c) | 1.5 | 3 | 4.5 | 6 |
|---|---|---|---|---|
| Grapes (c) | 1 | 2 | 3 | 4 |

**7.** If Luis had mowed 10 lawns, he would have earned $70.

**9.** In 3 hours, Rita could make 18 pairs of earrings.

**11.** It took Raul 15 minutes to walk 0.5 mile.

**13.** $579 = x$

**15.** The store should expect to sell 128 action figures in a year.

**17.** Marlene should expect to pay about $16.58 for gas.

## Lesson 1.5

**1.** Use the scaling method because it is easy to see that the numerator is multiplied by 10, so the denominator must also be multiplied by 10.

**3.** Use the means and extremes method because there are no clear relationships between the numbers.

**5.** Use the means and extremes method because there are no clear relationships between the numbers.

**7.** $x = 5$

**9.** $x = 2100$

**11.** $x \approx 8.67$

## Lesson 1.6

**1.** The unit rate is 28 ounces per dollar or about $0.04 per ounce.

**3.** The unit rate is about 0.84 pound of apples per dollar or about $1.20 per pound of apples.

**5.** The unit rate is 16 envelopes per dollar or about $0.06 per envelope.

**7.** Because $2 < $2.60, the 4 liter bottle is the better buy.

**9.** Because $1.25 < $1.75, the 20 pack is the better buy.

**11.** Because $0.42 < $0.50, the 12 pack is the better buy.

# Chapter 2

## Lesson 2.1

**1.**

| Hours Worked | Pay (dollars) |
|:---:|:---:|
| 2 | 24 |
| 3 | 36 |
| 5 | 60 |
| 10 | 120 |
| 15 | 180 |
| 20 | 240 |

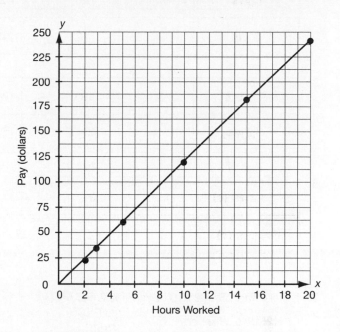

**3.**

| Number of Marbles Vanessa Takes | Number of Marbles Michelle Takes |
|:---:|:---:|
| 0 | 16 |
| 4 | 12 |
| 6 | 10 |
| 9 | 7 |
| 13 | 3 |
| 16 | 0 |

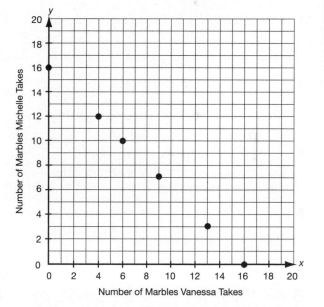

**5.**

| Square Side Length (inches) | Area (square inches) |
|---|---|
| 1 | 1 |
| 2 | 4 |
| 3 | 9 |
| 5 | 25 |
| 7 | 49 |
| 9 | 81 |

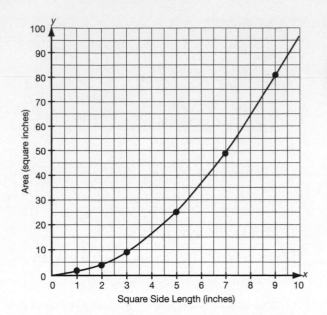

**7.**

| Hours Worked | Pay (dollars) |
|---|---|
| 1 | 50 |
| 2 | 70 |
| 3 | 90 |
| 4 | 110 |
| 6 | 150 |
| 8 | 190 |

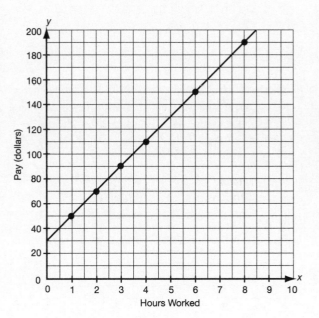

## Lesson 2.2

1. $\dfrac{\text{Glass}}{\text{Paper}} = \dfrac{2}{3}$

3. $\dfrac{\text{Number of Miles}}{\text{Number of Minutes}} = \dfrac{3}{4}$

5. $\dfrac{\text{Amount Heather Earns}}{\text{Number of Hours}} = 4.5$

7. $\dfrac{\text{Second Year Height}}{\text{First Year Height}} = 1.3$

9. $\dfrac{\text{Power Used}}{\text{Switch Setting}} = 14.5$

11. There are 15 teachers on the trip.

13. There are 9 dogs in the shelter.

15. There are 2385 fiction books in the library.

17. There are 39 catfish in the pond.

19. There are 37.50 pounds of phosphorus in the bag of fertilizer.

## Lesson 2.3

1. $p = 140$

3. $n = 27$

5. $g = 20$

7. $d \approx 8.57$

9. $x = 10$

11. $y = 49$

13. $x = 2500$

15. $x = 18$

## Lesson 2.4

1. The relationship is proportional because $\dfrac{5}{3} = \dfrac{30}{18}$.

3. The relationship is proportional because $\dfrac{18}{45} = \dfrac{28}{70}$.

5. The relationship is not proportional because $\dfrac{7}{18} \neq \dfrac{11}{26}$.

7. The relationship is proportional because $\dfrac{8}{6} = \dfrac{44}{33}$.

## Lesson 2.5

1.

| Number of Photos | Cost (dollars) |
|---|---|
| 2 | 0.2 |
| 5 | 0.5 |
| 8 | 0.8 |
| 12 | 1.2 |
| 15 | 1.5 |

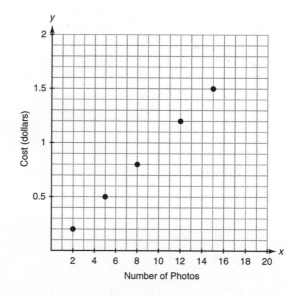

**3.**

| Area (square feet) | Number of Gallons |
| --- | --- |
| 175 | 0.5 |
| 700 | 2 |
| 875 | 2.5 |
| 1400 | 4 |
| 1750 | 5 |

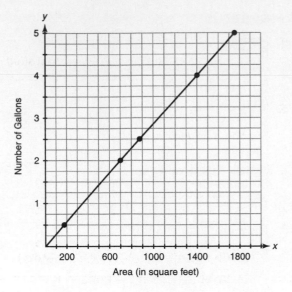

**5.**

| Time (hours) | Number of Feet |
| --- | --- |
| $\frac{1}{2}$ | 300 |
| 1 | 600 |
| 3 | 1 |
| $3\frac{1}{2}$ | 2 |
| 4 | 2400 |

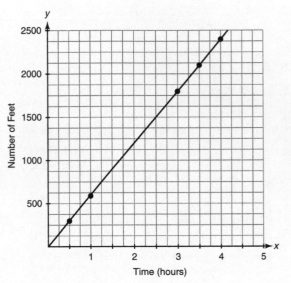

**7.** $k = \frac{3}{15}$ or $\frac{1}{5}$ or 0.2

The constant of proportionality means the distance between you and the storm increases by 1 mile for every 5 seconds between the lightning and the thunder. Or, the distance increases by 0.2 miles for every second counted.

**9.** $k = \frac{90}{100}$ or $\frac{9}{10}$

The constant of proportionality means that for every 10 pounds on Earth, the same object weighs 9 pounds on Venus. Or, the weight of an object on Venus is $\frac{9}{10}$ its weight on Earth.

**11.** $k = \frac{1}{3}$

The constant of proportionality means that for every 1 cup of water, 3 pounds of beef are needed. Or, $\frac{1}{3}$ cup of water is needed per pound of beef.

Answers

## Lesson 2.6

**1.**

| Hours Worked | Pipes Installed |
|:---:|:---:|
| $1\frac{1}{2}$ | 2 |
| 3 | 4 |
| 6 | 8 |

**3.**

| Time (in hours) | Distance (in kilometers) |
|:---:|:---:|
| 2 | 164 |
| 5 | 410 |
| 6 | 492 |

**5.**

| Peanuts (ounces) | Cost of Peanut Butter (dollars) |
|:---:|:---:|
| 1.5 | 5.07 |
| 3 | 10.14 |
| 3.5 | 11.83 |
| 4 | 13.52 |

**7.** The constant of proportionality is $1\frac{1}{2}$, and it represents the number of pages Shirley reads per minute.

**9.** The constant of proportionality is 3.5, and it represents the number of points each question is worth.

**11.** The constant of proportionality is 0.2, and it represents the distance a spring stretches in centimeters for every pound of weight attached to it.

**13.** It would take her 8.5 minutes to type 544 words.

**15.** If the length on the blueprint is 20.25 centimeters, then the length in the house is 27 feet.

**17.** Because he can only buy whole bags, Mr. Larson would need to buy 10 bags of grass seed.

## Lesson 2.7

**1.** The ratios are not constant, so the relationship between the number of hours and the amount charged is not directly proportional.

**3.** The ratios are constant, so the relationship between the size of a painting and the cost of the painting is directly proportional.

**5.** The points form a straight line, but the line does not go through the origin. Therefore, the relationship is not directly proportional.

**7.** The equation for the relationship is $d = 32g$, so $k = 32$. It is the number of miles Mr. Benson can drive on 1 gallon of gas.

**9.** The equation is in the form $y = kx$, with $k = 25$. It is the number of seconds it takes to deliver 1 newspaper.

**11.** The equation is in the form $y = kx$, with $k = \frac{4}{15}$. There are 4 advertisements for every 15 minutes of the television program.

**13.** Seven boys are needed.

**15.** The homeowner needs 10 rocks.

**17.** The fence would cost $600.

# Chapter 3

## Lesson 3.1

**1.** 20    **3.** 700    **5.** 48

**7.** 120    **9.** 27    **11.** 4

**13.** 20    **15.** 24    **17.** 32

**19.** 44

**21.** The estimated value is 10.

**23.** The estimated value is 2.

**25.** The estimated value is 20.

**27.** The estimated value is $5 \cdot 2 = 10$.

**29.** The estimated value is $20 \cdot 3 = 60$.

**31.** The estimated value is 3.

**33.** The estimated value is $5 + 2.50 = 7.50$.

**35.** The estimated value is 100.

**37.** The estimated value is 50 · 4 = 200.

**39.** The estimated value is 20 + 10 = 30.

**41.** The estimated sale price is $40 − $4 or $36.
The actual sale price is $39.90 − $3.99 = $35.91.

**43.** The estimated sale price is $80 − $16 or $64.
The actual sale price is $79.50 − $15.90 = $63.60.

**45.** The estimate sale price is $200 − $50 or $150.
The actual sale price is $199 − $49.75 = $149.25.

**47.** The estimated sale price is $60 − $24 or $36.
The actual sale price is $59.75 − $23.90 = $35.85.

**49.** The estimated sale price is $160 − $40 or $120.
The actual sale price is $159 − $39.75 = $119.25.

## Lesson 3.2

**1.** Fifteen is 30% of 50.

**3.** Forty-two is 60% of 70.

**5.** The number 112.50 is 75% of 150.

**7.** Eighteen is 12% of 150.

**9.** Seventy-eight is 26% of 300.

**11.** Twenty-five percent of the students in the class ride in a car to school.

**13.** Exactly 56.25% of the students in the class ride the bus to school.

**15.** Exactly 18.75% of the students in the class were born in September.

**17.** Exactly 37.5% of the students in the class were born in either April or October.

**19.** Exactly 18.75% of the students in the class have no siblings.

**21.** The original price of the table and chairs was $400.

**23.** Terrence gets $45 off the original price.

**25.** Rich pays $162.50 for the entertainment center.

**27.** The original price of the nightstand was $120.

**29.** Julian gets $405 off the original price.

## Lesson 3.3

**1.** Thirty-two is 20% of 160.

**3.** Fifty is 30% of about 166.67.

**5.** Forty-eight is 30% of 160.

**7.** The discount will be $9.50.

**9.** The tip will be about 17%.

**11.** The sales tax was 6.5%.

**13.** Nina saves 60% of her allowance.

**15.** There is 60 mL of total solution.

## Lesson 3.4

**1.** The simple interest is $27.

**3.** The simple interest is $105.

**5.** The simple interest is $133.02.

**7.** Ronna will earn $14.10 in interest.

**9.** Carmen will pay her parents an additional $4.60 in interest.

**11.** percent increase = 50%

**13.** percent increase ≈ 24%

**15.** percent decrease ≈ 23%

**17.** The price of the chair increased by 80%.

**19.** The value of the car decreased by about 24%.

**21.** The motorcycle depreciates $1350 in the first year.

**23.** The boat depreciates $1440 in the first year.

**25.** The value of the car after one year is $24,000 − $2880 = $21,120.

## Lesson 3.5

**1.** The regular cost of the jacket is $70.

**3.** The scientist made 40 grams of the mixture.

**5.** The secretary ordered a total of 300 pens.

**7.** They will devote 24 square feet to corn.

**9.** There are 14 roses in the ultimate bouquet.

**11.** There are 200 students in the sixth grade.

**13.** Tonya can paint 9 birdcages.

# Chapter 4

## Lesson 4.1

1. +4     3. +7     5. 0

7. −2     9. +6

11. $+2 + (−4) + 7 = +5$

13. $+6 + (−9) + 4 = +1$

15. $−5 + (−2) + 9 = +2$

17. $−3 + (−1) + 4 = 0$

19. $0 + (−8) + 2 = −6$

21. +8     23. +3     25. −4

27. +2     29. −4

31. $0 + (−5) + 3 = −2$

33. $−2 + (−4) + 1 = −5$

35. $−5 + (−2) + 4 = −3$

37. $0 + (−6) + 1 = −5$

39. $+7 + (−3) + 6 = +10$

41. $+5 + (−1) + 6 = +10$

43. $+12 + (−5) + 3 = +10$

45. $+14 + (−6) + 2 = +10$

## Lesson 4.2

1. The number that is 3 more than −5 is −2. Go to −5 on the number line and then move 3 units to the right.

3. The number that is 12 more than −8 is 4. Go to −8 on the number line and then move 12 units to the right.

5. The number that is 7 less than 3 is −4. Go to 3 on the number line and then move 7 units to the left.

7. The number that is 10 less than 2 is −8. Go to 2 on the number line and then move 10 units to the left.

9. $−3 + 8 = \underline{\ 5\ }$

$3 + (−8) + \underline{\ −5\ }$

$−3 + (−8) = \underline{\ −11\ }$

$3 + 8 = \underline{\ 11\ }$

11. $−4 + 10 = \underline{\ 6\ }$

$4 + (−10) = \underline{\ −6\ }$

$−4 + (−10) = \underline{\ −14\ }$

$4 + 10 = \underline{\ 14\ }$

13. $6 + (−8) = \underline{\ −2\ }$

$−6 + 8 = \underline{\ 2\ }$

$6 + 8 = \underline{\ 14\ }$

$−6 + (−8) = \underline{\ −14\ }$

15. $|4| = \underline{\ 4\ }$

$|−4| = \underline{\ 4\ }$

Each term is 4 units from 0.

17. $|−13| = \underline{\ 13\ }$

$|13| = \underline{\ 13\ }$

Each integer is 13 units from 0.

19. $|−8| = \underline{\ 8\ }$

$|8| = \underline{\ 8\ }$

Each integer is 8 units from 0.

21. $15 + \underline{\ −7\ } = 8$

23. $−4 + \underline{\ 9\ } = 5$

25. $6 + \underline{\ −8\ } = −2$

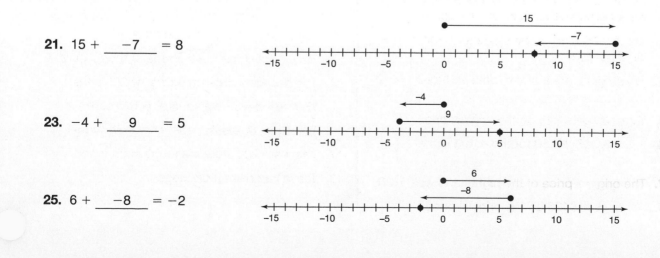

**27.** $8 + \underline{\quad -11 \quad} = -3$

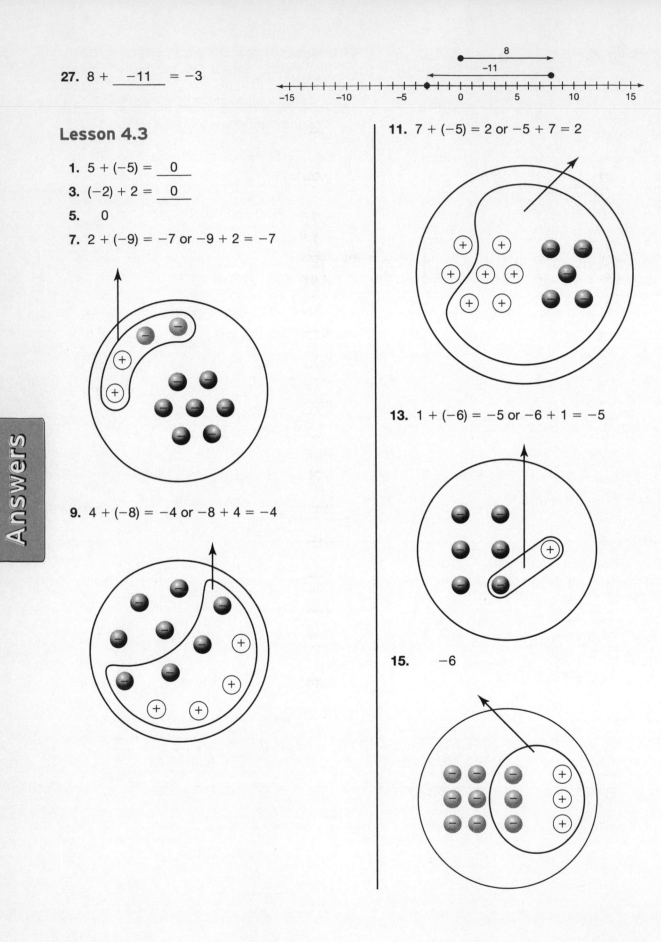

## Lesson 4.3

**1.** $5 + (-5) = \underline{\quad 0 \quad}$

**3.** $(-2) + 2 = \underline{\quad 0 \quad}$

**5.** $\quad 0$

**7.** $2 + (-9) = -7$ or $-9 + 2 = -7$

**9.** $4 + (-8) = -4$ or $-8 + 4 = -4$

**11.** $7 + (-5) = 2$ or $-5 + 7 = 2$

**13.** $1 + (-6) = -5$ or $-6 + 1 = -5$

**15.** $\quad -6$

**17.** −12

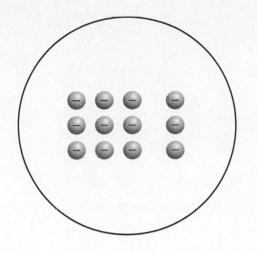

**19.** 3

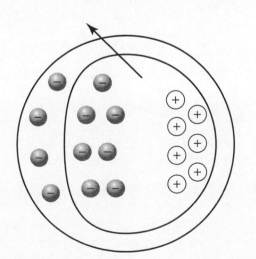

**21.** −4

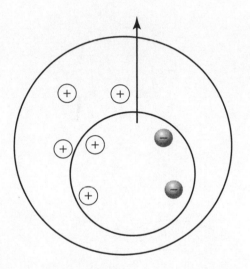

**23.** −18

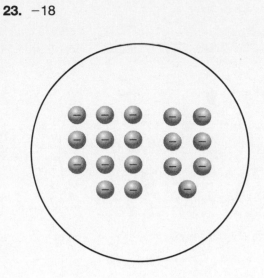

**25.** −2

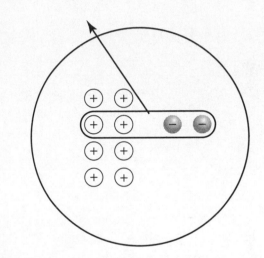

**27.** 8

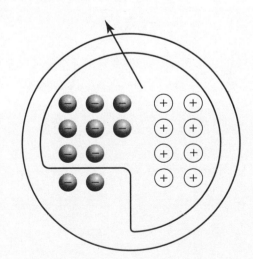

**29.** −5

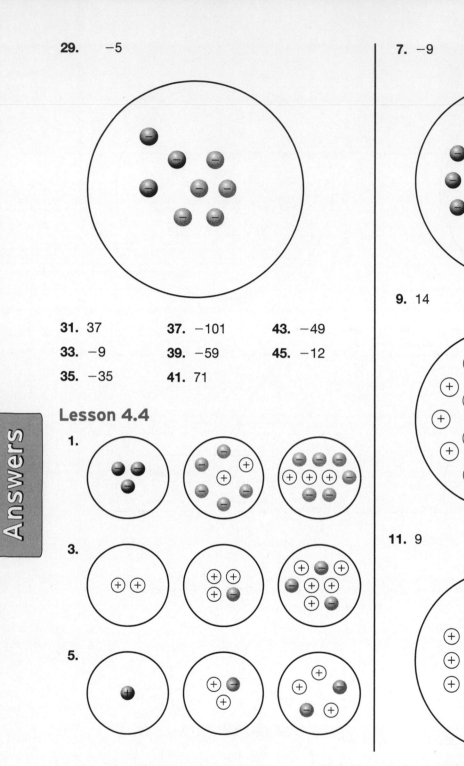

**31.** 37  **37.** −101  **43.** −49

**33.** −9  **39.** −59  **45.** −12

**35.** −35  **41.** 71

## Lesson 4.4

**1.**

**3.**

**5.**

**7.** −9

**9.** 14

**11.** 9

**13.** −4

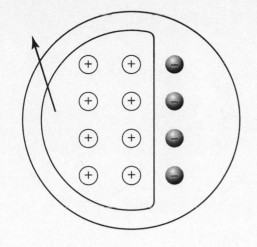

**15.** −5 − 7 = ___−12___

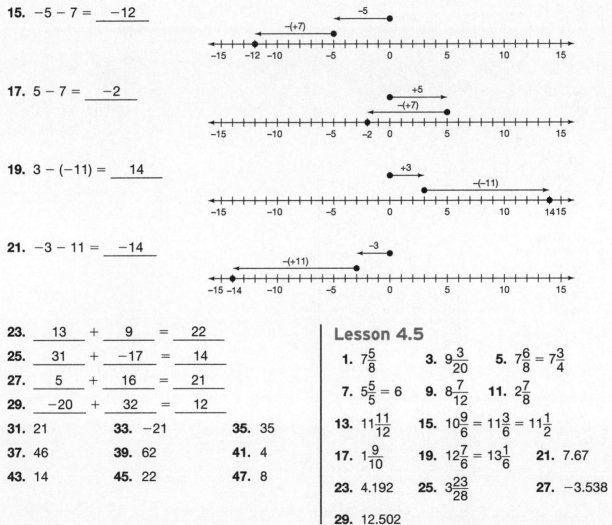

**17.** 5 − 7 = ___−2___

**19.** 3 − (−11) = ___14___

**21.** −3 − 11 = ___−14___

**23.** ___13___ + ___9___ = ___22___
**25.** ___31___ + ___−17___ = ___14___
**27.** ___5___ + ___16___ = ___21___
**29.** ___−20___ + ___32___ = ___12___
**31.** 21     **33.** −21     **35.** 35
**37.** 46     **39.** 62     **41.** 4
**43.** 14     **45.** 22     **47.** 8

## Lesson 4.5

**1.** $7\frac{5}{8}$    **3.** $9\frac{3}{20}$    **5.** $7\frac{6}{8} = 7\frac{3}{4}$

**7.** $5\frac{5}{5} = 6$    **9.** $8\frac{7}{12}$    **11.** $2\frac{7}{8}$

**13.** $11\frac{11}{12}$    **15.** $10\frac{9}{6} = 11\frac{3}{6} = 11\frac{1}{2}$

**17.** $1\frac{9}{10}$    **19.** $12\frac{7}{6} = 13\frac{1}{6}$    **21.** 7.67

**23.** 4.192    **25.** $3\frac{23}{28}$      **27.** −3.538

**29.** 12.502

# Chapter 5

## Lesson 5.1

**1.** −12

The expression 2 × (−6) means 2 groups of (−6).

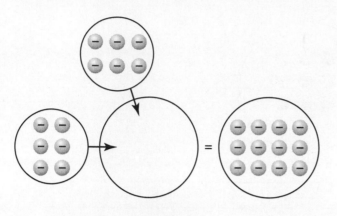

**3.** 21

The expression 7 × 3 means 7 groups of 3.

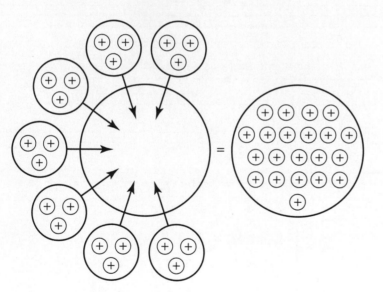

**5.** −10

The expression −2 × 5 means the opposite of 2 groups of 5.

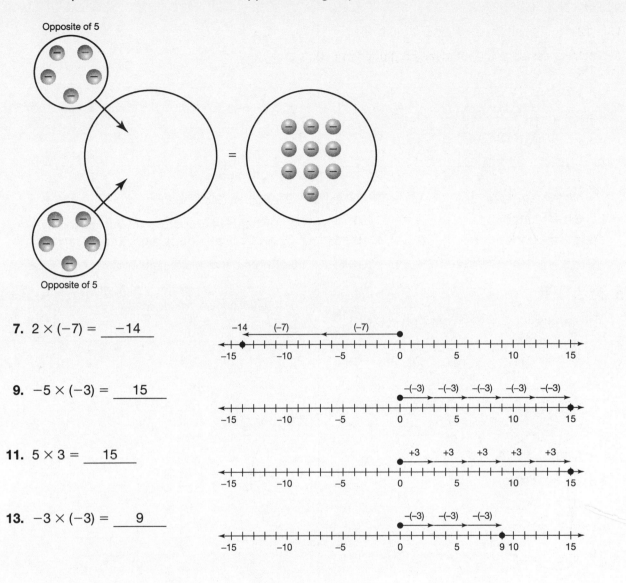

Opposite of 5

Opposite of 5

**7.** 2 × (−7) = _−14_

**9.** −5 × (−3) = _15_

**11.** 5 × 3 = _15_

**13.** −3 × (−3) = _9_

Answers

**15.** $(-7) + (-7) + (-7) + (-7) + (-7) + (-7) = -42$

**17.** $-(9 + 9 + 9) = -27$

**19.** $(-2) + (-2) + (-2) + (-2) + (-2) + (-2) + (-2) + (-2) + (-2) + (-2) = -20$

**21.** $-16; -12; -8; -4$

$-4 \times 0 = 0$

$-4 \times -1 = 4$

$-4 \times -2 = 8$

increasing

**23.** $18; 12; 6; 0$

$-6 \times 1 = -6$

$-6 \times 2 = -12$

$-6 \times 3 = -18$

decreasing

**25.** $96; -96; -96; 96$  **27.** $54; -54; -54; 54$

**29.** $7, -7$  **31.** $4$  **33.** $4$

**35.** $3 \times (-4) = -12$  **37.** $-2 \times 9 = -18$

$(-4) \times 3 = -12$  $9 \times (-2) = -18$

$-12 \div 3 = -4$  $-18 \div (-2) = 9$

$-12 \div (-4) = 3$  $-18 \div 9 = -2$

**39.** $7 \times (-3) = -21$

$-3 \times 7 = -21$

$-21 \div 7 = -3$

$-21 \div (-3) = 7$

**41.** $-9$  **43.** $5$  **45.** $24$  **47.** $-28$

## Lesson 5.2

**1.** $-\dfrac{128}{15} = -8\dfrac{8}{15}$

**3.** $33.15$

**5.** $-17.93$

**7.** $86.94$

**9.** $-44.46$

**11.** $-10$

**13.** $-9.30$

**15.** $8.20$

**17.** $-5.50$

**19.** $-4$

## Lesson 5.3

**1.** Addition; Subtraction

**3.** Distributive Property of Multiplication over Subtraction; Subtraction; Multiplication

**5.** Subtraction; Multiplication

**7.** Commutative Property of Multiplication; Multiplication; Multiplication

**9.** $9\dfrac{3}{5} + \left(3\dfrac{1}{4} + 2\dfrac{3}{4}\right) =$

$\qquad 9\dfrac{3}{5} + 6 =$

$\qquad\qquad 15\dfrac{3}{5}$

**11.** $-5.2(14.95) =$

$\qquad -77.74$

**13.** $\left(-4\dfrac{2}{3}\right) + 8\dfrac{2}{3} + 5\dfrac{1}{4} =$

$\qquad\qquad 4 + 5\dfrac{1}{4} =$

$\qquad\qquad\qquad 9\dfrac{1}{4}$

**15.** $\left(-\dfrac{12}{5} \times \dfrac{5}{12}\right) \times 4\dfrac{4}{5} =$

$\qquad\qquad (-1) \times 4\dfrac{4}{5} =$

$\qquad\qquad\qquad -4\dfrac{4}{5}$

**17.** $1\dfrac{3}{4} + \left(2\dfrac{1}{3} + 4\dfrac{2}{3}\right) =$     <u>Associative Property of Addition</u>

$1\dfrac{3}{4} + 7 =$     <u>Addition</u>

$8\dfrac{3}{4}$     <u>Addition</u>

**19.** $3.2(10.8 - 8.3) =$      Distributive Property of Multiplication over Subtraction

$3.2(2.5) =$      Subtraction

$8$      Multiplication

**21.** $\left(-\dfrac{5}{9}\right) \times \left(-\dfrac{9}{5}\right) \times \left(-\dfrac{3}{11}\right) =$      Commutative Property of Multiplication

$1 \times \left(-\dfrac{3}{11}\right) =$      Multiplication

$-\dfrac{3}{11}$      Multiplication

## Lesson 5.4

1. Edith can make 9 full batches.

   Edith will have $\dfrac{1}{8}$ cup of sugar left over.

3. Tomas can cut 6 pieces from the pipe.

5. The veterinarian can get 12 doses from one bottle. There will be no vaccine left in the bottle.

7. Each kitten drinks $3\dfrac{5}{8}$ ounces of milk.

9. The car will use $31\dfrac{1}{6}$ gallons of gas in $8\dfrac{1}{2}$ hours.

11. $-6\dfrac{2}{3}$

13. 13

15. $7\dfrac{3}{4}$

17. $-20$

19. $-5\dfrac{5}{8}$

## Lesson 5.5

1. The decimal equivalent is 0.15. The decimal is terminating.

3. The decimal equivalent is 0.8333 … or $0.8\overline{3}$. The decimal is non-terminating and repeating.

5. The decimal equivalent is 0.181818… or $0.\overline{18}$. The decimal is non-terminating and repeating.

7. The decimal equivalent is 0.1333… or $0.1\overline{3}$. The decimal is non-terminating and repeating.

9. The decimal equivalent is 0.3666… or $0.3\overline{6}$. The decimal is non-terminating and repeating.

11. 11.95

13. $-2.35$

15. 54.15

**17.** 25

**19.** 2.80

# Chapter 6

## Lesson 6.1

1. Let $h$ represent the number of hours you skate; $3 + 2h$

   a. You will pay \$7 to skate for 2 hours. $3 + 2(2) = 7$

   b. You will pay \$11 to skate for 4 hours. $3 + 2(4) = 11$

   c. You will pay \$10 to skate for $3\dfrac{1}{2}$ hours.

   $3 + 2\left(3\dfrac{1}{2}\right) = 10$

3. Let $s$ represent the number of snacks you bought; $15 - 1.75s$

   a. You will have \$9.75 left if you buy 3 snacks. $15 - 1.75(3) = 9.75$

   b. You will have \$6.25 left if you buy 5 snacks. $15 - 1.75(5) = 6.25$

   c. You will have \$1 left if you buy 8 snacks. $15 - 1.75(8) = 1$

5. Let $a$ represent the number of additional lessons you take; $\dfrac{a + 4}{10}$

   a. You will get 1 free lesson with 6 more lessons. $\dfrac{6 + 4}{10} = 1$

   b. You will get 2 free lessons with 16 more lessons. $\dfrac{16 + 4}{10} = 2$

   c. You will get 3 free lessons with 26 more lessons. $\dfrac{26 + 4}{10} = 3$

**7. a.** 40      **b.** −160      **c.** 0

**9. a.** 28      **b.** −17      **c.** 91

**11. a.** 40      **b.** 0      **c.** 50

**13. a.** 0      **b.** 14      **c.** −7

**15.**

| $b$ | $3b + 14$ |
|-----|-----------|
| −5 | −1 |
| −3 | 5 |
| 0 | 14 |
| 4 | 26 |

**17.**

| $v$ | 1 | 2 | 5 | −3.25 |
|-----|---|---|---|-------|
| $6.75 - 6v$ | 0.75 | −5.25 | −23.25 | 26.25 |

**19.**

| $s$ | $34 - 6s^3$ |
|-----|-------------|
| 3 | −128 |
| −1 | 40 |
| 2 | −14 |
| −3 | 196 |

**21.** −2.85

**23.** 44.64

**25.** $2\frac{5}{8}$

## Lesson 6.2

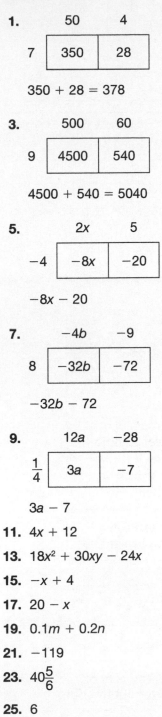

**1.**

| | 50 | 4 |
|---|---|---|
| 7 | 350 | 28 |

350 + 28 = 378

**3.**

| | 500 | 60 |
|---|---|---|
| 9 | 4500 | 540 |

4500 + 540 = 5040

**5.**

| | $2x$ | 5 |
|---|---|---|
| −4 | $-8x$ | −20 |

$-8x - 20$

**7.**

| | $-4b$ | −9 |
|---|---|---|
| 8 | $-32b$ | −72 |

$-32b - 72$

**9.**

| | $12a$ | −28 |
|---|---|---|
| $\frac{1}{4}$ | $3a$ | −7 |

$3a - 7$

**11.** $4x + 12$

**13.** $18x^2 + 30xy - 24x$

**15.** $-x + 4$

**17.** $20 - x$

**19.** $0.1m + 0.2n$

**21.** −119

**23.** $40\frac{5}{6}$

**25.** 6

## Lesson 6.3

**1.** $8(8x + 3)$

**3.** $4(9 - 2z)$

**5.** $-18a(2a - 1)$

**7.** $3m(14n + 9)$

**9.** $15c(2c - d + 3)$

**11.** $10x$

**13.** $-11m$

**15.** $6qr$

**17.** The expression is already simplified. The terms do not contain the same variables; they are not like terms.

**19.** The expression is already simplified. The terms do not contain the same variables; they are not like terms.

**21.** 9

**23.** 0

**25.** 168

**27.** 10

**29.** 11

**31.** $-3\frac{7}{12}$

## Lesson 6.4

**1.** $13 \neq 10$. The expressions are not equivalent.

**3.** $14 \neq -22$. The expressions are not equivalent.

**5.** $7 = 7$. The expressions may be equivalent.

**7.** $-25 - 4x = -25 - 4x$. The expressions are equivalent.

**9.** $2.7x \neq 27x$. The expressions are equivalent.

**11.** $-30x + 1.8 \neq -29.7x + 1.9$. The expressions are equivalent.

**13.**

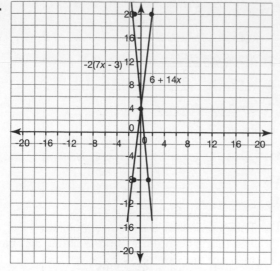

$-2(7x - 3)$

$6 + 14x$

The expressions are not equivalent.

**17.**

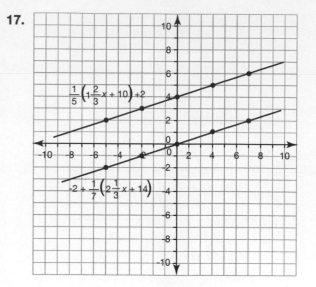

$\frac{1}{5}\left(1\frac{2}{3}x + 10\right) + 2$

$-2 + \frac{1}{7}\left(2\frac{1}{3}x + 14\right)$

The expressions are not equivalent.

**15.**

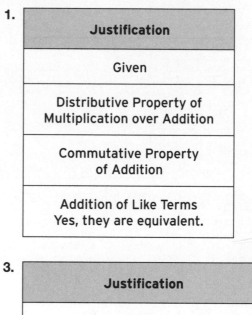

$\frac{-3}{10}\left(\frac{2}{3}x - \frac{5}{6}\right) + 2\left(\frac{1}{10}x + \frac{5}{8}\right)$

and

$12\left(\frac{4}{9}x - \frac{3}{8}\right) - 5\frac{1}{3}x + 6$

The expressions are equivalent.

## Lesson 6.5

**1.**

| Justification |
| --- |
| Given |
| Distributive Property of Multiplication over Addition |
| Commutative Property of Addition |
| Addition of Like Terms Yes, they are equivalent. |

**3.**

| Justification |
| --- |
| Given |
| Distributive Property of Multiplication over Subtraction |
| Commutative Property of Addition |
| Addition of Like Terms No, they are not equivalent. |

**5.**

| Justification |
|---|
| Given |
| Distributive Property of Division over Subtraction |
| Divide |
| Commutative Property of Addition |
| Addition of Like Terms<br>No, they are not equivalent. |

**7.**

| Step |
|---|
| $\dfrac{8x + 3(7 + x)}{10} + \dfrac{(9x - 1)}{10} =$ |
| $\dfrac{8x + 21 + 3x}{10} + \dfrac{9x + (-1)}{10} =$ |
| $\dfrac{8x + 3x + 21}{10} + \dfrac{9x + (-1)}{10} =$ |
| $\dfrac{11x + 21}{10} + \dfrac{9x + (-1)}{10} =$ |
| $\dfrac{11x}{10} + \dfrac{21}{10} + \dfrac{9x}{10} + \dfrac{(-1)}{10} =$ |
| $\dfrac{11}{10}x + \dfrac{9}{10}x + \dfrac{21}{10} + \left(-\dfrac{1}{10}\right) =$ |
| $\dfrac{20}{10}x + \dfrac{20}{10} =$ |
| $2x + 2$ |

**9.**

| Step | Justification |
|---|---|
| $-6(-4x + 8) + 10 + 3(-5x + 7) =$ | Given |
| $24x + (-48) + 10 + (-15x) + 21 =$ | Distributive Property of Multiplication over Addition |
| $24x + (-15x) + (-48) + 10 + 21 =$ | Commutative Property of Addition |
| $9x - 17$ | Addition of Like Terms |
| | Yes, they are equivalent. |

**11.**

| Step | Justification |
|---|---|
| $\dfrac{5 - 4(6x + 2)}{3} + \dfrac{7(12 + 8x)}{4} =$ | Given |
| $\dfrac{5 + (-24x) + (-8)}{3} + \dfrac{84 + 56x}{4} =$ | Distributive Property of Multiplication over Addition |
| $\dfrac{-3 + (-24x)}{3} + \dfrac{84 + 56x}{4} =$ | Combine Like Terms |
| $-\dfrac{3}{3} + \left(-\dfrac{24x}{3}\right) + \dfrac{84}{4} + \dfrac{56x}{4} =$ | Distributive Property of Division over Addition |
| $-1 + (-8x) + 21 + 14x =$ | Divide |
| $-8x + 14x + (-1) + 21 =$ | Commutative Property of Addition |
| $6x + 20$ | Combine Like Terms |
| | No, they are not equivalent. |

Answers

**13.** Left Side

| Step | Justification |
|---|---|
| $0.5(-3.2x + 2.4) + 6[1.7 + 4(0.9x + 0.8)] =$ | Given |
| $-1.6x + 1.2 + 6(1.7 + 3.6x + 3.2) =$ | Distributive Property of Multiplication over Addition |
| $-1.6x + 1.2 + 6(3.6x + 4.9) =$ | Combine Like Terms |
| $-1.6x + 1.2 + 21.6x + 29.4 =$ | Distributive Property of Multiplication over Addition |
| $-1.6x + 21.6x + 1.2 + 29.4 =$ | Commutative Property of Addition |
| $20x + 30.6 =$ | Combine Like Terms |

Right Side

| Step | Justification |
|---|---|
| $3.8(2x - 7) + 1.4(6 + 3x) =$ | Given |
| $7.6x - 26.6 + 8.4 + 4.2x =$ | Distributive Property of Multiplication over Addition |
| $7.6x + 4.2x + (-26.6) + 8.4 =$ | Commutative Property of Addition |
| $11.8x - 18.2$ | Combine Like Terms |

No, they are not equivalent.

# Chapter 7

## Lesson 7.1

**1.**

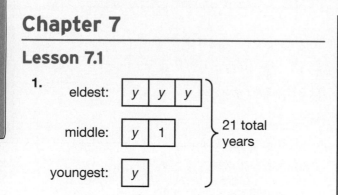

$3y + y + 1 + y = 21$ or $5y + 1 = 21$
The youngest child is 4 years old, the middle child is 5 years old, and the eldest child is 12 years old.

**3.**

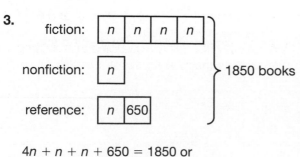

$4n + n + n + 650 = 1850$ or
$6n + 650 = 1850$
There are 200 nonfiction books, 850 reference books, and 800 fiction books.

**5.**

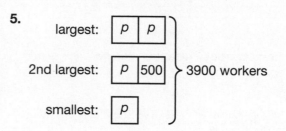

$2p + p + 500 + p = 3900$ or
$4p + 500 = 3900$
There are 850 workers in the smallest building, 1350 workers in the second-largest building, and 1700 workers in the largest building.

**7.**

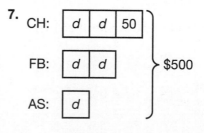

$2d + 50 + 2d + d = 500$ or $5d + 50 = 500$
The Petersons donated $90 to the animal shelter, $180 to the food bank, and $230 to the children's home.

## Lesson 7.2

**1.** 1 rectangle = 2 squares.
$$2x + 5 = 9$$

**3.** 1 rectangle = 2 squares.
$$7x = 2x + 10$$

**5.** 1 rectangle = 3 squares.
$$4 + 2x = 3x + 1$$

**7.** Add first, and then divide.
$$w = 7$$

**9.** Add first, and then multiply.
$$448 = y$$

**11.** Subtract first, and then divide.
$$10 = h$$

**13.** Subtract first, and then divide.
$$19 = h$$

**15.** The number is 8.

**17.** The number is 4.

**19.** The number is 7.

## Lesson 7.3

**1.** First subtract 12 from each side, then divide each side by 4.
$$x = 3$$

**3.** First subtract 13 from each side, then multiply each side by $-7$.
$$x = 49$$

**5.** First subtract 29 from each side, then multiply each side by 9.
$$x = 108$$

**7.** First add 14 to each side, then divide each side by 2.
$$3 = x$$

**9.** First subtract 35 from each side, then divide each side by 9.
$$-6 = x$$

**11.** $40p + 55 = 695$
Jerry took 16 lessons.

**13.** $1000 - 2s = 840$
There are 80 students on the honor roll in the first quarter.

**15.** $125 = 3c + 38$
Javier gives each of his friends 29 comic books.

## Lesson 7.4

**1.** $x = 4$

**3.** $x = -1$

**5.** $x = 4.4$

**7.** $2 = x$

**9.** $x = -4\frac{25}{28}$

**11.** $1185 = 15 + 45(x - 2)$
You will pay $1185 to take 28 classes.

**13.** $138.24(1 + x) + 25 = 173.61$
The sales tax was 7.5%.

**15.** $500 = x - 50 - 0.25x$
The original price of the laptop was $733.33.

## Lesson 7.5

**1.** $13 + 2b \leq 27$

**3.** $36 > 17 + p$

**5.** $15 > \frac{250}{g}$

**7.** The numbers 3, 4, 5, 6, and 7 make the inequality true.
Answers will vary. Three additional solutions for the inequality are 8, 9, and 10.

**9.** The numbers $-1$, 0, 1, 2, 3, 4, 5, 6, and 7 make the inequality true.
Answers will vary. Three additional solutions for the inequality are 8, 9, and 10.

**11.** The numbers $-2$, $-1$, 0, 1, 2, 3, 4, and 5 make the inequality true.
Answers will vary. Three additional solutions for the inequality are $-3$, $-4$, and $-5$.

Answers

**13.** $x > 7$

**15.** $x \leq 8$

**17.** $x \leq 3$

**19.** $-40 \leq x$

# Chapter 8

## Lesson 8.1

**1.**

| Number of Pages | Copier Use Charge (dollars) | Total Cost (dollars) |
|:---:|:---:|:---:|
| 1 | $1 | $1.50 |
| 2 | $1 | $2.00 |
| 5 | $1 | $3.50 |
| 8 | $1 | $5.00 |
| 10 | $1 | $6.00 |

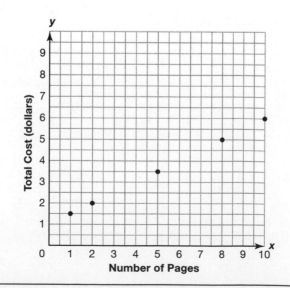

**3.**

| Number of Pecks | Cost of First Peck (dollars) | Total Cost (dollars) |
|---|---|---|
| 1 | $5 | $5 |
| 2 | $5 | $8 |
| 3 | $5 | $11 |
| 4 | $5 | $14 |
| 5 | $5 | $17 |

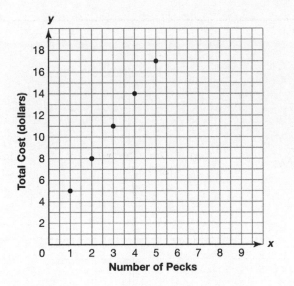

Answers

**5.**

| Number of Balloons | Cost of First Six Balloons (dollars) | Total Cost (dollars) |
|:---:|:---:|:---:|
| 6 | $18 | $18 |
| 7 | $18 | $20 |
| 8 | $18 | $22 |
| 9 | $18 | $24 |
| 10 | $18 | $26 |

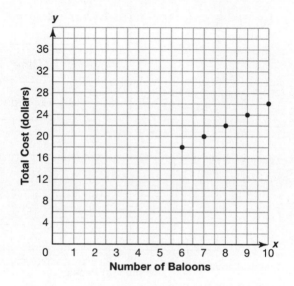

**7.** $t = 120 + 95(c - 1)$

One week of care for a family with 3 children will cost $310.

**9.** $t = 4.25 + 3.5(p - 1)$

The total cost of 3 pecks of peaches is $11.25.

**11.** $t = 14 + 1.5(c - 4)$

The total cost for 9 greeting cards is $21.50.

**13.** $3 = x$

**15.** $x = 8$

**17.** $4.5 = x$

## Lesson 8.2

**1.** $t = 169.90 + 15.99(g - 10)$

**3.** $t = 330 + 11.5(s - 20)$

**5.** $h = 4 + 3w$

**7.** Hector will have to wait 10.8 weeks for the plum tomato plants to be at least 5 feet tall.

**9.** For 20 guests, Mario's is the most affordable.

**11.** For a 1-year membership, King Gym is the least expensive fitness center.

## Lesson 8.3

**1.** $x = 16$

**3.** $x = 2$

**5.** $12 = x$

**7.** $x = 48$

**9.** $x = 1$

**11.** $18 = x$

**13.** $4 = x$

**15.** $x = 139$

**17.** $35x = 20 + 25x$

The fees would be equal at 2 grooming sessions.

**19.** $3\frac{1}{2}x + 11 = 25$

There will be 4 shelves on the bookshelf.

**21.** $\frac{5}{6}p = \frac{7}{8}p - 2\frac{1}{4}$

Peter is 54 inches tall.

## Lesson 8.4

**1.** 137     **3.** 98

**5.** $-42$     **7.** 9

**9.** 6     **11.** 4

**13.** Lea will have paid a total of $708 for her cell phone contract.

**15.** Tanya's mother will have to wait 15 minutes for Tanya to arrive at the finish line.

**17.** It will take Haru an additional 1.2 hours, or 1 hour 12 minutes, to finish the race.

## Lesson 8.5

**1.** $h = 10t$

| Time | Height |
|------|--------|
| seconds | meters |
| 0 | 0 |
| 1 | 10 |
| 2 | 20 |
| 3 | 30 |
| 4 | 40 |

**3.** $d = -0.25t$

| Time | Depth |
|------|-------|
| seconds | meters |
| 0 | 0 |
| 30 | $-7.5$ |
| 60 | $-15$ |
| 90 | $-22.5$ |
| 120 | $-30$ |

**5.** $d = -50 + 0.2t$

| Time | Depth |
|------|-------|
| seconds | meters |
| 0 | −50 |
| 30 | −44 |
| 60 | −38 |
| 90 | −32 |
| 120 | −26 |

**7.** The unit rate of change is 15 meters per second.

**9.** The unit rate of change is −14 meters per minute.

**11.** The unit rate of change is −18.5 meters per minute.

**13.** The hot air balloon will be 570 meters high.

**15.** The diver will be 15 meters below the surface.

**17.** The diver will take 1.5 minutes to reach the surface.

**19.** The submarine will be below the surface for about 3.5 minutes before reaching its goal depth.

## Lesson 8.6

**1.** There will be 10,500 gallons of water in the pool.

**3.** $10\frac{2}{3}$ months ago Roberto's savings account contained $1000.

**5.** $d = 10t$

| Time | Distance |
|------|----------|
| hours | miles |
| 0.1 | 1 |
| 0.2 | 2 |
| 0.3 | 3 |
| 1 | 10 |
| 2 | 20 |
| 2.6 | 26 |

**7.** $s = 1350 + 150t$

| Time | Savings |
|------|---------|
| months | dollars |
| 0 | 1350 |
| 1 | 1500 |
| 2 | 1650 |
| 3 | 1800 |
| 4 | 1950 |
| 5 | 2100 |

**9.**

| x | y |
|---|---|
| −4 | 18 |
| −2 | 14 |
| 0 | 10 |
| 2 | 6 |
| 4 | 2 |

$y = 10 - 2x$

# Chapter 9

## Lesson 9.1

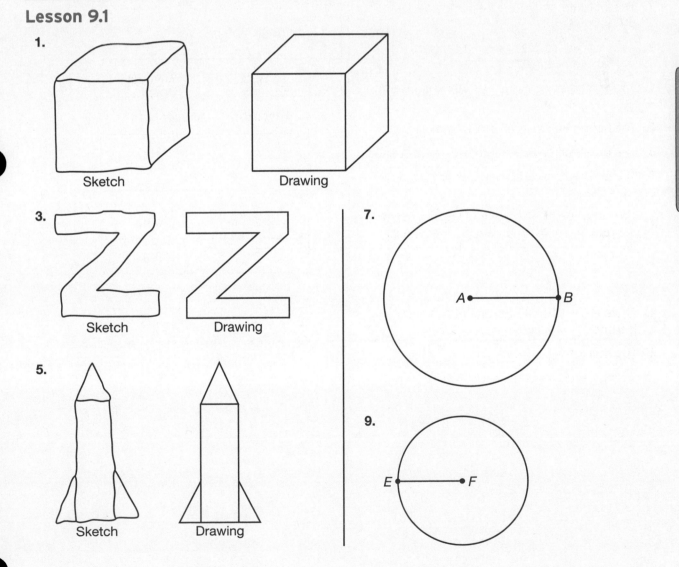

**1.**

Sketch

Drawing

**3.**

Sketch

Drawing

**5.**

Sketch

Drawing

**7.**

$A$ ●————● $B$

**9.**

$E$ ●————● $F$

**11.**

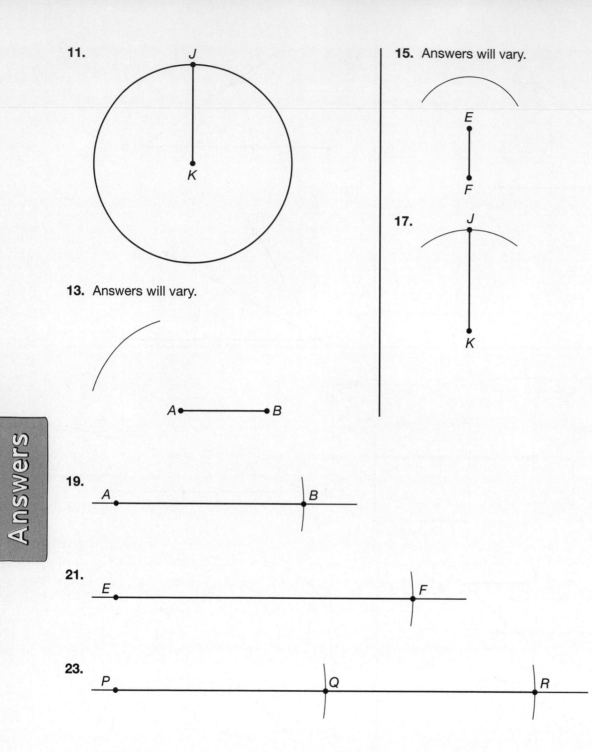

**13.** Answers will vary.

**15.** Answers will vary.

**17.**

**19.**

**21.**

**23.**

# Lesson 9.2

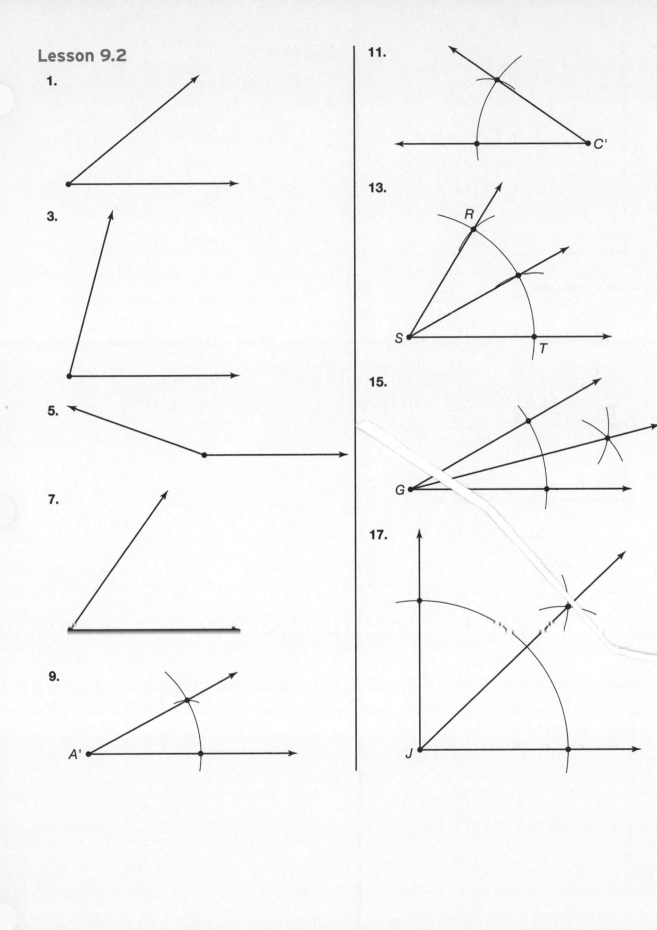

1.

3.

5.

7.

9.
A'

11.
C'

13.
R
S
T

15.
G

17.
J

**19.**

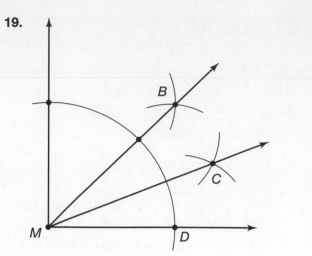

## Lesson 9.3

| | |
|---|---|
| **1.** 60° | **3.** 45° |
| **5.** 68° | **7.** 79° |
| **9.** 120° | **11.** 145° |
| **13.** 102° | **15.** 167° |

**17.**

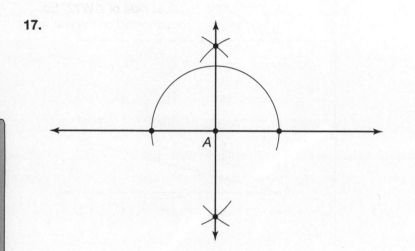

**19.**

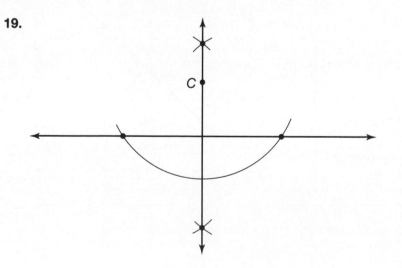

**21.**

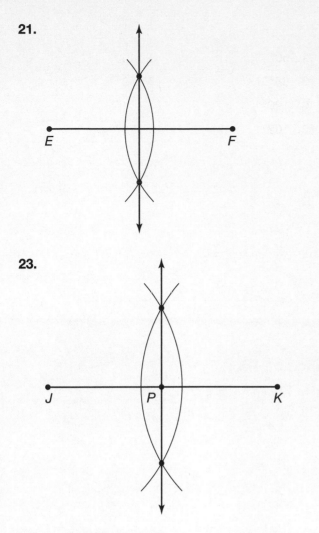

**23.**

**25.** ∠1 and ∠2, ∠2 and ∠3, ∠3 and ∠4, ∠4 and ∠1

**27.** ∠9 and ∠10, ∠10 and ∠11, ∠11 and ∠12, ∠12 and ∠9

**29.** ∠1 and ∠2 form a linear pair, ∠3 and ∠4 form a linear pair

**31.** ∠9 and ∠10 form a linear pair, ∠10 and ∠11 form a linear pair, ∠11 and ∠12 form a linear pair, ∠12 and ∠9 form a linear pair

**33.** ∠9 and ∠11 are vertical angles, ∠10 and ∠12 are vertical angles

# Chapter 10

## Lesson 10.1

**1.** $m\angle B = 65°$  **3.** $m\angle L = 117°$

**5.** $m\angle Y = 60°$

**7.** The shortest side of a triangle is opposite the smallest angle. So, the side lengths from shortest to longest are $a$, $b$, $c$.

**9.** The shortest side of a triangle is opposite the smallest angle. So, the side lengths from shortest to longest are $l$, $m$, $k$.

**11.** The shortest side of a triangle is opposite the smallest angle. Side $c$ is the longest side of $\triangle WXY$ and the shortest side of $\triangle WYZ$. So, the side lengths from shortest to longest are $b$, $a$, $c$, $d$, $e$.

**13.** Interior angles: ∠XYZ, ∠YZX, ∠ZXY
Exterior angle: ∠WXZ
Remote interior angles: ∠XYZ, ∠YZX

**15.** Interior angles: ∠EFG, ∠EGF, ∠FEG
Exterior angle: ∠FGH
Remote interior angles: ∠EFG, ∠FEG

**17.** Interior angles: ∠JKL, ∠JLK, ∠KJL
Exterior angle: ∠LKM
Remote interior angles: ∠JLK, ∠KJL

**19.** $49° = x$

**21.** $33° = x$

**23.** $30° = x$

**25.** $m\angle \underline{\;\;QRT\;\;} > m\angle RST$

$m\angle RTS \underline{\;\;<\;\;} m\angle QRT$

**27.** $m\angle TUV \underline{\;\;>\;\;} m\angle UWV$

$m\angle WVU \underline{\;\;<\;\;} m\angle TUV$

**29.** $m\angle LMN \underline{\;\;<\;\;} m\angle KLN$

$m\angle LNM \underline{\;\;<\;\;} m\angle KLN$

Answers

# Lesson 10.2

**1.** No.  **3.** Yes.  **5.** No.

**7.**

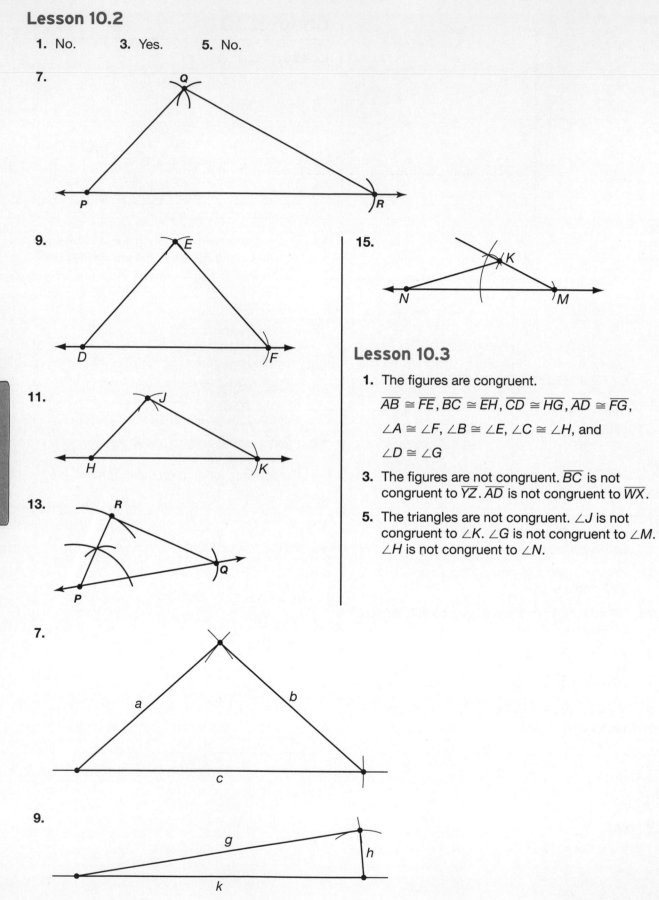

**9.**

**11.**

**13.**

**15.**

## Lesson 10.3

**1.** The figures are congruent.

$\overline{AB} \cong \overline{FE}, \overline{BC} \cong \overline{EH}, \overline{CD} \cong \overline{HG}, \overline{AD} \cong \overline{FG}$,

$\angle A \cong \angle F, \angle B \cong \angle E, \angle C \cong \angle H$, and

$\angle D \cong \angle G$

**3.** The figures are not congruent. $\overline{BC}$ is not congruent to $\overline{YZ}$. $\overline{AD}$ is not congruent to $\overline{WX}$.

**5.** The triangles are not congruent. $\angle J$ is not congruent to $\angle K$. $\angle G$ is not congruent to $\angle M$. $\angle H$ is not congruent to $\angle N$.

**7.**

**9.**

**11.**

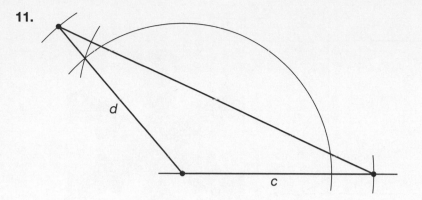

**13.**

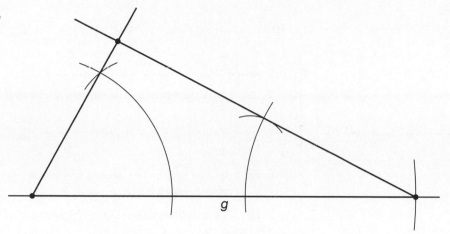

**15.** $\overline{MA} \cong \overline{JE}, \overline{AT} \cong \overline{EF}, \overline{MT} \cong \overline{JF}, \angle M \cong \angle J,$
$\angle A \cong \angle E, \angle T \cong \angle F$

**17.** $\overline{CA} \cong \overline{DO}, \overline{AT} \cong \overline{OG}, \overline{CT} \cong \overline{DG}, \angle C \cong \angle D,$
$\angle A \cong \angle O, \angle T \cong \angle G$

**19.** $\overline{PQ} \cong \overline{XY}, \overline{QR} \cong \overline{YZ}, \overline{PR} \cong \overline{XZ}, \angle P \cong \angle X,$
$\angle Q \cong \angle Y, \angle R \cong \angle Z$

## Lesson 10.4

**1.** $\angle H, \angle F, \angle G.$

**3.** $\angle P, \angle Q, \angle R.$

**5.** $\angle G, \angle F, \angle E.$

**7.** Yes.

**9.** No.

**11.** No.

**13.** Yes.

**15.** No.

**17.** $2 \text{ m} < AB < 18 \text{ m}$

**19.** $6 \text{ in.} < HI < 34 \text{ in.}$

**21.** $8 \text{ cm} < MN < 14 \text{ cm}$

# Chapter 11

## Lesson 11.1

**1.**

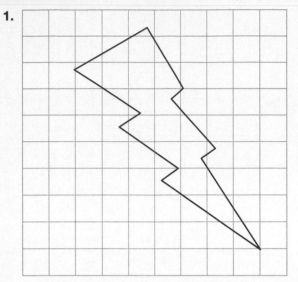

**3.**

**5.**

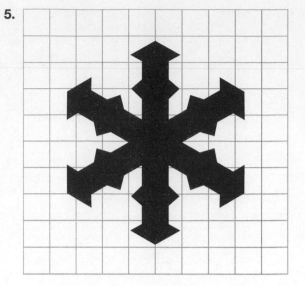

**7. a.** The actual car is 168 inches, or 14 feet long.

  **b.** The door on the model is 1.75 inches wide.

**9. a.** An actual Tyrannosaurus rex would have been 6 meters tall.

  **b.** The model is 0.30 meter long.

**11. a.** The actual ship is 80 feet long.

  **b.** The mast on the model is 0.50 foot, or 6 inches tall.

## Lesson 11.2

**1.** Rectangle B = 6 cm × 8 cm

**3.** Rectangle B = 24 cm × 32 cm

**5.** Rectangle B = 3 cm × 4 cm

**7.** Rectangle B = 15 in. × 5 in.

**9.** Rectangle B = 20 in. × 8 in.

**11.** Rectangle B = 27 in. × 18 in.

**13.** aspect ratio = 4 : 9

**15.** aspect ratio = 3 : 5

**17.** aspect ratio = 1 : 1

**19.** The redwood tree is 360 feet tall.

**21.** A single die is 0.5 inch tall.

**23.** The ranch style house is 20 feet tall.

Answers

## Lesson 11.3

**1.** 4 : 1     **3.** 1 : 2     **5.** 1 : 1

**7.** about 0.3 mile      **9.** about 1 mile

**11.** about 0.3 mile     **13.** 2 : 1

**15.** 1 in. : 25 ft.       **17.** 2 m : 1 cm

**19.** The scale model is smaller than the original object.

**21.** The scale model is smaller than the original object.

**23.** The scale model is larger than the original object.

**25.** The height of the original skyscraper is 350 meters.

**27.** The model is built at a scale of 1 : 100.

**29.** The height of the Washington Monument is 555 feet.

**3.**

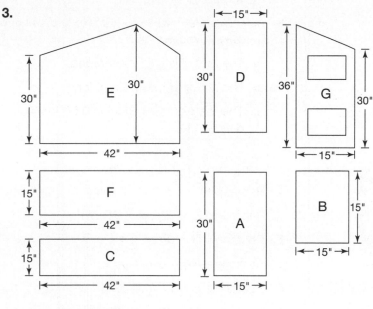

**5.** Answers will vary.

**7.** Answers will vary.

## Chapter 12

### Lesson 12.1

**1.** The circle shown is Circle *B*.

**3.** Sample answer.
Line segment *EF* is a diameter of the circle.

**5.** Sample answer.
Line segment *AC* is a radius of the circle.

## Lesson 11.4

**1.** Answers will vary.

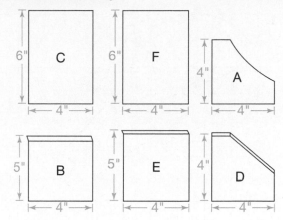

**7.** Sample answer.
Line segment *FG* is a diameter of the circle.

**9.** Sample answer.
Line segment *BC* is a radius of the circle.

**11.** Circle A and Circle D are congruent.

**13.** Circle A and Circle B are congruent.

**15.** Circle A and Circle B are congruent.

**17.** Circle A and Circle B are not congruent.

**19.**

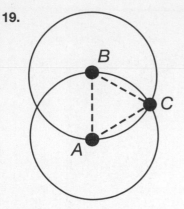

## Lesson 12.2

1. Answers will vary.
   The ratio should be $\approx 3.14$.

3. Answers will vary.
   The ratio should be $\approx 3.14$.

5. Answers will vary.
   The ratio should be $\approx 3.14$.

7. $C = 18.84$      9. $C = 23.55$

11. $C = 43.96$      13. $17.83 \approx d$

15. $35.92 \approx d$      17. $15.20 \approx d$

## Lesson 12.3

1. $P = 16.5$      3. $A \approx 12.38$

5. $P = 28$      7. $A = 49$

9. $P = 20$      11. $A = 27.5$

13. $P = 24$      15. $A = 42$

## Lesson 12.4

1. The pool will cover about 114.93 square feet.

3. Carlos needs 12.56 feet of rubber edging.

5. Eva needs at least 15.64 feet of the paper streamer.

7. The area of the shaded region is approximately 5.31 square centimeters.

9. The area of the shaded region is 156.96 square centimeters.

11. The area of the shaded region is 7.63 square centimeters.

# Chapter 13

## Lesson 13.1

**1.**

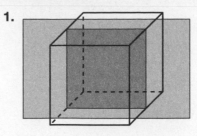

Answers may vary.

**3.**

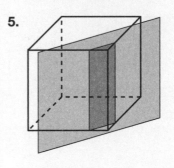

Answers may vary.

**5.**

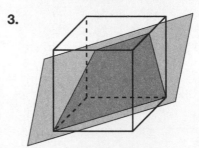

Answers may vary.

**7.**

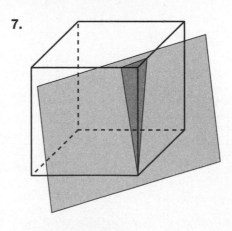

Answers may vary.

**9.** The cross-section is a rectangle.

**11.** The cross-section is a square.

**13.** The cross-section is a pentagon.

**15.** The cross-section is a hexagon.

## Lesson 13.2

**1.**

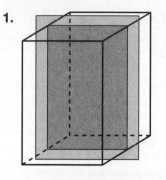

Answers may vary.

**3.**

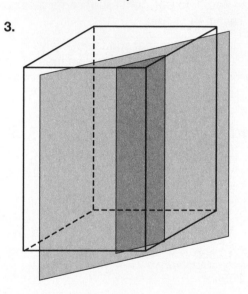

Answers may vary.

**5.**

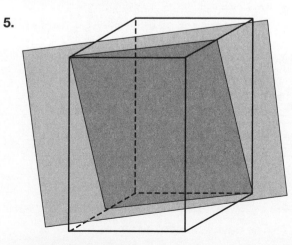

Answers may vary.

**7.**

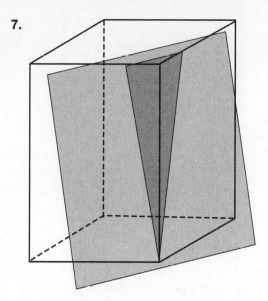

Answers may vary.

**9.** The cross-section is a triangle.

**11.** The cross-section is a rectangle.

**13.** The cross-section is a rectangle.

**15.** The cross-section is a trapezoid.

## Lesson 13.3

**1.**

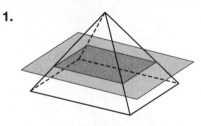

Answers may vary.

**3.**

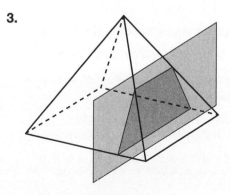

Answers may vary.

**5.**

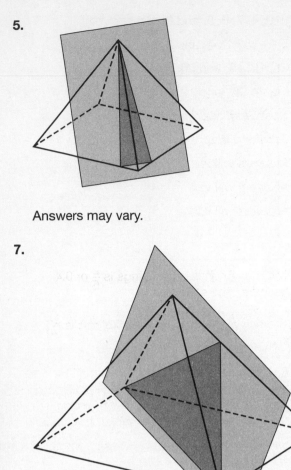

Answers may vary.

**7.**

Answers may vary.

9. The cross-section is a triangle.

11. The cross-section is a rectangle.

13. The cross-section is a triangle.

15. The cross-section is a triangle.

## Lesson 13.4

1. $V = 80$ in.$^3$

3. $V = 56$ m$^3$

5. $V = 64$ in.$^3$

7. Separate the solid into two rectangular prisms – one prism is the bottom of the "L", and the other prism is the top of the "L".

9. Separate the solid into two rectangular prisms – one prism is the top of the "T", and the other prism is the bottom of the "T".

11. Separate the solid into three rectangular prisms – two prisms are the vertical sides of the "H", and one prism is the horizontal middle of the "H".

13. $V = 5$ ft$^3$

15. $V = 36$ cm$^3$

17. $V = 42$ ft$^3$

19. $SA = 92$ m$^2$

21. $SA = 268$ cm$^2$

23. $SA = 294$ mm$^2$

25. There are 8 polygonal surfaces. Six surfaces are lateral faces in the shapes of rectangles. Two polygonal surfaces are bases that have an "L" shape.

27. There are 10 polygonal surfaces. Eight surfaces are lateral faces in the shapes of rectangles. Two polygonal surfaces are bases that have a "T" shape.

29. There are 14 polygonal surfaces. Twelve surfaces are lateral faces in the shapes of rectangles. Two polygonal surfaces are bases that have an "H" shape.

## Lesson 13.5

1. $SA = 132$ in$^2$

3. $SA = 2997$ m$^2$

5. $SA = 972$ in$^2$

7. $SA = 1827$ m$^2$

9. $SA = 10,000$ cm$^2$

11. $V = 300$ in$^3$

13. $V \approx 179.67$ cm$^3$

15. $V = 6600$ ft$^3$

17. $V = 20,286$ in$^3$

19. $V \approx 416,666.67$ yd$^3$

# Chapter 14

## Lesson 14.1

1. The data represent a sample.

3. The data represent a sample.

5. The data represent a census.

7. The data represent a sample.

9. The data represent a census.

11. The result is a statistic.

13. The result is a statistic.

15. The result is a parameter.

17. The result is a parameter.

19. The result is a statistic.

21. In the class, 9 out of 20 students are male.

23. In the class, 5 out of 20 students have blond hair.

25. In the class, 10% of the students do not carry a cell phone.

27. In the class, 3 of the students are male and spend at least 2 hours doing homework every week.

29. In the class, 20% of the students are female and chose Reality as their favorite type of TV show.

## Lesson 14.2

1. The sample is not random because team members whose last names start with consonants have no chance of being selected.

3. The sample is random because each team member has an equal chance of being selected.

5. The sample is not random because it only focuses on the early customers whose eating habits may be different from later customers.

7. The sample is not random because the first 50 nurses are the only ones who can participate. The first 50 may have arrived together by bus which would affect the results of the survey.

9. The sample is not random because not every student has an equal chance of participating. The students on the first row may all be friends or they may have been the last ones to arrive.

11. 2, 9, 4, 7, 8, 5, and 9.

13. 591, 383, 954, and 271.

15. 28, 12, 13, and 30.

17. 14, 24, 22, and 19.

19. Noah, Aki, and Sherwin.

21. Jada and Wei.

23. Answers will vary.

25. Answers will vary.

27. Answers will vary.

## Lesson 14.3

1. The mean number of siblings is $\frac{2}{5}$ or 0.4 based on the sample.

3. The actual mean number of siblings is $\frac{24}{20}$ or 1.2.

5. Answers will vary.
I selected Horace (17), Jasmine (26), Ramona (27), Rika (22), and Augustine (18) using line 2 of the Random Number Table. The mean number of pets is $\frac{13}{5}$ or 2.6 based on the sample.

7. The mean number of miles driven to work is $\frac{106}{5}$ or 21.2 miles based on the sample.

9. The actual mean number of miles driven to work daily is $\frac{271}{20}$ or 13.55 miles.

11. Answers will vary.
The employees I selected for my random sample are Ignatius (67), Gregory (64), Betty (52), Linda (69), and Tiffany (62) using line 16 of the Random Number Table. The mean years of experience is $\frac{22}{5}$ or 4.4 years based on the random sample.

Answers

## Lesson 14.4

**1.**

| Data | Mean | Deviation From the Mean | Absolute Value of the Deviation From the Mean |
|------|------|-------------------------|-----------------------------------------------|
| 35 |    | $35 - 41 = -6$ | 6 |
| 18 |    | $18 - 41 = -23$ | 23 |
| 58 | 41 | $58 - 41 = 17$ | 17 |
| 65 |    | $65 - 41 = 24$ | 24 |
| 29 |    | $29 - 41 = -12$ | 12 |
| **Mean Absolute Deviation** | | | 16.4 |

**3.**

| Data | Mean | Deviation From the Mean | Absolute Value of the Deviation From the Mean |
|------|------|-------------------------|-----------------------------------------------|
| 61 |      | $61 - 64.6 = -3.6$ | 3.6 |
| 55 |      | $55 - 64.6 = -9.6$ | 9.6 |
| 57 | 64.6 | $57 - 64.6 = -7.6$ | 7.6 |
| 64 |      | $64 - 64.6 = -0.6$ | 0.6 |
| 86 |      | $86 - 64.6 = 21.4$ | 21.4 |
| **Mean Absolute Deviation** | | | 8.56 |

**5.**

| Data | Mean | Deviation From the Mean | Absolute Value of the Deviation From the Mean |
|------|------|-------------------------|-----------------------------------------------|
| 24 |      | $24 - 37.8 = -13.8$ | 13.8 |
| 21 |      | $21 - 37.8 = -16.8$ | 16.8 |
| 66 | 37.8 | $66 - 37.8 = 28.2$ | 28.2 |
| 34 |      | $34 - 37.8 = -3.8$ | 3.8 |
| 44 |      | $44 - 37.8 = 6.2$ | 6.2 |
| **Mean Absolute Deviation** | | | 13.76 |

Answers

**7.** Minimum = 16; Q1 = 22

Maximum = 97; Q3 = 78

Median = 54

IQR = 56

**9.** Minimum = 16; Q1 = 45

Maximum = 96; Q3 = 74

Median = 62

IQR = 29

**11.** Minimum = 9; Q1 = 21

Maximum = 97; Q3 = 77.5

Median = 42

IQR = 56.5

**13.**

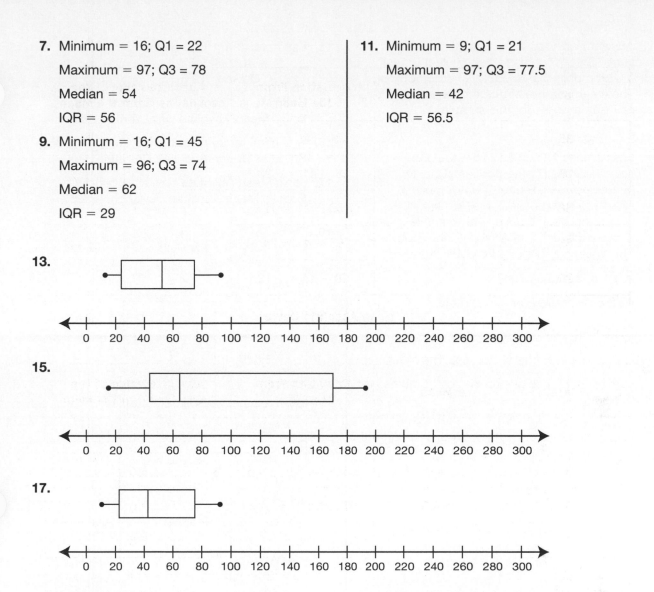

**15.**

**17.**

## Lesson 14.5

**1.** Answers will vary.
I used Line 1 of the Random Number Table to select Emily (5 hours) and Juan (10 hours). The mean number of hours spent online weekly is $\frac{15}{2}$ or 7.5 hours for this sample.

**3.** Answers will vary.
I used Lines 3 and 4 of the table to select Brian (25 hours), Jill (14 hours), Joelle (15 hours), June (0 hours), Hannah (0 hours), Daniel (10 hours), Gloria (7 hours), and Hyacinth (14 hours). The mean number of hours spent online weekly is $\frac{85}{8}$ or approximately 10.63 hours for this sample.

**5.** Answers will vary.
I used Line 5 of the table to select Juan (10 hours) and Gloria (15 hours). The mean number of hours spent watching television weekly is $\frac{25}{2}$ or 12.5 hours for this sample.

**7.** Answers will vary.
I used Lines 8 and 9 of the table to select Emily (20 hours), Jamal (14 hours), Gloria (15 hours), Brian (4 hours), Tony (20 hours), Jill (3 hours), Hector (5 hours), and Joelle (5 hours). The mean number of hours spent watching television weekly is $\frac{86}{8}$ or approximately 10.75 hours for this sample.

**9.** Answers will vary.
I used Line 10 of the table to select Ernest (7 automobiles) and Maeko (7 automobiles). The mean number of automobiles owned is $\frac{14}{2}$ or 7 automobiles for this sample.

**11.** Answers will vary.
I used Lines 12 and 13 of the table to select Marcus (7 automobiles), Charlie (5 automobiles), Rafael (3 automobiles), Robert (6 automobiles), Maeko (7 automobiles), Lonnie (2 automobiles), Jack (5 automobiles), and Allison (2 automobiles). The mean number of automobiles owned is $\frac{37}{8}$ or approximately 4.63 automobiles for this sample.

**13.** Answers will vary.
I used Line 14 of the table to select Rosa (1 home) and Rafael (2 homes). The mean number of homes owned is $\frac{3}{2}$ or 1.5 homes for this sample.

**15.** Answers will vary.
I used Lines 16 and 17 of the table to select Maeko (2 homes), Mike (3 homes), Adrian (4 homes), Kayla (2 homes), Rafael (2 homes), Charlie (3 homes), Robert (3 homes), and Thomas (1 home). The mean number of homes owned is $\frac{20}{8}$ or 2.5 homes for this sample.

# Chapter 15

## Lesson 15.1

**1.** The distribution of the girls' data is symmetric. The distribution of the boys' data is roughly symmetric, too.

**3.** The distribution of the teachers' data is skewed left. The distribution of the students' data is skewed left.

**5.** The distribution of Jan's data is symmetric. The distribution of Gavin's data is symmetric.

**7.** Estimate: girls = 7; boys = 10
    Actual: girls = 7
        boys = 10

**9.** Estimate: teachers = 9; students = 16
    Actual: teachers = 8.5
        students = 14.5

**11.** Estimate: Jan = 6; Gavin = 12
    Actual: = 6.5
        Gavin = 12.5

**13.** Girls' Mean Absolute Deviation: ≈ 0.86
    Boys' Mean Absolute Deviation: ≈ 2.57

**15.** Teachers' Mean Absolute Deviation: ≈ 1.38
    Students' Mean Absolute Deviation: ≈ 4.88

**17.** Jan's Mean Absolute Deviation: ≈ 1.33
    Gavin's Mean Absolute Deviation: ≈ 2.67

**19.**

|  | Girls | Boys |
|---|---|---|
| Minimum | 5 | 3 |
| Q1 | 6 | 8 |
| Median | 7 | 10 |
| Q3 | 8 | 11 |
| Maximum | 9 | 17 |
| IQR | 8 − 6 = 2 | 11 − 8 = 3 |

**21.**

|  | Teachers | Students |
|---|---|---|
| Minimum | 5 | 0 |
| Q1 | 7.5 | 12 |
| Median | 9 | 16.5 |
| Q3 | 10 | 19.5 |
| Maximum | 10 | 20 |
| IQR | 10 − 7.5 = 2.5 | 19.5 − 12 = 7.5 |

**23.**

| | Jan | Gavin |
|---|---|---|
| Minimum | 4 | 8 |
| Q1 | 6 | 10 |
| Median | 6 | 12 |
| Q3 | 7 | 15 |
| Maximum | 10 | 18 |
| IQR | 7 − 6 = 1 | 15 − 10 = 5 |

## Lesson 15.2

**1.** 85, 96, 52, 50, 66, 87

**3.** 63, 52, 91, 71, 72, 65

**5.** 296, 303, 263, 291, 293

**7.**  **Fund-raising Items Sold**

| Raffle Tickets Sold | | Candy Bars Sold |
|---|---|---|
| 8 | 0 | 03589 |
| 51 | 1 | 225 |
| 873 | 2 | 0 |
| 5200 | 3 | 0 |

1|2 = 12

The data for raffle tickets is skewed left and the data for candy bars is skewed right.

**9.**  **Students' Math Scores**

| Ms. Kinzer | | Mr. Hannon |
|---|---|---|
| 9876 | 7 | 9 |
| 65 | 8 | 4589 |
| 3110 | 9 | 00235 |

8|4 = 84

The data for Ms. Kinzer's class is symmetric and the data for Mr. Hannon's class is slightly skewed left.

**11.**

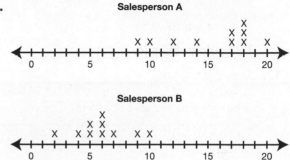

The data for Salesperson A is skewed left and the data for Salesperson B is symmetric.

**13.** median (skewed left)

**15.** median (skewed right)

**17.** median (skewed right)

## Lesson 15.3

**1.** Both sets of data are symmetric.

**3.** The data set on the left is symmetric and the set on the right is skewed left.

**5.** The data set on the left is symmetric and the data set on the right is skewed left.

Answers

**7.**

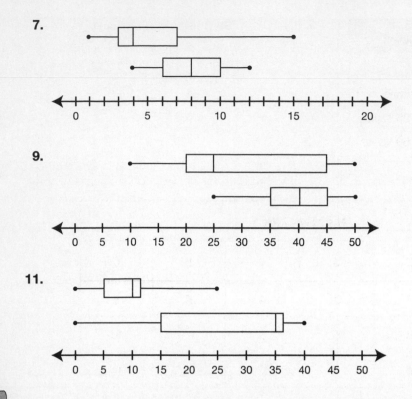

**9.**

**11.**

**13.** The data on the bottom is symmetric and the data on top is skewed right.

**15.** Both data sets have the same range, but the top data is more symmetric and the bottom data is more skewed right.

**17.** Both sets of data are symmetric.

# Chapter 16

## Lesson 16.1

**1.** The sample space is {Sunday, Monday, Tuesday, Wednesday, Thursday, Friday, Saturday}.

**3.** The sample space is {black sock, brown sock, blue sock}.

**5.** The sample space is {HH, HT, TH, TT}.

**7.** The outcomes for the event are 2 and 4.

**9.** The outcomes for the event are Saturday and Sunday.

**11.** The outcomes for the event are 1, 2, 3, 4, 5, and 6.

**13.** $P(\text{even number}) = \frac{1}{2}$

**15.** $P(\text{letter}) = \frac{1}{2}$

**17.** $P(\text{blue}) = \frac{1}{4}$

**19.** $P(\text{number} < 7) = 1$

**21.** The probability is about $\frac{1}{3}$.

**23.** The probability is about $\frac{2}{5}$.

**25.** The probability is about $\frac{3}{5}$.

**27.** The probability is about $\frac{9}{10} = 0.9 = 90\%$.

**29.** The probability is about $\frac{1}{3} \approx 0.33 = 33\%$.

**31.** The probability is about $\frac{1}{20} = 0.05 = 5\%$.

**33.** $P(\text{blue}) = \frac{1}{5}$

**35.** $P(\text{iced tea}) = \frac{1}{3}$

**37.** $P(\text{cherry}) = \frac{1}{4}$

**39.** $P(\text{male}) = \frac{7}{12}$

## Lesson 16.2

**1.** $P(\text{tails}) = 60\%$

**3.** $P(\text{brown}) = 20\%$

**5.** $P(\text{nickel}) = 36\%$

**7.** $P(\text{heads}) = 44\%$

**9.** $P(\text{orange}) = 32\%$

**11.** $P(\text{multiple of 3}) = 42.5\%$

**13.** $P(A)$: 3 times  $P(B)$: 4 times  $P(C)$: 5 times

**15.** $P(A)$: 15 times  $P(B)$: 20 times  $P(C)$: 25 times

**17.** $P(A)$: 36 times  $P(B)$: 48 times  $P(C)$: 60 times

## Lesson 16.3

**1.**

| | | Number Cube 1 | | | | | |
|---|---|---|---|---|---|---|---|
| | | **1** | **2** | **3** | **4** | **5** | **6** |
| **Number Cube 2** | **1** | 1 | 2 | 3 | 4 | 5 | 6 |
| | **2** | 2 | 4 | 6 | 8 | 10 | 12 |
| | **3** | 3 | 6 | 9 | 12 | 15 | 18 |
| | **4** | 4 | 8 | 12 | 16 | 20 | 24 |
| | **5** | 5 | 10 | 15 | 20 | 25 | 30 |
| | **6** | 6 | 12 | 18 | 24 | 30 | 36 |

$P(\text{multiple of 6}) = \dfrac{5}{12}$

**3.**

| | | First Spin | | | |
|---|---|---|---|---|---|
| | | **2** | **4** | **6** | **8** |
| **Second Spin** | **2** | 4 | 6 | 8 | 10 |
| | **4** | 6 | 8 | 10 | 12 |
| | **6** | 8 | 10 | 12 | 14 |
| | **8** | 10 | 12 | 14 | 16 |

$P(\text{sum} < 8) = \dfrac{3}{16}$

**5.**

| | | First Spinner | | | | | |
|---|---|---|---|---|---|---|---|
| | | **0** | **1** | **2** | **3** | **4** | **5** |
| **Second Spinner** | **0** | 0 | 0 | 0 | 0 | 0 | 0 |
| | **5** | 0 | 5 | 10 | 15 | 20 | 25 |
| | **10** | 0 | 10 | 20 | 30 | 40 | 50 |

$P(\text{multiple of } 10) = \frac{7}{18}$

**7.** $x = 15$ times

**9.** $x = 35$ times

**11.** $x = 50$ times

**13.** Experimental.

**15.** Experimental.

**17.** Theoretical.

## Lesson 16.4

**1.** Sample answers are shown.

| Result | Tally | Total | Percent (total/30) |
|---|---|---|---|
| Left | ‖‖‖ ‖‖‖ ‖‖‖ | 13 | ≈ 43% |
| Right | ‖‖‖ ‖‖‖‖ | 9 | 30% |
| Straight | ‖‖‖ ‖‖‖ | 8 | ≈ 27% |

30%

**3.** Sample answers are shown.

| Result | Tally | Total | Percent (total/25) |
|---|---|---|---|
| 1, 2, 3, or 4 (trout) | ‖‖‖ ‖‖‖ ‖‖‖ | 15 | 60% |
| 5 or 6 (not trout) | ‖‖‖ ‖‖‖ | 10 | 40% |

40%

**5.** Sample answers are shown.

| Trial Number | Number Correct | Trial Number | Number Correct |
|:---:|:---:|:---:|:---:|
| 1 | 1 | 6 | 0 |
| 2 | 2 | 7 | 2 |
| 3 | 1 | 8 | 0 |
| 4 | 3 | 9 | 3 |
| 5 | 1 | 10 | 1 |

40%

**7.** Sample answer:
Use a spinner with 4 equal sections. Label one section "coupon" and label the other 3 "no coupon." One trial would consist of spinning the spinner 1 time. Count how many trials you perform until it lands on "coupon."

**9.** Sample answer:
Divide a spinner into 5 equal sections. Label 1 section "ringer" and the other 4 as "not a ringer." One trial is spinning the spinner 3 times. Determine the percent of trials that result in 3 ringers.

**11.** Sample answer:
Label 4 slips of paper as "strike out" and 6 slips of paper as "no strike out." Put the papers in a bag. One trial is selecting a paper from the bag 8 times. Be sure to return the paper you chose back to the bag before choosing again. Determine the percent of trials that result in 5, 6, 7, or 8 "strike outs."

## Lesson 16.5

**1.** Sample answer:
Enter = *RANDBETWEEN(1, 2)* in cell A1. Copy the formula down through cell A50.
Let 1 represent heads and 2 represent tails.

**3.** Sample answer:
Enter = *RANDBETWEEN(1, 10)* in cell A1. Copy the formula to the right into cell B1. Copy this row down through row 40. Let the numbers 1, 2, and 3 represent that the bus is late.

**5.** Sample answer:
Enter = *RANDBETWEEN(1, 10)* in cell A1. Copy the formula to the right through cell E1. Copy this row down through row 25. Let the number 10 represent a loss.

Answers

**7.** Sample answers are shown.

| Trial Number | Days on Time | Trial Number | Days on Time | Trial Number | Days on Time |
|---|---|---|---|---|---|
| 1 | 2 | 6 | 1 | 11 | 1 |
| 2 | 2 | 7 | 3 | 12 | 1 |
| 3 | 3 | 8 | 2 | 13 | 3 |
| 4 | 0 | 9 | 3 | 14 | 2 |
| 5 | 3 | 10 | 2 | 15 | 1 |

$\frac{1}{3}$

**9.** Sample answers are shown.

| Trial Number | Number Correct | Trial Number | Number Correct |
|---|---|---|---|
| 1 | 4 | 11 | 4 |
| 2 | 2 | 12 | 2 |
| 3 | 2 | 13 | 4 |
| 4 | 4 | 14 | 5 |
| 5 | 1 | 15 | 5 |
| 6 | 0 | 16 | 4 |
| 7 | 6 | 17 | 1 |
| 8 | 1 | 18 | 4 |
| 9 | 4 | 19 | 1 |
| 10 | 3 | 20 | 3 |

0%

Answers

**11.** Sample answers are shown.

| Trial Number | Results | Bottles Bought | Trial Number | Results | Bottles Bought |
|---|---|---|---|---|---|
| 1 | 3, 2 | 2 | 16 | 2 | 1 |
| 2 | 5, 1 | 2 | 17 | 3, 4, 5, 1 | 4 |
| 3 | 1 | 1 | 18 | 1 | 1 |
| 4 | 1 | 1 | 19 | 5, 3, 5, 1 | 4 |
| 5 | 5, 3, 4, 1 | 4 | 20 | 4, 2 | 2 |
| 6 | 4, 5, 4, 4, 2 | 5 | 21 | 3, 1 | 2 |
| 7 | 5, 3, 2 | 2 | 22 | 5, 5, 1 | 3 |
| 8 | 3, 1 | 2 | 23 | 5, 1 | 2 |
| 9 | 4, 3, 3, 2 | 4 | 24 | 4, 3, 5, 1 | 4 |
| 10 | 2 | 1 | 25 | 2 | 1 |
| 11 | 5, 3, 1 | 3 | 26 | 4, 2 | 2 |
| 12 | 4, 2 | 2 | 27 | 1 | 1 |
| 13 | 4, 3, 5, 1 | 4 | 28 | 2 | 1 |
| 14 | 4, 1 | 2 | 29 | 2 | 1 |
| 15 | 4, 3, 3, 5, 1 | 5 | 30 | 4, 4, 2 | 3 |

The average of the number of bottles bought is 2.4. So I predict you need to buy 2 or 3 bottles before getting a winner.

# Chapter 17

## Lesson 17.1

1. The model is a uniform probability model.

3. The model is a uniform probability model.

5. The model is a non-uniform probability model.

7. $P(4) = \frac{5}{25}$

9. $P(\text{less than } 6) = \frac{14}{25}$

11. $P(\text{odd}) = \frac{8}{25}$

13. $P(B) = \frac{5}{20}$

15. $P(\text{not } C) = \frac{18}{20}$

17. $P(\text{not } A) = \frac{18}{20}$

## Lesson 17.2

1. Possible outcomes: BBB, BBG, BGB, BGG, GGG, GGB, GBG, GBB

| Outcome | 0 boys | 1 boy | 2 boys | 3 boys |
|---|---|---|---|---|
| Probability | $\frac{1}{8}$ | $\frac{3}{8}$ | $\frac{3}{8}$ | $\frac{1}{8}$ |

The probability that the first 3 students that enter the classroom are boys is $\frac{1}{8}$.

3. Possible outcomes: BBB, BBW, BWB, BWW, WWW, WWB, WBW, WBB

| Outcome | 0 blue | 1 blue | 2 blue | 3 blue |
|---|---|---|---|---|
| Probability | $\frac{1}{8}$ | $\frac{3}{8}$ | $\frac{3}{8}$ | $\frac{1}{8}$ |

The probability that spinning the spinner 3 times will result in only 1 blue is $\frac{3}{8}$.

5. Possible outcomes: PP, PY, PO, YY, YP, YO, OO, OP, OY

| Outcome | 0 purple | 1 purple | 2 purple |
|---|---|---|---|
| Probability | $\frac{4}{9}$ | $\frac{4}{9}$ | $\frac{1}{9}$ |

The probability that only 1 of the chosen stones is purple is $\frac{4}{9}$.

Answers

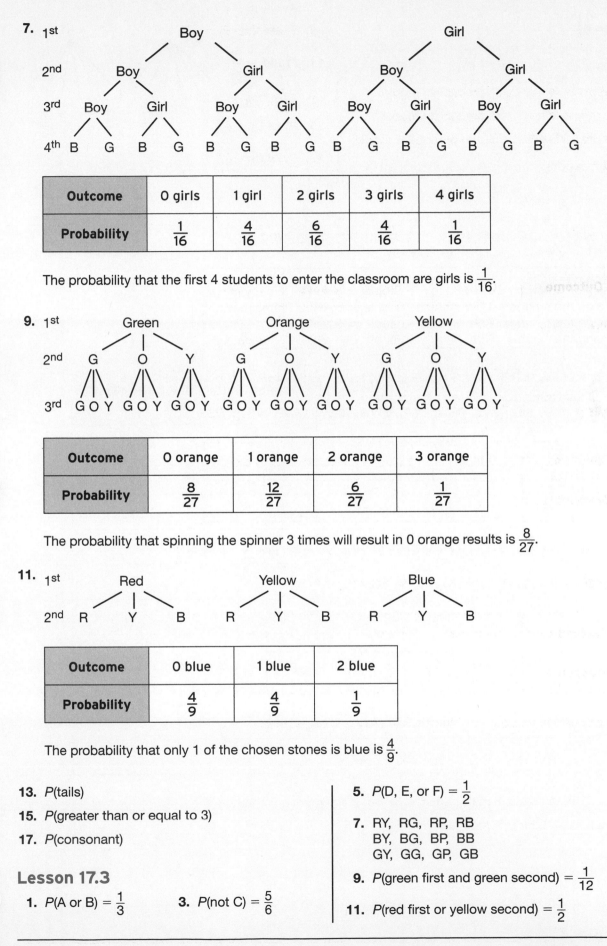

**7.**

| Outcome | 0 girls | 1 girl | 2 girls | 3 girls | 4 girls |
|---|---|---|---|---|---|
| Probability | $\frac{1}{16}$ | $\frac{4}{16}$ | $\frac{6}{16}$ | $\frac{4}{16}$ | $\frac{1}{16}$ |

The probability that the first 4 students to enter the classroom are girls is $\frac{1}{16}$.

**9.**

| Outcome | 0 orange | 1 orange | 2 orange | 3 orange |
|---|---|---|---|---|
| Probability | $\frac{8}{27}$ | $\frac{12}{27}$ | $\frac{6}{27}$ | $\frac{1}{27}$ |

The probability that spinning the spinner 3 times will result in 0 orange results is $\frac{8}{27}$.

**11.**

| Outcome | 0 blue | 1 blue | 2 blue |
|---|---|---|---|
| Probability | $\frac{4}{9}$ | $\frac{4}{9}$ | $\frac{1}{9}$ |

The probability that only 1 of the chosen stones is blue is $\frac{4}{9}$.

**13.** $P$(tails)

**15.** $P$(greater than or equal to 3)

**17.** $P$(consonant)

## Lesson 17.3

**1.** $P$(A or B) $= \frac{1}{3}$　　**3.** $P$(not C) $= \frac{5}{6}$

**5.** $P$(D, E, or F) $= \frac{1}{2}$

**7.** RY, RG, RP, RB
BY, BG, BP, BB
GY, GG, GP, GB

**9.** $P$(green first and green second) $= \frac{1}{12}$

**11.** $P$(red first or yellow second) $= \frac{1}{2}$

**13.** Spinner

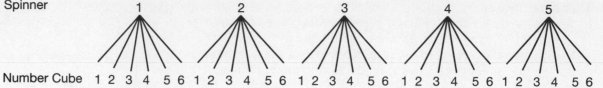

Number Cube    1 2  3  4  5 6    1 2  3  4  5 6    1 2  3  4  5 6    1 2  3  4  5 6    1 2  3  4  5 6

**15.** $P(\text{odd and odd}) = \frac{3}{10}$

**17.** $P(\text{spin greater than 3 or roll greater than 3}) = \frac{7}{10}$

**19.** $P(\text{spin 6 or roll 6}) = \frac{1}{6}$

## Lesson 17.4

**1.** Sample answer.
Assign the numbers 00 to 30 to the people who rent a Comedy movie.
Assign the numbers 31 to 72 to the people who rent a Drama movie.
Assign the numbers 73 to 94 to the people who rent a Science Fiction movie.
Assign the numbers 95 to 99 to the people who rent a Documentary.

| Trial Number | Numbers | Number of Customers Who Rent a Comedy |
|---|---|---|
| 1 | 65, 28, 59, 71, 12 | 2 |
| 2 | 13, 85, 30, 10, 94 | 3 |
| 3 | 11, 58, 38, 16, 56 | 2 |
| 4 | 10, 04, 43, 51, 61 | 2 |
| 5 | 20, 17, 26, 45, 27 | 4 |
| 6 | 38, 22, 93, 01, 18 | 3 |
| 7 | 16, 43, 81, 09, 97 | 2 |
| 8 | 66, 56, 92, 98, 56 | 0 |
| 9 | 95, 50, 95, 63, 97 | 0 |
| 10 | 54, 31, 19, 99, 25 | 2 |

Out of the 10 trials, 8 trials had at least 1 customer rent a comedy.

$P(\text{at least 1 customer rents a comedy}) = \frac{8}{10}$

$$= 0.8$$

**3.** Sample answer.

Assign the numbers 00 to 31 to students who prefer football.
Assign the numbers 32 to 61 to students who prefer baseball.
Assign the numbers 62 to 87 to students who prefer basketball.
Assign the numbers 88 to 99 to students who prefer hockey.

| Trial Number | Numbers | Number of Students Who Prefer Hockey |
|:---:|:---:|:---:|
| 1 | 64, 49, 09, 92, 15 | 1 |
| 2 | 84, 98, 72, 87, 59 | 1 |
| 3 | 19, 10, 71, 47, 33 | 0 |
| 4 | 24, 55, 02, 80, 67 | 0 |
| 5 | 68, 89, 43, 84, 90 | 2 |
| 6 | 24, 21, 66, 34, 44 | 0 |
| 7 | 21, 28, 30, 70, 44 | 0 |
| 8 | 92, 72, 93, 72, 84 | 2 |
| 9 | 13, 21, 13, 74, 85 | 0 |
| 10 | 11, 41, 53, 64, 57 | 0 |

Out of the 10 trials, 4 trials had at least 1 student who prefers hockey.

$$P(\text{at least 1 student prefers hockey}) = \frac{4}{10}$$
$$= 0.4$$

**5.** Sample answer.
Assign the numbers 1 to 2 of a number cube to a white car.
Assign the numbers 3 to 6 of a number cube to a car that is not white.

| Trial Number | Numbers | Number of Cars to Enter the Parking Lot Before A White Car |
|:---:|:---:|:---:|
| 1 | 4, 4, 1 | 2 |
| 2 | 5, 2 | 1 |
| 3 | 4, 1 | 1 |
| 4 | 1 | 0 |
| 5 | 6, 4, 5, 3, 5, 4, 6, 4, 4, 3, 2 | 10 |
| 6 | 6, 5, 4, 2 | 3 |
| 7 | 1 | 0 |
| 8 | 4, 2 | 1 |
| 9 | 6, 1 | 1 |
| 10 | 4, 5, 5, 1 | 3 |

$$\frac{2 + 1 + 1 + 0 + 10 + 3 + 0 + 1 + 1 + 3}{10} = 2.2$$
$$\approx 2$$

On average, about 2 cars will enter the parking garage before a white car enters the parking garage.